NEW COMEDIES
for
TEEN-AGERS

New Comedies

for

Teen-Agers

*A collection of one-act, royalty-free
comedies, farces, and melodramas*

By EARL J. DIAS

Publishers   *PLAYS, INC.*   Boston

ONCE MORE—FOR EDITH

Contents

NEW COMEDIES
for
TEEN-AGERS

The Touch of Genius

Characters

BRAD THURMAN, *city editor of the Glenfield "Daily Echo"*
ANNETTE BRADSHAW, *the society editor*
DIANA CHARLES, *writer of the "Advice to the Lovelorn" column*
ART LAKELAND, *an ace reporter*
THROCKMORTON HAMMER, *a drama critic*
BILLY, *the copy boy*
SPENCER LATTIMORE, *a young and brilliant publisher*
LIEUTENANT MORROW, *of the Glenfield Police Department*
NEVERMORE NEVINS, *a literate bank robber*
PICKLES DILL, *an illiterate bank robber*
MA DILL, *a sweet-faced, dignified old lady*

SCENE 1

SETTING: *The city room of the Glenfield "Daily Echo."*
There are five desks at right and center. There is a door
left and another up center.

AT RISE: BRAD THURMAN *is at his cluttered desk, correct-*
ing copy with savage strokes of his pencil. The other
desks are occupied by ANNETTE BRADSHAW, THROCK-
MORTON HAMMER, ART LAKELAND, *and* DIANA CHARLES.
All are working busily.

BRAD (*Putting finishing touches on copy*): Copy boy!

BILLY (*Enters hurriedly at left*): You want me, Mr. Thurman?

BRAD (*Sarcastically*): No, I was just yelling to improve my voice. I'm giving a concert at Carnegie Hall tonight.

ART: That'll set music back fifty years.

BRAD: Keep your nose to the typewriter, Art. I want that story on the department store fire before deadline time.

ART (*Bowing his head*): As you wish, O beloved master.

BRAD (*Handing copy to* BILLY): Take this down to the pressroom, Billy, and don't spare the horses.

BILLY: Yes, sir. (*He exits hurriedly left.*)

BRAD (*Picking up another piece of copy paper and crossing out something*): Don't they teach spelling in schools nowadays, Annette?

ANNETTE (*In affected manner*): I'll have you know that I attended Miss Finch's Finishing School. You wouldn't know about such places, because only the cream of society is found at Miss Finch's.

BRAD: Well, the cream must have soured. "Receive" is spelled "ei," not "ie." For Pete's sake, don't you know the rule?

ART (*Speaking in falsetto voice*): "I" before "e" except after "c"—

THROCKMORTON (*Also falsetto*): Or when pronounced "eigh" as in "neighbor" or "weigh."

BRAD: You guys are wasting your talents here. Do you have that review of *Macbeth* ready yet, Throckmorton?

THROCKMORTON: As the Bard himself would put it, I'll have it in "one fell swoop."

BRAD: Save the highbrow talk for our young publisher. (*Pause*) Why his father had to retire, I don't know. The old boy was in good health.

DIANA (*Looking up from her desk*): He wanted Spencer to take over the paper.

ART: Spencer? Since when have you been on a first-name basis with the young genius? I thought you carried a torch only for me, Diana.

DIANA: Don't be conceited, Art.

ART: I'm not conceited. I just happen to be the best reporter on the Glenfield *Daily Echo*—and I know it.

ANNETTE: Perhaps I should use that as an item on the society page. (*Distastefully*) Although I do try to keep my writing and subject matter on a high level.

ART: Sure. Go ahead and use it. And use my picture, too. That'll double the circulation.

BRAD: Anyway, since Spencer Lattimore took over the paper from his old man, this place has changed. That guy is a real egghead.

DIANA: He happens to be a genius. Can he help it?

THROCKMORTON: You know, Brad, you seem to distrust brains.

BRAD: Brains don't belong in a newspaper office. That's why you're all here.

ANNETTE: Well, our Spencer has brains, all right—in addition, of course, to social prominence, which is even more important. Imagine, he graduated from Harvard when he was only nineteen! And I heard something else the other day. Professor Crocker over at State—a fine man from an excellent family—told me that when Spencer was tested back in prep school, his I.Q. was nearly 180.

THROCKMORTON: When Spencer was a kid, he was a legend. He could read when he was a year old. At three he was studying algebra. And at six, he could recite parts of the *Iliad*—in Greek, no less.

BRAD: So what? That doesn't make him a newspaperman. I may not know the *Iliad*—either in Greek or English —but I can smell a good story a mile away.

DIANA: Maybe Spencer can, too.

THROCKMORTON: He's helpful, but he knows so much it's uncanny. He said to me last week, "You know, Throckmorton, you missed the essential point of Ibsen's *The Wild Duck* in your last review." Then he analyzed the play brilliantly, practically quoting the last act by heart.

ANNETTE: That's nothing. I was doing an article on old Glenfield houses a while ago, and I couldn't find a thing about the history of the Captain Stormer house. I talked with many of my friends—and, as you know, my friends belong to the best-informed old families in the city— but I could learn nothing. Spencer discovered I was having trouble. So he told me, "The Captain Stormer house was built in 1707; the architect was James Bull-meadow; the cost was 3,450 pounds." He just never forgets anything.

BRAD: And he sticks his nose into everything.

DIANA: But, after all, he does own the paper.

BRAD: So did his old man. But he kept out of our way. Anyway, Diana, I'll bet he doesn't help you much with your "Advice to the Lovelorn" column. It's not egg-heady enough for him.

DIANA (*Wistfully*): I wish he would. He's cute.

ART: Please—let's not get nauseating. It'll be time for lunch in an hour or so.

BILLY (*Entering hurriedly left and coming to* BRAD): Lieutenant Morrow wants to see you, boss. He says it's important.

ART: So the police department's after you, Brad. What did you do—double-park again?

BRAD: Did he give you any idea of what he wants?

BILLY: No, but he sounds angry.

BRAD: Swell. That's just peachy. All I need to make my morning complete is an angry cop. Well, send him in here. (BILLY *exits left*.) How's that review coming, Throckmorton?

THROCKMORTON (*With a flourish*): Done! Some of the most deathless prose I've ever written. (*He rises and brings copy to* BRAD.) If any of the big words floor you, I'll be glad to explain them.

BRAD: Oh, you drama critics are clever boys.

THROCKMORTON: That we are. We're the only intellectuals left in the newspaper world. (*Going toward left*) Now I think I've earned a cup of coffee.

BRAD (*Calling after him*): Don't talk to me about intellectuals. It's bad enough that the publisher is one.

THROCKMORTON (*About to exit, almost collides with* LIEUTENANT MORROW): Sorry, Lieutenant. (THROCKMORTON *exits as* LIEUTENANT *goes to* BRAD.)

ART: I didn't know that any of Glenfield's finest were up before noon.

LIEUTENANT (*Speaking toughly*): Save your cracks for the funny papers, Art. Hello, Annette. Hello, Diana.

ANNETTE: Hello, Lieutenant.

DIANA: Nice to see you, Lieutenant.

BRAD: So what's cooking?

LIEUTENANT: Plenty. I'm up here on the commissioner's orders. He's really sore.

BRAD (*Pretending fright*): O-oh! That's terrible! I'm all goose pimples!

LIEUTENANT: And he has a right to be sore. That was a crazy editorial in last night's *Echo*.

BRAD: So that's it! Well, Lieutenant, I had nothing to do

with that editorial. That was the young genius's idea—our brilliant publisher. I told him he was going out on a limb. But the boy won't listen to me.

LIEUTENANT: It makes the police department look like a bunch of idiots.

ART (*With mock dismay*): Oh, how terrible!

LIEUTENANT: We know who pulled the robbery at the Glenfield National Bank. It was Pickles Dill and Nevermore Nevins. They were identified.

DIANA (*Loyally*): That was Mr. Lattimore's point in the editorial. You know who did it, but you can't find them. They've vanished.

ANNETTE: Like ships that pass in the night.

LIEUTENANT: But your young publisher was pretty nasty about things. (*He takes a newspaper clipping from his pocket.*) This sounds like double talk to me. (*He reads.*) "It seems to us that if the police department used the processes of reasoning and logical thinking and made deductions from existing evidence, the whereabouts of Pickles Dill and Nevermore Nevins could easily be determined."

BRAD (*Shaking his head*): Look, I'm on your side. I told Lattimore he was biting off more than he could chew.

ART: You see, Lieutenant, our fair-haired boy still thinks he's wowing them at Harvard. He's still up in his ivory tower.

DIANA: That's not fair, Art.

ANNETTE: Art may be correct, though. At Miss Finch's we were taught that there's sometimes a big difference between pure theory and actual practice.

LIEUTENANT: So what does this Lattimore expect us to do? Use a crystal ball or consult a fortune-teller? We've been going over this whole area with a fine-toothed comb.

We're working day and night on the case. And then some bright guy with a bug in his ear starts taking swipes at us.

ART: I agree with you, too. But what am I supposed to do? I'm only one of the slaves here. (SPENCER *enters left*.)

SPENCER: Good morning, all. (*He goes to* DIANA's *desk*.) Miss Charles, I've been thinking about that little problem addressed to you from "Heartbroken." In your answer, I think you should remind her that we must never forget Emerson's law of compensation. Let's see if I can remember Emerson's words correctly.

DIANA (*Admiringly*): I'm sure you can.

SPENCER (*Closing eyes*): Ah, yes, I have it. "Punishment is a fruit that unsuspected ripens within the flower of the pleasure which concealed it." I think that will answer "Heartbroken."

ART: That is, if she understands Emerson.

SPENCER: Doesn't everybody?

DIANA: Thank you so much, Mr. Lattimore. I certainly will use the quotation.

BRAD: Lieutenant Morrow has a bit of a complaint, Mr. Lattimore.

SPENCER (*Smiling*): I can guess its nature.

LIEUTENANT: You were pretty hard on us, Mr. Lattimore. We don't mind fair criticism, but yours was unreasonable.

SPENCER (*Quietly and pleasantly*): Unreasonable? I hardly think so. I believe wholeheartedly what I said in that editorial. Reason is the tool that distinguishes us from the lower animals. I still think that knowing what you do about the lives, characters, and backgrounds of Pickles Dill and Nevermore Nevins, you should be able, through logical deduction, to discover where they are hiding out.

LIEUTENANT: That sort of Sherlock Holmes stuff might work in books, Mr. Lattimore, but this is real life. And Pickles Dill and Nevermore Nevins are a couple of cagey guys.

SPENCER (*Smiling*): Then the police ought to be cagey, too.

LIEUTENANT: Let me get this straight. You actually think that with what we already know about these two hoods, we should be able to deduce where they're hiding?

SPENCER: I most certainly do.

LIEUTENANT (*Pointedly*): Could *you* do it?

SPENCER: I think so. I've already thought about it.

LIEUTENANT: Let me call your bluff, Mr. Lattimore. I'll give you all the information we have on these two crooks. And I'll make a little bet with you. I'll bet you a good dinner at the Glenfield Country Club that you'll be just as much in the dark about where those guys are hiding as we are.

ANNETTE: Imagine celebrating the arrest of two hoodlums at Glenfield's most select club.

SPENCER: Lieutenant, I'll take you up on that. And I don't need any information from you. We have in our morgue a complete file on Pickles and Nevermore. That's all the data I'll need.

LIEUTENANT: I know you're bright, Mr. Lattimore. I know all about your college career. But you're going to find out that police work isn't like life on an ivy-covered campus. (*Holding out hand*) Let's shake hands on that bet. This is one time when I'm betting on a sure thing.

SPENCER (*Shaking hands*): We'll see. I don't pretend to be infallible, but I have a great respect for human reason. One more thing, though. I'd like to add a stipulation to our little wager. If I am able to lead you to the whereabouts of Pickles and Nevermore, I want you to bring them here before you take them to the station for booking. I want to talk with them.

ART: You want those hoods in here?

ANNETTE: I can't think of anything more distasteful. (*Haughtily*) Bringing those unsavory characters here! I certainly don't want any social dealings with criminals. It would be highly improper for a woman of my position.

DIANA: I think it might be fun.

LIEUTENANT: O.K. I'll do it. The chances of your ever being able to give us a good tip, Mr. Lattimore, are as slim as a skeleton, anyway. (*Ironically*) Do you want to tell me where they are now?

SPENCER (*Smiling good-humoredly*): All in good time, Lieutenant. I have my homework to do first. Let's say that by tomorrow morning, if all goes well, I'll be able to supply you with the information.

LIEUTENANT: You're an optimist, Mr. Lattimore. But it's a deal. (*He goes toward left.*) The prices at the Glenfield Country Club are a bit steep for me, anyway. (*He grins and exits.*)

SPENCER: Miss Charles, will you please get me the files on Pickles Dill and Nevermore Nevins?

DIANA: Right away, Mr. Lattimore. (*She exits quickly left.*)

BRAD: You're the boss, Mr. Lattimore, and I should probably keep my mouth shut. But I don't like this. News of this little bet will get out, and if you don't deliver the goods, this paper will become a laughingstock.

SPENCER: Look at the other side of the picture, Brad. If

we're successful, it will be invaluable publicity for the paper.

ANNETTE: I think I can speak for the cream of Glenfield society when I say that we shall be utterly thrilled by your success, Mr. Lattimore. Some of us, I am happy to say, understand the importance of intellect.

ART: I spend most of my time with the sour milk of Glenfield society. So it won't make much difference.

DIANA (*Entering left, carrying two bulky folders*): Here they are, Mr. Lattimore.

SPENCER (*Taking folders*): Thank you. May I use your desk for a moment?

DIANA: Of course.

SPENCER (*Sits at* DIANA's *desk and opens one of folders*): This is devoted to Nevermore Nevins' life and works. (*He removes some clippings from folder and begins to read them.* DIANA *looks with interest over his shoulder.*) Here's something most interesting, Art. I had no idea that you ever knew our friend, Nevermore.

ANNETTE: Art—how could you ever stoop so low?

ART: It was easy. I went up to State Prison where he was serving time a few years ago. He was a great reader and was working in the prison library. I did an interview called "The Literary World of Nevermore Nevins."

SPENCER: I note that Nevermore says his favorite writer is Edgar Allan Poe.

ART: Sure. That's where he got his nickname. From Poe's poem, "The Raven".

SPENCER: And that his favorite Poe story is "The Purloined Letter." Mm-m. Most revealing.

THROCKMORTON (*Entering left*): Nothing like a cup of coffee to steady the nerves after writing an unfavorable review.

ANNETTE: Sh-h. Mr. Lattimore's thinking.

SPENCER: Throckmorton. Just the man I want to see. I haven't read "The Purloined Letter" since I was in prep school. I recall the plot, but, as I remember, the point of the story is really its theme. Am I correct, Throckmorton?

THROCKMORTON: Yes, the plot is that an important letter has disappeared and the police cannot find it. Then the great detective, Auguste Dupin, guarantees to find the letter. It turns out to be in the room in which the police have been looking.

SPENCER: Right. I remember. It was hidden on a table with other letters. That's the point: it has been hidden in the most obvious place of all—so obvious that the police overlooked it.

ART: As Nevermore remarked to me, "That Poe could have made a fortune in my business. He had some magnificent ideas."

SPENCER: Exactly. (*Opening the other folder*) And now for Pickles Dill. (*He looks at clippings.*) I notice that his mother, Ma Dill, appears in most of this material about him.

ART: I know good old Ma. Quiet and law-abiding.

ANNETTE: I saw her once at an antique show. Nice, dignified old lady.

SPENCER: She seems ashamed of her son, Pickles, though. I note that the most frequent quote from her in this material is, "I don't understand my boy. I've tried to raise him to be a good citizen. I just will not have any more to do with him."

ART: That's Ma, all right. Stands up for law and virtue every time.

SPENCER: Yet after Pickles was released from jail last time, he and Ma took a cruise to the West Indies. (*Thoughtfully*) Suggests a great deal, doesn't it?

BRAD (*Looking at a clipping*): And this item is most informative. Pickles has managed to break out of jail twice—both times with the aid of a prisoner who was a trusty.

DIANA: A trusty is a prisoner whom the authorities allow to do odd jobs, isn't he? Don't they even let him have the keys to cells, sometimes?

BRAD: Right you are.

SPENCER: I think I see a few clues in all this data. (*He rises with folders.*) Miss Charles, will you come into my office, please? I may need you.

DIANA: Of course.

SPENCER: Good. Let's put the reasoning process to work. I suspect that we may really come up with something. (*He and* DIANA *exit up center.*)

BRAD (*Shaking his head*): You know what they say—these geniuses burn themselves out young. Too much thinking. That boy is cracking up.

THROCKMORTON: Don't sell him short, Brad.

ART: I agree with Brad for once. Spencer may be bright, but now he's acting like a kid playing cops and robbers.

BRAD: Well, we have a paper to get out. (*Harshly*) What do you say, Annette? I want that story on the Hanscom wedding.

ANNETTE: Right. It was a lovely affair. Only the best people were present.

BRAD: And, Throckmorton, this *Macbeth* review will have to be cut. (*He begins to cross out parts of copy.*)

THROCKMORTON: That's right. We need more space for football games and bowling tournaments. But for Shakespeare—no room at the inn.

BRAD: Come over some night, and you can cry on my shoulder. Copy boy! (BILLY *rushes in at left.*) Take this to the pressroom. (BILLY *takes copy and exits hurriedly.*)

ART (*Rising and coming to* BRAD): Here's the fire story. It's a masterpiece.

BRAD: That's the laugh of the week. (*Staring thoughtfully into space*) "The Purloined Letter", by Poe. Ma Dill. West Indies cruise. Trusties. (*He shakes his head.*) That Spencer is really way out. Of all the newspapers in the country, I have to land with this one! (*He begins to pencil copy savagely, as the curtain falls.*)

* * * * *

SCENE 2

TIME: *About ten o'clock the next morning.*

SETTING: *Same as Scene 1.*

AT RISE: DIANA *and* ANNETTE *are standing at center.*

ANNETTE: Where is Brad?

DIANA: In the pressroom for a moment. Art's out on a story. And Throckmorton isn't in yet. He was at an opening last night, and he's probably catching up on his sleep.

ANNETTE: I know it is bad taste to pry into another's affairs. (*She sits behind* BRAD's *desk.*) But I have been wondering how Spencer's thinking went yesterday.

DIANA: He went over the files for about an hour and then made several phone calls. Then he took the files home with him last night. (*Sighing*) I had a wonderful talk with him. Do you know that he's a lonely man?

ANNETTE: With all his brains, and money, and high social position? I can scarcely believe it.

DIANA: But he really is lonely. Being so brilliant has set him apart. What that man needs is affection.

ANNETTE: And I suppose that you'd like to give it to him.

DIANA: There's no use in my denying it. I know it's obvious to all of you here in the office. (*Sighing*) But it's not obvious to Spencer. I don't think he even knows I'm a girl.

ANNETTE: You must remember that he is a man of good taste. And people of good taste—I know this for I, of course, meet them socially—do not wear their hearts on their sleeves.

DIANA: I suppose not.

ANNETTE (*More kindly*): However, I sympathize with you.

DIANA: Thanks.

ANNETTE: But what I really want to know is whether Spencer did come up with an idea about where Pickles Dill and Nevermore Nevins are hiding? My, what horrible names!

DIANA: Well—yes.

ANNETTE: Where?

DIANA: I'm sorry, Annette, but all I can tell you is that he phoned Lieutenant Morrow about eight this morning. (*Looking at watch*) That was two hours ago. He told the Lieutenant where he thinks Pickles and Nevermore may be.

ANNETTE: And just where is this place?

DIANA: Spencer swore me to silence, so I can't tell. Brad and Art know that Spencer gave the information to the police, but they don't know the place he mentioned either.

BRAD (*Entering left*): Cut the gossiping, girls. There's work to be done. And, Annette, I'd like my desk, if you don't mind.

ANNETTE (*Rising*): There's such a thing as common courtesy, Brad.

BRAD: I'm common—but I'm not courteous. I've never made the society page. (ANNETTE *goes to her own desk and* DIANA *to hers.* BRAD *sits down and looks at his watch.*) The police aren't exactly burning the telephone wires with cries of joy about finding those two crooks. I'm afraid our boy Spencer overestimated his own brilliance.

DIANA: It's still early.

ART (*Entering wearily at left, goes to his desk and sits*): Do me a favor, Brad, will you? The next time you want a City Council meeting covered, send Billy. Those guys are steaming up the place with hot air. (*Looking at watch*) Any reports on the genius's educated guess?

BRAD: None—and there won't be any. The whole thing's the failure of the century. When the news leaks out, we won't be able to hold up our heads in this town. (THROCKMORTON *enters left.*) How nice of you to come in, Throckmorton. Are you sure you've had enough rest? May I fix you a sandwich? You want to lie down on the sofa in the boss's office for a while?

THROCKMORTON: Spare me your witticisms, Brad. I saw a play last night that may mean the end of the theater in the twentieth century. It was ghastly. (*Sitting at his desk*) And speaking of ghastly matters, any news about Pickles and Nevermore?

ART: Those two boys are probably counting their money and happily sipping their morning coffee right now.

SPENCER (*Enters up center.* DIANA *looks up at him expectantly. He meets her inquiring look and shakes his head*): I haven't heard a thing yet. But I'm sure I must be right. Given the characters and backgrounds of those two men, I don't see how there can be any other answer. (*Looking at watch*) The police have had two hours to round up Pickles and Nevermore. I don't understand the delay.

BRAD: You could have been wrong, you know.

SPENCER: I've said before that I don't pretend to be infallible. But the human reason can accomplish a great deal if it is used properly.

BILLY (*Entering hurriedly left*): A police car just drove up, Mr. Lattimore!

SPENCER (*Perking up*): Who's in it?

BILLY: Quite a crowd. The only one I recognized was the Lieutenant.

SPENCER: Go down, Billy, and hurry them up here. (*Smiling*) This suspense is bad for the nerves. (BILLY *exits left.*)

ART: I could use something to calm me down right now.

ANNETTE: I hope you've been successful, Mr. Lattimore, but I shudder to think that we may shortly be visited by two horrible creatures.

THROCKMORTON: Everybody can't be in the social register, Annette. (BILLY *returns, followed by* NEVERMORE NEVINS, PICKLES DILL, MA DILL, *and* LIEUTENANT MORROW. NEVERMORE *and* PICKLES *are handcuffed together.* BILLY *stands entranced at doorway through rest of scene.*)

LIEUTENANT (*Admiringly*): I don't know how you did it, Mr. Lattimore, but you had these guys pegged to a "T." And is my face red! They were actually right under our noses in the city jail!

BRAD (*Open-mouthed with astonishment*): In the what!

ANNETTE: The city jail!

THROCKMORTON: The age of miracles has not passed.

SPENCER (*Happily*): Of course they were in the city jail. Where else could they be?

THROCKMORTON: Mr. Lattimore, how did you ever figure it out?

ART: It's unbelievable.

SPENCER: I'll be happy to answer your question, Throckmorton. Let me begin with Mr. Nevins.

NEVERMORE: I am Nevermore Nevins and obviously at your service—although somewhat reluctantly, as the Lieutenant can tell you.

SPENCER: Well, Mr. Nevins, I began with your literary tastes. What's your favorite Poe story?

NEVERMORE: Ah, the immortal Poe! What a magnificent partner he would have made! A man of great creative imagination—not at all like this fellow here. (*He nods toward* PICKLES.)

PICKLES: Listen to who's talking. You're the guy who figured out the hiding in jail bit.

NEVERMORE: Pay no attention to him. He is most uncouth. In reply to your query, my favorite Poe story is undoubtedly "The Purloined Letter."

SPENCER: I know. Its basic theme appeals to you.

NEVERMORE: Indeed it does.

PICKLES: Say, what is this? It's enough to be grilled by the cops. Take me to my lawyer.

NEVERMORE: Please forgive these rude outbursts. Yes, as I was saying, the theme—that the best way to hide anything is to put it in the most obvious place—is a most provocative one.

SPENCER: Exactly. Now certainly the city jail is about as obvious a place as one can find.

NEVERMORE: Indubitably. But how did you know?

SPENCER: I discovered from reading your newspaper file that Pickles had broken out of jail twice with the aid of a trusty. I said to myself, "Why couldn't he break *into* jail in the same way?" And why couldn't you and Pickles, with the help of a trusty, change places with two other prisoners?

LIEUTENANT: They did just that. They changed places with two old pals of theirs—Sam the Sniper and Joe the Gyp. The trusty had keys to the cells and to a side door.

SPENCER: I had a suspicion that after a week or two, once the heat was off, Nevermore and Pickles would escape, collect the swag, and be off to Mexico or somewhere. I assume the money was in the place I indicated, Lieutenant?

LIEUTENANT: It sure was.

NEVERMORE: How did you ever deduce that we had hidden the swag at Ma's?

SPENCER: Very obvious. Ma lives only two blocks from the Glenfield National Bank, doesn't she?

MA: It's a lovely apartment. I'd like to have you all over some time. I'll make a special batch of cookies.

SPENCER: I suspected that Ma has always been in on Pickles' deals, despite the quotes she's given the newspapers.

MA: I don't understand my son. I've tried to raise him to be a good citizen. I just will not have anything more to do with him.

PICKLES: Nuts.

ANNETTE: You might show some respect for your mother, Mr. Dill.

MA: Thank you, my dear.

SPENCER: I think your question is answered, Mr. Nevins. Despite all that Ma says, she and Pickles took a cruise together not long ago.

NEVERMORE (*Admiringly*): I follow your reasoning very well. Mr. Lattimore, I must hand it to you.

PICKLES: I'd like to hand him something.

MA: Now, son, behave like a gentleman.

NEVERMORE (*Earnestly*): Mr. Lattimore, perhaps circumstances are such that I shall be removed from the daily ranks of society for a considerable period. But when I return to my activities, you and I should get together. We could go far. What a partnership ours would be, with your intellect and my experience!

SPENCER: Well, thank you, Mr. Nevins, but I have a newspaper to run.

MA: I don't understand all this. The boys just dropped in a couple of days ago for a cup of tea. Pickles is very partial to my tea and homemade cookies.

LIEUTENANT: We found the two hundred thousand smackers in Ma's coal bin.

MA: It's a mystery to me.

LIEUTENANT: Come off it, Ma. You're not forgetting that we found your bank books, are you? Eighteen different bank books, Mr. Lattimore—and a mighty tidy sum. Looks as if Pickles has been good to you, Ma.

MA (*Sweetly*): Just a few dollars for my old age.

NEVERMORE: I am still of the opinion that you are wasting your talents in the newspaper business, Mr. Lattimore. I estimate—and this is conservative—that we could make a million dollars together.

THROCKMORTON: Look me up instead, Mr. Nevins. I'm brainy, too.

ART: So am I.

NEVERMORE: Why, you're my old friend, Art Lakeland. That was a delightful story you did about me a few

years ago. It occupies a cherished place in my scrap-
book.

ART: Nevermore, that's really touching. (*Placing hand over heart*) Sort of gets me right here.

NEVERMORE: To speak candidly, I thought we had hoodwinked everybody.

PICKLES: Yes, we hoodwinked 'em, all right. (*Jingling handcuffs*) That's why we're wearing these bracelets.

LIEUTENANT: Satisfied now, Mr. Lattimore?

SPENCER: Very satisfied. This has been a most provocative morning. I feel positively exhilarated.

MA (*Admiringly*): Such a vocabulary! (*To* PICKLES) You see, son, how you might have sounded if you'd studied.

PICKLES: But it was you who took me out of the sixth grade.

MA: Now, son, good boys don't talk back to their mothers.

LIEUTENANT: Well, Mr. Lattimore, you win. It'll be a pleasure to buy you that dinner at the Glenfield Country Club.

SPENCER: It'll be a pleasure to be your guest.

LIEUTENANT: And now we'll take these characters down to the station for booking. (*He nudges* PICKLES *and* NEVERMORE *and beckons to* MA.) Let's go.

NEVERMORE: My proposition is still open, Mr. Lattimore.

PICKLES: I'll give the lug a proposition.

THROCKMORTON: "Quoth the Raven, 'Nevermore.'"

LIEUTENANT (*Guides* NEVERMORE, PICKLES *and* MA *toward left, then turns and grins*): I'm afraid these boys are going to be out of circulation for a long time. (*Exits with his charges, followed by* BILLY.)

MA (*Just before exit*): This is all a mistake. The boys just dropped by for a cup of tea. (*She exits still talking.*)

THROCKMORTON: Mr. Lattimore, you deserve a reward.

DIANA (*Impulsively kissing* SPENCER *on the cheek*): I'm so happy! (SPENCER *is momentarily taken aback by the kiss.* DIANA *looks very embarrassed.*)

ANNETTE: Yes, it was a triumph of reason, Mr. Lattimore.

SPENCER: Thank you.

ANNETTE: When I was a student at Miss Finch's, I learned that great thinkers really know how to face the important problems—the big issues of life, death, and bank robberies. But I remember something else from my literature courses at Miss Finch's—a really splendid school. You have read Pascal, haven't you, Mr. Lattimore?

SPENCER (*Puzzled*): Yes.

ANNETTE: Then you must know his famous statement, "The heart has its reasons that reason cannot know."

SPENCER (*Slowly*): "The heart has its reasons—"

DIANA: Annette, you shouldn't—

SPENCER (*Smiling suddenly*): Oh, yes, she should. (*He takes* DIANA's *arm.*) Miss Charles, I want to discuss something personal with you in my office. (DIANA *looks alarmed as he leads her to up center. He stops at door, turns, and smiles.*) Maybe I have neglected the obvious right under my own nose. But that's over. (*He grins.*) And I'd like to announce, friends, that we're not going into this office to exercise any powers of reasoning. (DIANA *smiles happily as she and* SPENCER *exit.*)

ART (*To* ANNETTE): I didn't have you pegged as the sentimental type, Annette.

ANNETTE: You have a great deal to learn, Art. At Miss Finch's, we were taught that to do an occasional good deed was worthy.

THROCKMORTON: What do you think of the boy genius now, Brad?

BRAD (*Huffily*): All right. So I was wrong. A man's entitled to one mistake in a lifetime. (*Gruffly*) Back to work. Get going on that City Council story, Art. And, Throckmorton, write your bilious reactions to that lousy play you saw. Annette, let's have that bit on the Women's Club meeting. (*They all begin working.*) I'm going to get a volume of Edgar Allan Poe, and, by golly, I'm going to read it word for word. (*All laugh.*) Copy boy! (*Curtain falls.*)

THE END

Production Notes

THE TOUCH OF GENIUS

Characters: 8 male; 3 female.

Playing Time: 35 minutes.

Costumes: Modern dress. Brad wears a green eyeshade and is in his shirt sleeves. Annette wears a floppy hat and stylish suit. Lieutenant Morrow wears a trench coat and a hat pulled down over his brow. Pickles and Nevermore should wear shabby clothes.

Properties: Papers, pencils, typewriters, assorted office equipment, newspapers and clippings, two large folders containing clippings and papers, wrist watches, handcuffs.

Setting: The city room of the Glenfield *Daily Echo*. There are five desks with typewriters, pencils, paper, etc., at right and center. There is a door at left and another at up center. Telephones, books, newspapers, bulletin boards and other appropriate items should complete the newspaper office atmosphere.

Lighting: No special effects.

Summer Stock à la Carte

Characters

SALLY HUME, *an attractive girl of eighteen*
LOUISE FARRELL, *a pretty girl of the same age*
CAP HOLMES, *counterman at the Bridge Diner*
JOE BURNS, *a truck driver*
DEWITT CROPPER, *a veteran actor*
CECIL SOMERSBY-THORNTON, *a British tourist*
MRS. SOMERSBY-THORNTON, *his wife*
DIANA CRAIG, *a flamboyant actress*
JERRY BUNCE, *a summer theater director*
MABEL, *a waitress*

TIME: *A summer morning.*
SETTING: *The Bridge Diner, located at one end of Fairview Bridge. At rear, there is a counter behind which are a few coffee makers. On counter, there may be several glass cases containing pies, doughnuts, the usual paraphernalia of a diner. There are stools at the counter. Downstage are several tables and chairs. Up left, a door leads into the kitchen. There is another door at right.*
AT RISE: SALLY HUME *and* LOUISE FARRELL *are seated at a center table.* CAP HOLMES, *the counterman, is con-*

versing across the counter with JOE BURNS, *a truck
driver. Also seated at the counter is* DEWITT CROPPER.

CAP (*As honking of horns is heard offstage*): Joe, they've
done it again!

JOE (*Getting up quickly from stool, going to door right,
and looking out*): Cap, you're right. The same old
story! Those bridge guys must have rocks in their heads!

SALLY (*Interestedly*): What's the matter?

JOE (*Going to* SALLY's *and* LOUISE's *table*): I hope you
girls aren't in a hurry to get anywhere. (*Smiling*) We
may be here a long time.

SALLY: A long time?

JOE: Yes, the drawbridge is stuck again—for the third
time this week. Whenever they open the thing lately,
they have a tough time getting it closed. Something
about expansion in hot weather. Took them three
hours last time.

LOUISE (*Looking at watch*): And we're supposed to be at
Camp Fairview by eleven. It's after ten now.

JOE: Nice place, Camp Fairview.

CAP: Are you girls counselors there?

SALLY: We hope to be. We're going for interviews today.
I'm Sally Hume, and this is Louise Farrell.

JOE: Pleased to meet you. I'm Joe Burns.

CAP: Likewise.

CROPPER (*Rising from stool, going to right, and looking
out*): Fie on modern machinery! It has us in its power.
(*Looks at watch*) I'm supposed to be at a rehearsal in exactly thirty minutes.

CAP: Are you working at the Fairview Summer Theater?

CROPPER (*Returning to counter*): Working is the word.
When one performs in a play with that celebrated ac-

tress, Diana Craig, one works—like a galley slave. She's a she-devil.

CAP: I've heard tell she's a bit of a tartar.

CROPPER: Compared to Diana Craig, Madame Defarge and Lucretia Borgia were Girl Scouts. I have performed in the theater for more years than I care to mention. The name of DeWitt Cropper is known on two continents, but Diana Craig surpasses anyone else I have ever encountered for sheer unpleasantness and unmitigated conceit. (*He sits at stool and sips coffee.* MABEL *enters up left, carrying a plate with a sandwich on it.*)

MABEL (*Placing plate on counter*): Here's your sandwich, Joe. Ham on rye as usual.

JOE (*Returning to counter as sound of honking is heard once more*): Thanks, Mabel. (*Sitting*) That goofy bridge. And I have a load of fish on the truck that ought to be at the Fairview Market right now.

MABEL: Cheer up, Joe. The fish aren't complaining. (MABEL *goes to end of counter, picks up a magazine, sits, and begins to read.*)

CAP: Mabel, if you can tear yourself away from *True Romances* for a couple of minutes, there are two girls over there who haven't been waited on.

MABEL (*Looking up*): Sorry. But don't forget, Cap, that *True Romances* is the only contact I have with real life. Nothing ever happens around this one-horse town. (*Going to* SALLY's *and* LOUISE's *table*) What'll you girls have?

LOUISE: Just coffee—and maybe a doughnut.

SALLY: I'll have the same.

MABEL: Right. (*She goes behind counter to fill the order.*)

SALLY (*Nodding toward* CROPPER *and speaking in low tone to* SALLY): It's so thrilling to be on the premises with a real live actor.

LOUISE (*Smiling*): He looks and talks like an old Shakespearean ham.

SALLY (*Sighing*): I suppose we'll be late for our interviews. Actually, I don't care if I never get to Camp Fairview. Even if I got the job, I'd be wishing I were somewhere else.

LOUISE: Think of the beautiful sunshine and all that wonderful fresh air.

SALLY: Think of being cooped up in a cabin all summer when what I really want to be doing is acting in some summer theater. But getting a stage job is so difficult.

LOUISE: Well, you'll be off to drama school in the fall. Plenty of time to rival Julie Harris and Helen Hayes then.

SALLY: But that's not the point, Louise. I feel as though the entire summer will be wasted. I could be getting valuable experience, but instead I may be playing nursemaid to a lot of little girls, teaching them arts and crafts and how to swim and how to sail a boat.

LOUISE (*Dramatically*): The youth of America need us.

MABEL (*Returning with a tray holding two cups of coffee and two doughnuts*): Here you are, girls. (MABEL *goes to door right and looks out.*) Wow! There's a real line of traffic out there now!

JOE: Waiting in line has become Fairview's favorite sport. That bridge is a bottleneck.

CROPPER: A pox on mechanical bridges and automobiles. Men were happier when they used only the horse for transportation. (MABEL *returns to her counter stool and begins to read her magazine once more.* MR. *and* MRS. CECIL SOMERSBY-THORNTON, *who enter at right, are typically British in appearance.*

CECIL (*Going to counter*): I say, this is a beastly bore, isn't it? I've always read that you Americans were so deucedly efficient, but you can't seem to close that frightful bridge.

CAP: You've got us there, sir. British, aren't you?

CECIL: Right. My wife and I thought we'd see your country, and we're on an automobile tour. Beautiful scenery and all that—and so big, too. (*To wife*) What will you have, my dear?

MRS. SOMERSBY-THORNTON: A nice cup of tea would taste good, Cecil.

CECIL: Quite. But I suppose, my good fellow, that you brew tea with one of those frightful tea bags. Not the right method, you know. Tea should be brewed in a pot—lots of tea—and it should steep for a good long time.

MRS. SOMERSBY-THORNTON (*Quickly*): A tea bag will be all right, Cecil.

CECIL: And I'll have the same, though I should jolly well know better.

CAP: I'll have the waitress bring the tea to a table.

CECIL: Thanks, old boy.

CROPPER (*Staring at* MRS. SOMERSBY-THORNTON): It can't be!

CECIL (*Looking at him*): Something wrong, old man?

CROPPER (*Rising, going to* MRS. SOMERSBY-THORNTON *and extending his hand*): Sybil Merriwether—what a surprise!

MRS. SOMERSBY-THORNTON: Why, DeWitt Cropper. (*Shaking his hand enthusiastically*) After all these years!

CROPPER: To coin a phrase, it's a small world.

MRS. SOMERSBY-THORNTON: DeWitt, I'd like you to meet my husband, Mr. Cecil Somersby-Thornton—Mr. De-Witt Cropper.

CROPPER (*As the two men shake hands*): Delighted. I knew Sybil years ago. In fact, she once played Viola to my Orsino in *Twelfth Night*.

MRS. SOMERSBY-THORNTON: At the Drury Lane in London.

CAP: Mabel, will you take this tea to a table?

MABEL (*Rising from stool*): Right. (MABEL *takes tea to a table.* MR. *and* MRS. SOMERSBY-THORNTON *go to table and sit.* CROPPER *joins them.*)

CROPPER: No longer on the stage, Sybil?

CECIL: Mind you, I've nothing against you theater people—salt of the earth and all that—but when Sybil and I were married, I insisted she give up her career. It's career enough to be Mrs. Somersby-Thornton—old family, and all that, a seat in Parliament, good many social obligations.

CROPPER: I understand.

MRS. SOMERSBY-THORNTON: We do lead a busy life.

CECIL: That's why it's so jolly good to get some free time for this tour. Always wanted to see something of this country. (*He sips tea and grimaces.*) Fine country—but Americans just can't brew tea. Tastes like tepid dishwater.

MRS. SOMERSBY-THORNTON (*Smiling*): You want to remember, dear, that Americans say we don't know how to make coffee.

CECIL: Nonsense. Our coffee is awfully good. (SALLY *and* LOUISE *have been conversing softly.* SALLY *suddenly rises with an air of determination.*)

SALLY: I'll do it. (*She takes a piece of paper from her hand-bag and goes to* CROPPER'S *table.*)

SALLY: Pardon me, Mr. Cropper, but may I have your autograph?

CROPPER (*Beaming*): Why, of course, my dear. A poor thing but mine own, as the Bard would phrase it. (SALLY *hands him the paper, and he takes a pen from his coat pocket.*) What is your name, my dear?

SALLY: Sally Hume.

CROPPER: I shall write, then, "Compliments of DeWitt Cropper to Sally Hume, who is pretty enough to grace any stage."

SALLY: Oh, thank you. (CROPPER *begins to write.*)

MRS. SOMERSBY-THORNTON: Are you interested in the theater, Miss Hume?

SALLY: Very much. I want to be an actress, but everyone tells me that competition in the theater is terrific. My parents think I've made the wrong decision—to go to drama school in the fall. But I've dreamed about acting since I was a little girl.

CECIL: Stars in your eyes and all that sort of thing, what?

SALLY: I suppose so.

MRS. SOMERSBY-THORNTON: My advice is not to give up. If you really think you have the ability to become an actress, have faith in yourself. I was on the stage before my marriage.

SALLY: You were?

CROPPER (*Handing paper to* SALLY): She was, indeed. Acted with her myself, and she was perfectly charming.

MRS. SOMERSBY-THORNTON: Thank you, DeWitt.

CROPPER: Not at all like Diana Craig, with whom I have the current misfortune of appearing.

SALLY: Miss Craig's a good actress, though, isn't she?

CROPPER: Miss Craig knows her way about the stage—she can tread the boards with skill. But she is a most exasperating woman, and when she doesn't get her own way, she's a tigress.

CECIL: Oh, I say, she must be frightfully interesting.

CROPPER: A pox on women who are interesting in that way.

SALLY: All I know is that I'd change places with her any day—tigress or not.

MRS. SOMERSBY-THORNTON: Who knows, Miss Hume? Perhaps some day you will have what you Americans call a "break." Do you know how I became an actress? It might encourage you. I merely went into a Lyons Shop in London one day for tea. I ordered it, and, standing behind me, was Sir Gregory Challingsworth, one of the great producers of the day. He spoke to me—I remember his exact words. "Young woman," he said, "you have a positively charming voice. You should be in the theater." And, within a month, with his encouragement, I had a walk-on part in a Mayfair comedy.

CECIL: Good, too. Saw her in it. Said to myself, "Cecil, that's the girl you're jolly well going to marry."

SALLY: How romantic! Thank you for the story; it is encouraging. And thank you for the autograph, Mr. Cropper.

CROPPER: A pleasure. (SALLY *returns to her table.* DIANA CRAIG *and* JERRY BUNCE *enter.* DIANA, *theatrical and imperious, goes to counter.*)

DIANA (*Dramatically*): A cup of coffee, darling. I'm no good in the morning until I've had my first cup anyway.

CAP: Coming right up, ma'am.

JERRY: Make mine the same. Let's sit at a table, Diana.

DIANA: All right, darling. That bridge is one of the scourges of civilization. We'll be late for rehearsal again.

SALLY: (*Excitedly to* LOUISE): That's Diana Craig, the famous actress!

LOUISE: I thought I recognized her from television. (JERRY *and* DIANA *go to table next to* SALLY'S. *As* JERRY *and* DIANA *sit down, she turns and sees* CROPPER.)

DIANA (*With exaggerated sweetness*): DeWitt, darling, how nice to see you up and around. (*Acidly*) The way you plodded through our last scene yesterday, I thought you might be coming down with the black plague.

CROPPER: Ah, Diana, my dear, still your customary sweet self, I see. Spreading sweetness and light wherever you go.

DIANA: Save your wit for rehearsals, darling. (*She sits and turns to* JERRY.) And speaking of rehearsals, Jerry, where did the glorious Fairview Summer Theater ever dig up that girl who is playing my daughter? She has no more talent than a backward baboon. And, besides, she's suffering from an advanced case of adenoids.

JERRY: She comes well recommended, Diana.

DIANA (*Sweetly*): By whom, darling—King Kong or Count Dracula?

JERRY: Don't be hard on the girl.

DIANA: Look, Jerry darling, whether a theater is on Broadway or out in the miserable sticks like this one, every time I step onstage, I have my reputation to consider. I will not have an audience laughing at me—and how can they help laughing when I begin to exchange dialogue with that adenoidal creature? (MABEL *brings two cups of coffee and sets them on table*.) Thank you, darling. (MABEL *returns to the counter and her magazine*. DIANA *takes a sip of the coffee*.) No, darling, that girl must go—to Mars preferably. There's a clause in my contract for this engagement that says I can exercise control over the rest of the cast. And that's just what I'm going to do. As the director of this little opus, it's up to you to break the sad news to Little Miss Mumbly.

JERRY (*With exasperation*): Be reasonable, Diana. Where am I going to get a replacement at this late date? The show opens next week.

DIANA (*Gesturing flamboyantly*): Scour the country, darling. Call the agents. Get in touch with your friends— who, I am sure, are numerous. But do it. Or the Fairview Summer Theater will be in for a nice breach of contract suit. (*Sipping coffee*) And I'm not fooling, darling. I will not step on the stage with that lamebrain.

JERRY (*Shaking his head*): You're a hard woman, Diana.

DIANA: When it concerns my career, darling, I'm as hard as concrete. And don't you forget it.

CROPPER (*Who has been eavesdropping*): Amen!

DIANA (*Picking up her cup and shaking it menacingly at* CROPPER): No remarks from the peanut gallery, Mr. Hamlet of 1920, or I'll bounce this off your noggin.

CROPPER: Always the lady, Diana. As the Bard says, "Her voice was ever soft, gentle, and low—an excellent thing in woman." (*Angrily*) And I last played Hamlet last summer, not 1920. 1920 is in your mind because I suspect it was the year in which you were born.

DIANA: You cad! I came into the world long after 1920.

CROPPER: Again to quote the Bard, "A star danced when I was born."

DIANA: Blah to you, DeWitt. (*She rises, goes to door right and looks out.*) The bridge is still open as wide as ever.

JOE: Lady, it'll be that way for a long time.

DIANA: What a mess! (*Returning to table*) You'd think, darling, that in this marvelous age of science and technology, they'd be able to tackle so trifling a problem as a bridge that won't close.

JERRY: Don't be restless, Diana. There's nothing we can do.

DIANA: You'd think that a couple of those egghead scientists at Fairview College would be able to suggest something. Anyway, the longer we stay here, the less time I have to look at that bad excuse for an actress— and she's supposed to be my daughter.

JERRY: Look, Diana, I promise I'll do something about her. But give me time. Young actresses don't grow on trees.

DIANA: I don't know about that. She looks as though she'd just climbed down from one. And when she speaks, she mumbles like an engine running on only two cylinders.

SALLY (*Amused and excited by what she has overheard; dramatically*): "Speak the speech, I pray you, as I pronounced it to you, trippingly on the tongue; but if you mouth it, as many of your players do, I had as lief the town crier spoke my lines."

DIANA (*Perking up with interest, rising, and going quickly to* SALLY's *table*): Darling, that was from *Hamlet*, wasn't it?

CROPPER: Even an idiot could recognize those lines.

DIANA (*Turning on him angrily*): DeWitt, do me a favor, will you? Go outside and jump off that miserable bridge. Tie a rock around your neck first.

CROPPER (*Sarcastically*): Usually I will do anything to oblige a lady. (*Looking about him*) But inasmuch as the request does not come from a lady, I shall have to decline.

JERRY: Now, now—

DIANA (*Advancing on* CROPPER): You ham! You two-bit stock company player—

JERRY (*Grabbing her by the arm and leading her, struggling, back to* SALLY'S *table*): You were going to say something to this young woman, Diana.

DIANA (*Smiling sweetly*): Forgive my little outburst. I usually am as gentle as the proverbial lamb. But that man (*She points theatrically at* CROPPER) brings out the latent beast in me.

CROPPER: Latent! Ha!

CECIL: Oh, I say, none of this is really cricket, you know. Not in good taste at all.

MRS. SOMERSBY-THORNTON: Remember, we're in America, dear. Things are different here.

DIANA: What I was going to say, darling, was that I once played Ophelia years ago. (*Catching herself*) Well, not so many years ago. Of course, I began my career when I was very young—a child really. I'm Diana Craig.

SALLY: Yes, I know, Miss Craig. I recognized you at once. This is my friend, Louise Farrell. And I'm Sally Hume.

DIANA: Charmed, darlings. Forgive my being personal, Sally, but how old are you?

SALLY: Eighteen.

DIANA: This handsome fellow is Jerry Bunce, who directs the goings-on at the Fairview Summer Theater. Isn't this a pretty girl, Jerry?

JERRY (*Eying* SALLY *and* LOUISE *appreciatively*): They're both pretty girls.

DIANA: And just think of it, darling, Sally quotes Shakespeare. Now, I ask you, how many pretty girls do you know who can quote the Bard—or, for that matter, have even heard of him?

CECIL (*Joining in the discussion he has overheard*): Oh, I say, a good many attractive young women in England are acquainted with Shakespeare. Fine system of education there, don't you know. Really gives them the best of everything.

SALLY (*Smiling at* DIANA): I've been interested in the theater since I was a little girl.

LOUISE: Sally's going to drama school in the fall.

DIANA: Well, bless you, darling. The theater is a rat race, but it gets in one's blood. And I can tell you that an actress faces plenty of problems—girls with adenoids, producers with no brains, old ham actors who think they know everything—

CROPPER: I resent that!

DIANA: If the shoe fits, darling, wear it on your size twelve foot.

JERRY: Diana, I told you I'd try to do something about that girl in the play.

DIANA (*Sweetly*): If you don't, darling, I'll boil you in oil. (*To* MABEL) Another cup of coffee, please. It looks as though we're going to be stranded here until doomsday. Well, nice to have met you, darlings. And, Sally, keep up your yen for Shakespeare—he's a winner.

SALLY: Thank you, Miss Craig, I will. (DIANA *and* JERRY *return to their table, where* MABEL *brings the coffee, then returns to her magazine.*) Isn't she glamorous?

LOUISE: Yes, but I'm inclined to agree with Mr. Cropper. She's a pretty tough specimen.

SALLY: Louise, you just don't understand. All good actresses are temperamental. It's all part of being a creative artist. All I know is that I'd gladly change places with her. I'm just fated to read bedtime stories to kids at camp and to see that they don't get their feet wet.

JOE (*Rising*): Think I'll take a look around outside, Cap. Sort of cheer the boys on.

CAP: I guess the boys could stand some cheering. (JOE *exits right.* DIANA *and* JERRY *have been conversing earnestly in low tones.*)

DIANA: Darling, I'm almost certain it would work.

JERRY: Look, Diana, be sensible. You can't take just anybody and put her in a part like that.

DIANA: You did, when you cast Little Miss Adenoids in the role.

JERRY: But this girl—

DIANA: Haven't you ever heard of talented people being discovered, darling? Where's your faith? The girl has the looks for the part. She's the right age.

JERRY: Don't you see that the big question is—can she act?

DIANA (*Rising*): Well, darling, let's find out if she can act. What's so difficult about that? (*She and* JERRY *go to* SALLY's *table.*) Darling, I have a proposition for you.

SALLY: A proposition?

DIANA: You'd like to be in the theater, wouldn't you?

SALLY: That's all I dream about.

JERRY: Here's the situation. Miss Craig is not satisfied with the girl who is playing her daughter in the Fairview Summer Theater production which opens next week.

DIANA: Not satisfied! I'm appalled by her! She's a walking zombie.

JERRY: Miss Craig thinks you're the right type for the role. But I may as well be frank with you. I don't agree with all of Miss Craig's sudden inspirations. Acting takes talent. It's not just a lark.

LOUISE (*Loyally*): Sally's acted in lots of high school

plays, and she's done plenty of work with the little theater group back home, too.

JERRY: Really? What parts have you done?

SALLY: I played Juliet in *Romeo and Juliet* and Emily in *Our Town*, and—

JERRY: So you played Juliet. Can you remember any of the lines?

SALLY (*Proudly*): I've never forgotten any of them. I loved the role.

DIANA: There you are, darling! What did I tell you? The girl has talent.

JERRY: Not so fast, Diana. She played the role, but the question is—how did she play it?

CROPPER (*Who has been listening with interest*): Let us, as the Bard says, brave "the slings and arrows of outrageous fortune." I have played Romeo many times. (*He rises.*) And I should be happy to be the Romeo to your Juliet, young lady.

DIANA: You'd be more suited to Rip Van Winkle, after his twenty-year sleep.

CROPPER: Fie on your unkind comments, Diana! I shall rise above them. What do you say, young lady? Are you willing?

SALLY (*Swallowing*): W-well, I s-suppose so.

CROPPER: Good, I am positive I remember most of the lines. Young lady, stand behind the counter.

JERRY: Good idea. We can get an idea of how her voice carries.

CECIL: Oh, I say, how jolly! Shakespeare in a diner. It just could not happen in England.

MRS. SOMERSBY-THORNTON: Isn't it exciting!

CAP: It's not every day we get an audition in this eatery. Stand over here, miss. (*He points behind the counter.*

SALLY *goes slowly behind counter. She is obviously nervous.*)

CROPPER (*Standing importantly at center*): We'll try part of the balcony scene. We'll assume you've just completed the "Romeo, Romeo, wherefore art thou Romeo?" speech, not knowing I'm hidden in the shadows of the balcony. Suddenly, I reveal myself and speak.

DIANA (*To* SALLY): Give it all you've got, darling, despite the fact that Romeo is woefully miscast.

CROPPER: A pox on you, Diana. (*He now assumes a theatrical pose.*)

"I take thee at thy word.

Call me but love, and I'll be new baptiz'd;

Henceforth I never will be Romeo."

DIANA: That's for sure.

SALLY:

"What man art thou, that, thus bescreen'd in night,

So stumblest on my counsel?"

CROPPER:

"By a name

I know not how to tell thee who I am:

My name, dear saint, is hateful to myself,

Because it is an enemy to thee;

Had I it written, I would tear the word."

(JOE *enters at right and stands in doorway watching the scene.*)

SALLY:

"My ears have not yet drunk a hundred words

Of thy tongue's uttering, yet I know the sound:

Art thou not Romeo and a Montague?"

JERRY: Not bad. Let's cut now to the cue for your long speech, Sally. Give her the cue, DeWitt. The "I am no pilot" bit.

CROPPER:

> "I am no pilot; yet wert thou as far
> As that vast shore wash'd with the farthest sea,
> I should adventure for such merchandise."

SALLY:

> "Thou know'st the mask of night is on my face,
> Else would a maiden blush bepaint my cheek
> For that which thou hast heard me speak tonight.
> Fain would I dwell on form, fain, fain deny
> What I have spoke: but farewell compliment!
> Dost thou love me? I know thou wilt say 'Ay';
> And I will take thy word: yet, if thou swear'st,
> Thou may prove false. At lovers' perjuries,
> They say, Jove laughs. O gentle Romeo,
> If thou dost love, pronounce it faithfully;
> Or if thou think'st I am too quickly won,
> I'll frown and be perverse, and say thee nay—"

JERRY: That's enough.

CROPPER: I have a fine speech coming up. You might at least let me get to it.

DIANA: Save your ham for some other time, DeWitt. (*To* SALLY) That was lovely, darling. I knew I was right. Well, Jerry? (SALLY *comes timidly from behind counter to table.*)

CAP: I don't know much about Shakespeare, but I liked that.

MRS. SOMERSBY-THORNTON: It was sweet.

CECIL: Deucedly good. The Bard's sometimes a bit above my head and all that, but I thought this little scene was simply ripping.

SALLY (*Anxiously to* JERRY): How did I do?

JERRY: You're not Katharine Cornell. (SALLY's *face falls.*) But don't be disturbed. (*Smiling*) Not many actresses are. Let me put it this way. You have possibilities. I think that with training and experience, you might make it.

DIANA: Of course she'll make it, darling. And she's going to start by playing my daughter.

JERRY: I'm going to surprise you, Diana. I agree with you. I think that with proper guidance—which I'll do my best to give—she can play the part.

LOUISE (*Hugging* SALLY): Congratulations! I'll miss you at camp—if I get the job—but I'll come over to see you in the show.

SALLY (*Sinking into chair*): I'm speechless.

JERRY (*Grinning*): Well, don't stay that way. Actresses have to talk.

DIANA: Darling, I'm so happy all this is settled. We'll have your first rehearsal this afternoon.

LOUISE: I'll explain at the camp interview why you didn't appear, Sally. And I'm sure there are plenty of other candidates for counselors' jobs, so you won't really be letting anybody down.

JERRY: Right. And, Miss Farrell, when you want to come over to watch Sally perform, just give me a ring at the theater. I'll be glad to drive over to camp to pick you up.

LOUISE: Thank you.

SALLY: And, Mr. Cropper, I want to thank you for playing Romeo for me.

CROPPER: A pleasure, my dear. Took me back to the days of my youth.

DIANA: And, darling, that is far back.

CECIL: Dash it all, I do hope you're making the right decision, young lady. The theater can be a deucedly dangerous place for a young girl. I have nothing against stage folks—I keep an open mind and all that sort of thing—but some of them are a bit wild, don't you know?

MRS. SOMERSBY-THORNTON: Why, Cecil? Aren't you forgetting that I was on the stage?

CECIL: Different case, my dear. Rescued you from all that.

MRS. SOMERSBY-THORNTON (*Going to* SALLY *and taking her hand*): Don't mind Cecil, my dear. He's really very sweet, but sometimes he does say silly things. I'm very happy for you. And I want to give you something to wear on your opening night. (*She reaches into her handbag and takes out a ring.*) This ring was given to me by a very dear friend—

CECIL: Oh, I say, my dear, I've never heard about this. Wasn't a beastly male, was it?

MRS. SOMERSBY-THORNTON (*Smiling*): Set your mind at rest, my dear. The friend was a very generous woman— the Duchess of Drysdale. It is the ring that the great Ellen Terry wore on the night that she made her glorious debut as Portia in *The Merchant of Venice*. (*She hands ring to* SALLY.) I wore it on my own opening night in London, and I want you to wear it on yours here in Fairview.

SALLY: Oh, how wonderful! I've read so much about Ellen Terry!

MRS. SOMERSBY-THORNTON: It's a sort of good luck charm.

SALLY: You're so kind. But I wonder if I should take such a treasure.

MRS. SOMERSBY-THORNTON: Just regard it as a loan for opening night. After your debut, you can return it to me.

CECIL: But we won't be here, my dear. We'll be on our way to the jolly old open spaces of the Wild West. Always wanted to see some genuine redskins.

MRS. SOMERSBY-THORNTON (*Firmly*): We will be here, Cecil. We shall return for Sally's opening.

CECIL: But I say—that will mean quite a lot of driving, won't it?

MRS. SOMERSBY-THORNTON: But we'll do it, won't we, Cecil? (*She plants a kiss on his forehead.*)

CECIL (*Melting*): Of course, my dear. Anything to make you happy.

JOE (*Going to right and looking out*): The bridge is closing, folks. The age of miracles isn't over. Well, back to my fish. See you later, Cap. So long, Mabel. Good luck, folks.

CAP: So long, Joe.

MABEL (*Looking up from her magazine*): Be good, Joe. (JOE *exits right.*)

DIANA: Let us give thanks for small favors. I thought, darlings, that we might be cooped up here until we were eligible for Social Security. Sally, why don't you come to the theater with Jerry and me? You'll need a copy of the script, and you'll have to study hard.

SALLY: I'm perfectly willing, Miss Craig. Would you mind, Louise?

LOUISE: Not at all. I'll drive the car to camp, have the interview, hope I get the job, and explain why you aren't with me.

SALLY: Wonderful.

DIANA: Then come on, darlings, there's work to be done.

JERRY: Right. Coming, girls?

SALLY (*Exultantly*): With bells on! This is the happiest

day of my life! (*They walk toward right, and at door* SALLY *turns.*) Thank you again for the ring; I'll be thrilled to wear it, and I'll love having you in the audience.

MRS. SOMERSBY-THORNTON: The pleasure is mine, my dear.

SALLY: And thanks again to you, Mr. Cropper. You've been very kind.

CROPPER (*Modestly*): It was delightful. To quote the Bard, I am only "a poor player, who struts and frets his hour upon the stage."

DIANA: I'll buy that, DeWitt. And don't forget, you've got some strutting and fretting to do at rehearsal this morning. So get with it. (SALLY, LOUISE, DIANA *and* JERRY *exit right.*)

CROPPER: You heard what Lady Macbeth said. I must get back to the salt mines. Splendid to have seen you, Sybil, and you, Mr. Somersby-Thornton.

MRS. SOMERSBY-THORNTON: You were excellent as Romeo, DeWitt. And I'm happy that Cecil and I will be seeing you perform next week.

CECIL: We had better be on our way, too, my dear. America is jolly well out there waiting to be explored.

MRS. SOMERSBY-THORNTON: Very well, Cecil. (CECIL, MRS. SOMERSBY-THORNTON, *and* CROPPER *go toward right.*)

CAP: Good luck with Miss Craig, Mr. Cropper. (CROPPER *grimaces.*) And have a pleasant trip, folks. Hope you take some happy memories back to England.

CECIL: Decent of you to say so, old boy. Ta-ta. (*They exit right.*)

CAP: Well, Mabel, that's our quota of excitement until the bridge refuses to close again.

MABEL (*Looking up from her magazine*): Right. (*She sighs.*) Golly, this is a dull place. (*She yawns.*) Nothing ever happens around here. (CAP *looks at her, shakes his head and shrugs his shoulders as the curtain falls.*)

THE END

Production Notes

SUMMER STOCK À LA CARTE

Characters: 5 male; 5 female.

Playing Time: 25 minutes.

Costumes: Sally and Louise wear casual summer clothing. Mabel and Cap wear white aprons over their clothing. Joe wears work clothes. Mr. and Mrs. Somersby-Thornton may be more conservatively dressed than the others; he may wear a monocle. Cropper, Diana and Jerry should wear striking and colorful clothes; Cropper wears an ascot.

Properties: Coffee cups, plates, sandwiches, tray, magazine, for Mabel; handbags for the other women; wrist watches for Louise and Cropper; paper for Sally; pen for Cropper; ring for Mrs. Somersby-Thornton.

Setting: The Bridge Diner. At rear there is a counter behind which are several coffee makers. On the counter are a few glass cases containing pies, doughnuts, the usual paraphernalia of a diner. There are stools at the counter. Downstage are several tables and chairs. Door up left leads to the kitchen. Door at right leads outside.

Sound: Honking of horns offstage.

Mountain Madness

Characters

PAW CRUMM, *a typical hillbilly*
MAW CRUMM, *his wife*
ZENOBIA CRUMM, *their eighteen-year-old daughter*
GRANDMAW CRUMM, *a hillbilly philosopher*
BOXWELL BLUSTER, *a film director*
TY MONOTONE, *a film star*
SELINA SLINK, *a film actress*
MAW PARSNIP, *a hillbilly woman*
HANK PARSNIP, *her handsome son*
PAW JONES, *another hillbilly*
SADIE JONES, *his sixteen-year-old daughter*
EMMELINE JONES, *his eighteen-year-old daughter*
ABNER JONES, *his nineteen-year-old son*
FELIX FERRET, *a supposed federal agent*

SETTING: *A room in the hillbilly cabin of the Crumm family.*

AT RISE: PAW CRUMM *is seated on a box near center table, whittling a piece of wood.* GRANDMAW CRUMM *is seated in rocking chair, humming tunelessly, an unlit corncob pipe in her mouth.* MAW CRUMM, *seated on a box at right of table, is peeling potatoes.* ZENOBIA CRUMM *is modeling a new dress.*

ZENOBIA (*Turning around slowly*): Like it, Maw? Marked down from $22.89 to $8.67 at Funk's General Store. Lem Funk says it's a real Dior.

MAW CRUMM: Dior? Looks like plain wool, Zenobia.

ZENOBIA: Oh, Maw, Dior's a famous dress designer—from way over in Paris, France.

PAW CRUMM: Never heard tell of the critter. But, Zenobia, I don't want you to be sportin' those glad rags when those Hollywood slickers get here. Maw, mosey out to the sundial and see what time of day it's gettin' to be.

MAW CRUMM (*Sighing and rising*): A body can't get a mite of work done around here. Always somethin' interferin'. (*She exits.*)

ZENOBIA: I hate to change this dress. After all, it's what I'm going to be married in. (*Closing eyes and speaking dreamily*) Married to Hank Parsnip.

GRANDMAW: Shucks, child, you've known that there Hank since he was knee-high to a caterpillar. The Parsnip cabin's no more than a half mile from here.

ZENOBIA: Hank is so handsome, Grandmaw. I never realized it until lately.

GRANDMAW: Looks the same to me as he ever did. And, girl, don't you think that dress is a bit frilly? I don't hold with city ways. Your Paw spoiled you by sendin' you to that school in Rattlesnake Hollow.

PAW CRUMM: Stop your jabbering, Grandmaw. If Zenobia wasn't schooled proper, we'd never have been able to make out that letter from that Hollywood what's-his-name.

ZENOBIA: Boxwell Bluster, Paw. He's a famous film director. (MAW CRUMM *enters.*)

MAW CRUMM (*Returning to potato peeling*): The dial says exactly twenty-three and three-quarters minutes before two.

PAW CRUMM: If that's what it says, that's it. That there sundial is the best in the hills. And those Hollywood critters are about due. (*Looks around room*) I hope they won't be thinkin' we're too fancy here. They're lookin' for what they call a real hillbilly place. These boxes are nearly new, and the sofa's no more than fifty years old.

GRANDMAW: It's nigh on to fifty-eight. Grandpaw gave me that on our tenth anniversary. He sure was a good provider. He gave me somethin' else, too—a real fancy pin. It was a prize he got in a box of Crackerjacks he bought at the County Fair. (*Wipes eyes with a red handkerchief*) Never will be another like Grandpaw. And he never held with those city ways, either.

PAW CRUMM: City ways or no city ways, this fellow Bluster promises to give us $500 if we let him use our place for his new movin' picture. But he says we have to be typical of hill folk. Trouble with those dudes is they get their ideas of us from all them funny papers. Well, I wasn't born yesterday. If they expect us to be feudin' and fussin' all the time, they'll get plenty of feudin' and fussin'. Maw Parsnip and Hank know what they have to do, Zenobia?

ZENOBIA: Yes, Paw. They're going to pretend to be feuding with us. But Maw Parsnip wants $50 for her share.

MAW CRUMM: Always was greedy as a crow in a cornfield.

PAW CRUMM: Only thing worryin' me is that blamed Jones crowd. Paw Jones heard about the letter, and he claims his place is better than ours for the movin' picture. Says he's goin' to prove it to Bluster. Never did trust the Joneses. Now, Zenobia, you get that there dress changed.

ZENOBIA: All right, Paw. (*She exits left.*)

MAW CRUMM: I'll bet the Joneses have somethin' up their sleeves.

PAW CRUMM: Well, so have we—'specially with Maw Parsnip and Hank in on the act. With $500 ready to be dropped in my pocket, I'm not lyin' down on the job. (*There is the sound of an automobile horn from outside.* MAW *goes to window and looks out.*)

MAW CRUMM (*Excitedly*): It's them Hollywood dudes all right. There are three of 'em—two male critters and a female. She's all dressed up like a real queen—just like in the Sears Roebuck catalogue.

PAW CRUMM: Come away from that window, Maw. We don't want 'em to think we're jumpy. I'll give 'em a scare to start things off. (MAW *returns to her seat. As* PAW *picks up shotgun from table, there is a knock at the door.* PAW *goes to door, opens it, and levels shotgun at visitors.*)

PAW CRUMM: Don't nobody make a move!

GRANDMAW: Calm yourself, son.

MAW CRUMM (*Softly to* GRANDMAW): Hush, Grandmaw, Paw's just actin' the way the Hollywood slickers expect him to.

GRANDMAW: I never did hold with them city ways.

BLUSTER (*Appearing in doorway*): I'm Boxwell Bluster, my man.

PAW CRUMM (*Backing away*): Shucks, I thought you might be one of them no-good Parsnips. I was goin' to shoot. (BLUSTER *enters room and looks around.*)

BLUSTER: Marvelous! Marvelous! Marvelous! (*Calling,*

off) Selina. Ty. Come in at once. True primitive simplicity. (SELINA SLINK, *a flamboyant movie actress*, and TY MONOTONE, *a film hero, enter.*)

SELINA: Looks like a road company set for *Tobacco Road*.

BLUSTER: And just what we need. Oh, marvelous, marvelous! (*Bowing to* GRANDMAW) How do you do, madam. Ah, perfect, perfect!

GRANDMAW (*Eying him sullenly*): I don't hold with them city ways.

BLUSTER: You hear that, Selina? You hear that, Ty? The heart of rural America. The pulse of the nation.

SELINA: For heaven's sake, darling, stop talking like the sound track of a two-bit travelogue.

BLUSTER: Introductions are in order. (*As he gestures*) This is Selina Slink, a brilliant star in the Hollywood galaxy. (*Pointing to* TY) And this is Ty Monotone, the toast of the women of America.

MAW CRUMM: Pleased to meet you all. I'm Maw Crumm. And that's Grandmaw Crumm. Guess you already know Paw.

TY (*Looking nervously at* PAW's *gun*): Mr. Crumm, I'd be happy if you'd put that thing down. My nerves are not strong.

PAW CRUMM (*Placing gun on table*): You city fellers don't have any idea what goes on in these here hills. I have to keep an eagle eye out for them thievin', connivin' Parsnips.

BLUSTER: Priceless! Priceless! You hear that, Selina? You hear that, Ty? A genuine feud.

TY (*Nervously*): There's not going to be any trouble around here, is there?

SELINA (*Sarcastically*): If your fans could only hear you now! Where's the brave scout who takes on the whole

Sioux tribe single-handed, or the Foreign Legion captain who walks fifty miles through the burning desert to save Fifi O'Toole, the darling of the regiment?

PAW CRUMM (*Interested*): You've done all that, son?

SELINA: Only in the movies, pop. Away from the cameras, he's about as courageous as Minnie Mouse.

BLUSTER: Now, Selina, behave yourself. (*He watches with great interest as* GRANDMAW *rocks and hums.*) Isn't she a gem? We must use her somewhere in the film. (*To* GRANDMAW) Do you always smoke a pipe, madam?

GRANDMAW: I don't hold with them city ways. I'm against tobacco.

TY: Then why do you have a pipe?

GRANDMAW: It's just somethin' to rest my teeth on.

BLUSTER: Magnificent! Magnificent! This is the real thing. This is the local color we're after. (ZENOBIA, *barefoot and wearing a ragged dress, enters left.*)

TY (*Eying her appreciatively*): And speaking of local color—wow!

PAW CRUMM: This here's my daughter Zenobia.

BLUSTER: A veritable flower of the hills. How do you do, my dear. I am Boxwell Bluster. This is Selina Slink. And this handsome dog is Ty Monotone.

ZENOBIA (*Shyly*): Oh, Mr. Monotone, I saw you once at a picture show in Rattlesnake Hollow. You were an Air Force ace. And, my goodness, I never saw anyone so brave.

TY (*Pleased*): That was *Anger in the Sky*. (*Posing*) If I do say so myself, I was good in that.

SELINA: Not according to the critic in *The New York Times*. He said your acting made a cigar store Indian look lively by comparison.

TY: Jealousy. Those film critics hate to see a fellow get

ahead. (*There is the sound of a shot from outside.* PAW *grabs gun from table.*)

PAW CRUMM: I'll bet that's those pesky Parsnips. Zenobia, you been seein' that Hank again?

ZENOBIA: No, Paw, I—

PAW CRUMM: Don't lie to me, girl. You know that no Crumm can ever marry up with a Parsnip.

BLUSTER: Amazing! Amazing!

MAW CRUMM (*Getting in on the act*): Maw Parsnip told me she'd come a-shootin' if Zenobia and Hank started romancin'.

PAW CRUMM: She winged me in the shoulder a year ago. (*He rubs shoulder.*) Still bothers me somethin' fierce in damp weather.

BLUSTER: Stupendous! Just like *Romeo and Juliet*—a pair of star-crossed lovers. I tell you, we'll be able to film the very spirit of the hills.

PAW CRUMM: If that's Maw Parsnip loose with her shotgun, we might all be spirits before long.

TY (*Very nervously*): I—I—I think I'll go out and sit in the car.

SELINA (*Sarcastically*): Where? In the trunk?

TY: Be nasty if you will, Selina, but I don't relish the thought of being made to look like a piece of Swiss cheese. (MAW PARSNIP, *shotgun in hand, appears suddenly in doorway.*)

MAW PARSNIP: Stand where you are, you ornery galoots!

GRANDMAW: Close the door. There's a draft.

MAW PARSNIP (*Pointing gun at* PAW CRUMM *who, in turn, points his gun at her*): I gave you warnin', Paw Crumm, that if that Zenobia kept chasin' my Hank, I'd fill you full of holes.

PAW CRUMM: You fire that gun, Maw Parsnip, and I'll fire mine.

BLUSTER (*Enthusiastically*): Tremendous! Tremendous!

TY (*Moving center*): I have an appointment.

MAW PARSNIP (*Pointing gun at him*): Stay where you be, dude. Nobody leaves here till I say what I have to say.

TY (*As he continues timidly toward door*): But— (MAW PARSNIP *jabs* TY *with gun. He falls to the floor in a faint.*)

ZENOBIA: He's fainted! (MAW CRUMM *takes jug of water from table and pours water on* TY.)

MAW CRUMM: That ought to bring him around. (ZENOBIA *goes to* TY *and bends over him, as* SELINA *laughs heartily.* TY *moves, gasps, sits up.*)

TY: Close the dam, boys. The water is rising.

ZENOBIA: Are you hurt?

TY (*Looking dazedly up at her*): This must be heaven— and you're an angel.

SELINA: Oh, brother. That line is right out of his last film, *Dr. Scalpel's Revenge*. (HANK PARSNIP *appears in doorway*.)

HANK (*Wresting gun from* MAW PARSNIP): Maw, drop that gun! Must we always have blood and violence?

BLUSTER: Wonderful! We'll use that line in the film.

MAW PARSNIP: The only good Crumm is a dead Crumm.

GRANDMAW: That's what Grandpaw used to say about you Parsnips.

ZENOBIA: Oh, Hank, I'm so glad you've come.

HANK (*Embracing her*): Zenobia.

BLUSTER: Beautiful! Beautiful! True love in all its pristine innocence. We'll have to work that into the script.

PAW CRUMM (*To* ZENOBIA *and* HANK): Don't you two be

actin' like lovebirds. There can't be any love between a Crumm and a Parsnip.

TY (*Shakily getting to his feet and wiping water from his face*): I hope my jacket isn't ruined. It's genuine, hand-woven Donegal tweed. (ZENOBIA *begins to wipe water from* TY's *jacket.*)

HANK: Now wait a minute. I don't want any goings-on between you and a city slicker, Zenobia.

ZENOBIA: But, Hank, he's been ill.

HANK: No girl of mine is goin' to make eyes at a dude.

PAW CRUMM: She's not your girl, Hank Parsnip.

SELINA (*To* BLUSTER, *wearily*): Look, Boxwell, haven't we seen enough of this? If this is what you're looking for, why not give them a check, close the deal, and begin location work for the film here tomorrow?

BLUSTER: I tell you, Selina, all this is fascinating. Positively fascinating. But you're right. I've seen enough to know that this is it. (*He takes checkbook from his pocket.*) Let me see now, Mr. Crumm, I believe our agreement is for $300.

PAW CRUMM: No, it isn't. Zenobia read your letter to me because I can't rightly make out printin' and writin'. But I can make out numbers. Seems to me there was a five and two noughts.

ZENOBIA (*Sweetly*): What Paw means is that the letter said $500—not $300.

GRANDMAW: I never did hold with those city ways. Can't trust a city slicker.

BLUSTER (*Laughing*): My mistake, my mistake.

TY: Write the check, Boxwell, and let's get out of here. (*Eying* HANK *nervously*) My nerves are simply shattered.

BLUSTER: All right, $500 it is. (MAW PARSNIP *and the* CRUMMS *grin happily, and* HANK *and* ZENOBIA *gaze romantically at each other, as* BLUSTER *goes to table and starts to make out check. Center door opens, and* PAW JONES *enters with a man who is gagged and whose hands are tied behind his back.* PAW JONES *is followed by his two daughters,* SADIE *and* EMMELINE, *and his son,* ABNER. *They are all barefoot.*)

PAW CRUMM: What are you doin' in these parts, Paw Jones?

SELINA (*To* BLUSTER): This is beginning to look like a mob scene in a Cecil B. DeMille epic.

TY (*Eying* EMMELINE *and* SADIE): My, they grow them pretty in the hills.

PAW JONES (*Leading his prisoner to center*): Are you Mr. Boxwell Bluster?

BLUSTER (*Bowing*): At your service. (*Looking at prisoner*) But who is this poor fellow? He looks uncomfortable. (*The prisoner gives muffled groans.*)

PAW JONES: This here is one of them miserable federal agents. Felix Ferret is his name. We caught him snoopin' and peepin'. He thought we were holding out on our taxes.

BLUSTER: That's against the law!

PAW JONES: Don't know about the law. Only know my boy Abner here (ABNER *grins proudly.*) caught him prowling around on our property. He crept up behind the varmint and tied him up.

EMMELINE: That's right, Paw.

PAW JONES: Speak only when spoken to, Emmeline.

SADIE: Caught him like a rat in a trap.

PAW JONES: And you'd better hold your tongue, too.

SADIE: Only tryin' to help, Paw.

PAW CRUMM: There hasn't been a federal agent around here in years. Smells fishy to me, Paw Jones.

MAW PARSNIP: You Joneses don't have an honest bone in your bodies.

ABNER: Don't you be insultin' us, Maw Parsnip.

BLUSTER: Phenomenal. Phenomenal. Typical hill folk, if I ever saw them.

PAW CRUMM (*Worried*): Now, Mr. Bluster, these Joneses are no more typical than the Crumms.

PAW JONES: Don't pay him any heed, Mr. Bluster. Our place is the one for that there movin' picture. We're the genuine article, living alone, way up in the hills. We know nothin' about the outside world—fact is, we're not even sure there is an outside world. (*Looking around the room scornfully*) Why, this Crumm place is like a palace compared to ours.

BLUSTER (*Impressed*): Really? Wonderful! Mr. Crumm, perhaps I've been too hasty in deciding on your place.

MAW PARSNIP: Don't believe Paw Jones, Mr. Bluster.

PAW JONES (*Triumphantly*): I'll bet there's no captured federal agent in this Crumm territory. Besides, we Joneses can sing, too. (*He holds up his hand to get his family's attention. They form a group at center.*) Ready. One. Two. Three. (*The JONES family all sing hillbilly song, with typical hillbilly gestures. BLUSTER listens delightedly.*)

BLUSTER (*Excitedly*): A slice of genuine rural life! You hear that, Selina? You hear that, Ty? Simply pulse-quickening. Mr. Jones, you are sent from heaven. I must see your home—your isolated home.

PAW CRUMM: Now see here, Mr. Bluster, we had an agreement.

MAW CRUMM: You're not goin' back on your word, are you?

MAW PARSNIP: I saw you about to sign the check.

BLUSTER: My dear Mr. Crumm, the letter offered only a tentative proposition.

PAW CRUMM: What's that mean?

SELINA: Boxwell means that he promised nothing definite.

HANK: I've a mind to blow these Joneses off the planet. (*He fingers trigger of gun.*)

TY: Now don't be hasty, Hank. You're the boy who said you're against violence.

EMMELINE (*Coyly*): Hank wouldn't shoot. He's as mild as spring rain.

SADIE: And he's real cute, too.

ZENOBIA: You stop flirting with Hank. He's all spoken for.

PAW JONES: You come up to our place, Mr. Bluster, and we'll be showin' you a real whiz-bang shindig. We're havin' a party tonight—all the relatives comin' from over the hills. There'll be Clem Jones, Zem Jones, Lem Jones—

BLUSTER: You hear that, Selina? You hear that, Ty? We can have a camera there and shoot the party as background. I'll win an Oscar for this.

PAW JONES: Yeah. Oscar Jones'll be there, and he's a champion fiddler, too.

BLUSTER: Thrilling! Thrilling!

TY (*Nervously*): One thing bothers me, though, Mr. Jones. Don't you think you'd better release Felix Ferret, the federal agent? It doesn't do to lock horns with the government. (*The prisoner nods vigorously.*)

GRANDMAW: No good ever comes from cruelty, Paw Jones.

BLUSTER: Just as a matter of curiosity, Mr. Jones, what did you plan to do with this man?

PAW JONES: We'll think of somethin'.

ABNER (*Ominously*): Shootin' is too good for him.

PAW CRUMM: He's a-pullin' your leg, Mr. Bluster. There's nobody had trouble with the federal agents in these parts for years. We're law-abidin'.

HANK (*Proudly*): We are honest, upright citizens of the glorious U.S.A.

SELINA: You tell him, handsome.

BLUSTER: Well, Mr. Jones, I am a humane man. I'm afraid I shall have to insist that you release Mr. Felix Ferret —that is, if you want to do business with us.

PAW JONES: $500 worth of business, isn't it?

BLUSTER: That's the general idea.

EMMELINE: Better untie him, Paw.

SADIE: $500 is $500.

MAW CRUMM: You Joneses were always a graspin' bunch.

ABNER: Seems to me, you Crumms are pretty graspin', too.

BLUSTER: Well, Mr. Jones?

PAW JONES (*Sighing*): Untie him, Abner. Dollars is dollars. (ABNER *unties* FERRET's *hands and loosens the gag.*)

FERRET (*Rubbing hands vigorously*): This outrage will not go unchallenged. (SELINA *looks at* FERRET *with great interest. She goes to him and stares fixedly at him.*)

SELINA: What did you say this man's name is?

PAW JONES: Felix Ferret, that's who he is.

SELINA (*Still staring*): Well, I'll be a monkey's uncle!

BLUSTER: Really, Selina, you might try for more elegance of language.

SELINA: I know this man. And if he's Felix Ferret, federal agent, then I'm Martha Washington.

PAW JONES (*Uncomfortably*): Caught him red-handed, we did—snoopin' and peepin' around our place.

SELINA: Come off it, pop. This is Montgomery Stokes. I

went to school with him in Raspberry Gulch—not ten miles from here.

ABNER: This can't be the same varmint! He's a pesky agent, I say.

SELINA: Cat got your tongue, Montgomery? Why don't you speak up?

FERRET: You're making a mistake! I'm Felix Ferret, federal agent.

SELINA: Roll up the sleeve on his right arm! I'm sure you'll find a scar there. He got it when Lon Cronker pushed him out the window when we were in the sixth grade.

FERRET: Now, hold it. I'm not— (HANK *goes quickly to* FERRET, *who tries to elude him, but* HANK *wrestles him to the floor, sits on his chest, and proceeds to roll back* FERRET'*s right sleeve.*)

HANK (*Triumphantly*): You're right. He's got a scar—a big one.

SELINA: Of course he has—and he's no federal agent. In the first place, he never got beyond the sixth grade. He spent four of the best years of his life there. You never were much of a one for the books, were you, Monty?

PAW CRUMM: Paw Jones, you're a snivelin', no-good rattlesnake! Tryin' to impress Mr. Bluster, were you, with all this hogwash about federal agents.

GRANDMAW: There never was a Jones you could trust.

MAW PARSNIP: Truer words were never spoken.

TY: Selina, I never knew you grew up in the hills.

SELINA: I don't advertise it, hero-boy. But there comes a time when one has to speak up.

ZENOBIA: We're so grateful to you, Miss Slink.

GRANDMAW: I've got a long memory, I have. I've heard tell of this Montgomery Stokes, but I've never seen him before. He's a cousin of the Joneses on Ma Jones' side. She was a Stokes before she married.

BLUSTER: Aha! So that is it—a family conspiracy.

FERRET: We'd better throw in the towel, Paw Jones. I told you it would never work.

PAW JONES (*Coaxingly*): Now, Mr. Bluster, you're not goin' to let a little joke break up our business deal, are you?

EMMELINE: It was all in fun.

SADIE: Just real good mountain fun.

MAW CRUMM: It was dishonest, that's what it was. Never had any use for dishonest critters.

PAW CRUMM (*Virtuously*): Makes a man ashamed to see how low his fellow critters will stoop.

PAW JONES (*Still hopeful*): Don't forget, Mr. Bluster, we're havin' a real wing-ding tonight. And there'll be singin', too. (*He raises his hand for attention. The* JONES *family form a group at center.*) One. Two. Three. (*They again begin to sing a hillbilly song.*)

BLUSTER (*Angrily breaking in*): Enough! I am a man of integrity, and I loathe deception of any kind. My advice to you, Mr. Jones, is to take your family and return to your isolated home in the hills. And take cousin Montgomery with you.

PAW CRUMM: Now you're talkin', Mr. Bluster.

PAW JONES: Don't be sore, Bluster.

HANK (*Pointing gun at* PAW JONES): Do what Mr. Bluster says, Paw Jones.

GRANDMAW: There's no good Jones but a dead Jones.

ABNER (*Looking nervously at gun*): Better do what he says, Paw. The jig is up.

PAW JONES: You're missin' the boat, Mr. Bluster. We

would have been great singin' and dancin' in your movin' picture.

HANK (*Menacingly*): Get out. (PAW JONES *goes reluctantly to center door, followed by his family and* MONTGOMERY.)

SELINA: And, Monty, remember me to the folks in Raspberry Gulch.

MONTGOMERY (*Looking back*): I will, Selina. (*Proudly*) And I'm in the eighth grade now.

SELINA: Swell. By the time you graduate, your grandchildren will be in the same class. (*The* JONESES *and* MONTGOMERY *exit*)

PAW CRUMM (*Shaking his head*): Shameful, that's what it is. Mr. Bluster, I hope you don't think all us hill folk are like the Joneses.

BLUSTER: I'll be frank with you, Mr. Crumm. My faith in human nature has been somewhat shaken. But I am thankful that there are still honest people like yourself in the world.

HANK: And if it's singin' you're after, Zenobia and I can warble a nice duet.

BLUSTER: Splendid! Splendid! (*Goes to table, takes out pen, and writes check, which he hands to* PAW CRUMM) There you are, Mr. Crumm—$500. My camera crew will be here tomorrow morning to begin work. And I do hope that you settle your feud with the Parsnip family before then. (*Indicating* ZENOBIA *and* HANK) I think that these two young people were made for each other.

MAW PARSNIP: I'm willin' to let bygones be bygones.

BLUSTER: You hear that, Selina? You hear that, Ty? Terrific! Terrific!

MAW CRUMM: That's a generous sentiment, Maw Parsnip.

MAW PARSNIP: And heartfelt, too, Maw Crumm.

BLUSTER: Perfect! Perfect! I feel that we have accomplished something here today. Now, Mr. Crumm and Mrs. Parsnip, will you two shake hands with each other and give your blessing to the speedy marriage of these two young people?

PAW CRUMM: I'm not refusin', Mr. Bluster. (*He holds out his hand to* MAW PARSNIP, *who shakes it heartily.*)

SELINA: The orchestra will now play "Hearts and Flowers."

BLUSTER: Don't be cynical, Selina. We are witnessing a beautiful and touching scene.

TY: Let's get going now, Boxwell. This has been a trying day—and I don't feel at all well.

SELINA: Ty's right for once, Boxwell. Let's get back to Crackerbarrel City to rest in what is laughingly described as a hotel. We've got plenty of work ahead of us tomorrow.

BLUSTER: Right. (*He goes to* GRANDMAW) Goodbye, madam.

GRANDMAW: I never did hold with them city ways.

BLUSTER (*Shaking hands with* MAW CRUMM): Goodbye, Mrs. Crumm. (*Shaking hands with* PAW CRUMM) Goodbye, Mr. Crumm. (*Shaking hands with* HANK) Goodbye, Mr. Parsnip. You're a lucky young man. (*Shaking hands with* MAW PARSNIP) You must be a proud mother. (*Going to* ZENOBIA) May I kiss the prospective bride?

ZENOBIA: Oh, Mr. Bluster. (*He kisses her on the cheek.*)

TY: Say, that's a good idea. (*He advances toward* ZENOBIA. HANK *aims the gun.* TY *looks at* HANK *and backs away.*) I was only kidding, Mr. Parsnip.

SELINA: Come on, lover boy. Save your romance for the

big film. (BLUSTER, TY, *and* SELINA *go toward center door.*)

PAW CRUMM: You folks come to supper tomorrow night. I'll have Maw cook up a mess of roast squirrel, grits, and skunk cabbage.

BLUSTER (*Delighted*): You hear that, Selina? You hear that, Ty? True rural hospitality. Pure hill simplicity. Oh, I tell you, we've really found it! (*They exit.* PAW CRUMM *sighs with relief*)

MAW PARSNIP: We've done it!

MAW CRUMM: $500.

PAW CRUMM (*Waving the check*): More money than we've ever seen in all our lives. Zenobia, you and Hank can have a real honeymoon—over at that big hotel in Crackerbarrel City.

ZENOBIA (*Rushing to him and kissing him*): Oh, Paw. You're so generous.

PAW CRUMM: And I'll be gettin' Maw a real stove. And, by golly, I'll get Grandmaw a new pipe. That one's gettin' kind of worn. (*He grasps* MAW CRUMM *around the waist, and they begin to do a dance.* MAW PARSNIP *joins in, doing a solo jig.* ZENOBIA *and* HANK *laugh delightedly and embrace.* GRANDMAW *chuckles and begins to rock rapidly. In the midst of this,* SELINA *appears in the doorway, but they do not see her at first. Then* ZENOBIA *catches sight of her*)

ZENOBIA (*Struggling from* HANK's *embrace*): Oh, it's Miss Slink! (*All stop their dancing abruptly.*)

SELINA (*Laughing*): Don't let me interrupt the revels.

PAW CRUMM (*Uncomfortably*): We were just—

SELINA: Look, Mr. Crumm, you don't have to explain anything to me. I had to come back, though, because I want to tell you something.

MAW CRUMM: Nothin' bad, I hope.

SELINA: No, but I just wanted you to know that I know your secret.

ZENOBIA: Secret?

SELINA: Remember, I grew up in these hills. I know there hasn't been a feud around here for fifty years. And these boxes don't fool me. I'll bet you've got some pretty good furniture hidden somewhere.

PAW CRUMM: Well—

SELINA: But, don't worry. My lips are sealed. In fact, I'm going to persuade Boxwell to use Zenobia and Hank as extras. You're certainly pretty enough for the movies, Zenobia. And Hank's a fine hunk of man. It'll mean a bit more money for you.

ZENOBIA: Oh, thank you, Miss Slink.

HANK: That's right generous of you.

GRANDMAW: I never did hold with them city ways.

MAW PARSNIP: My son, the movie star.

SELINA (*Going toward door*): After all, we hill folk have to stick together. (*Smiling broadly*) We can outsmart those city slickers every time. (*Waving*) See you tomorrow! (SELINA *exits.*)

MAW PARSNIP: That girl's a credit to these hills.

ZENOBIA (*Going over to embrace* GRANDMAW): Did you hear her, Grandmaw? Hank and I will be rich. Come on, everyone, give it a whirl! (*All resume hillbilly dancing and singing, as the curtain falls.*)

THE END

Production Notes

Mountain Madness

Characters: 7 male; 7 female.

Playing Time: 35 minutes.

Costumes: Selena and Ty wear flashy Hollywood outfits. Bluster wears sport jacket, slacks, and ascot. He carries a checkbook and pen. Ferret wears suit and long-sleeved shirt. Others wear typical hillbilly dress. Grandmaw has a pipe and a red handkerchief. Zenobia first appears in new dress, then changes to ragged one, and wears no shoes. Hank and the Joneses are also barefoot. Hank wears blue shirt and jeans.

Properties: Wood and knife for whittling, potatoes, paring knife, shotguns for Paw Crumm and Maw Parsnip.

Setting: A room in the Crumms' cabin. At center is a large wooden table, on which are a shotgun and a jug of water. Boxes serve as chairs. Down right is a dilapidated sofa, down left is an old rocking chair. Exit up center leads to outside; a small window is at one side. Exit at left leads to another room.

Lighting: No special effects.

Sound: Automobile horn, gun shot, as indicated in text.

Don't Tell the Folks Back Home

Characters

SANDRA LEE, *a young singer*
MAY HUME, *an aspiring actress*
BETTY JACKSON, *an aspiring painter*
MRS. GRIMSHAW, *their hardhearted landlady*
DELIA DANFORTH, *society editor of the "Springville Daily Echo"*
WENDY FLEMING, *a young dancer*
CAROLYN COLLINS, *a successful actress*
GERT DREXEL, *publicity director for "High Life Magazine"*
MOLLY⎫
HETTY⎭ *beatnik guitarists*
LENA, *a beatnik poet*
LUCY, *a beatnik painter*

SETTING: *The living room of a shabby apartment in Greenwich Village, New York.*

AT RISE: SANDRA *is standing near sofa, practicing scales.* BETTY, *dressed in a smock, is putting the finishing touches on a painting.* MAY, *in slacks and sweater, stands perfectly still at center, with eyes closed, and arms raised above her head.*

BETTY (*As* SANDRA's *voice increases in volume*): You're in great voice today, Sandra. I'll bet you can be heard as far as Brooklyn.

SANDRA: I wish somebody at the Metropolitan Opera could hear me. (*Looking at* MAY) Just what are you supposed to be doing, May?

MAY (*Keeping eyes closed*): I'm practicing being a tree— one of Professor Levosky's favorite exercises in drama class. The only trouble is that playwrights don't seem to be writing many parts for trees this season. (*Opens eyes*) Now for a few interpretive dance steps. As the professor says, "Mees Hume, the grace must be developed in the body. The great actress—she must know how to move." (SANDRA *begins singing again, and* MAY *begins to dance slowly around the room.*)

BETTY (*Standing off to look critically at her painting*): I think there's just a bit too much blue in that sky.

MAY (*Dancing over to painting and looking at it*): And if there's one thing true about our own personal skies, Betty, it's that they're not blue. A depressing, desolate gray would be more appropriate.

SANDRA (*Pausing in her singing*): Gray or a nice funereal black. When I went downstairs for the milk this morning, who blocked my path but the terror of Greenwich Village, Mrs. Grimshaw.

BETTY: Did she ask you for the rent?

SANDRA: She really lit into me. She was waving that mop of hers, and I thought she was going to conk me on the noggin with it. She says that if we don't pay our rent soon, she's going to throw us out on our ears.

BETTY: I guess that means we're really in trouble.

MAY (*Gloomily*): Trouble is all we've had since we came to New York.

SANDRA: Well, grin and bear it, May. You're an actress, aren't you?

MAY: An unemployed one.

BETTY: That's what makes us such a jolly trio. We have one thing in common. You're an unemployed actress, I'm a painter who can't sell any pictures, and Sandra is a singer whom no one will listen to.

SANDRA: You've forgotten one other thing we have in common—we can't pay the rent.

MAY: I've just been thinking. Wouldn't it be something if Delia Danforth could see us now?

BETTY: I'll say. Those clippings my mother sends us are out of this world. Delia's column is full of stories about three hometown girls who've taken New York by storm. The readers of the *Springville Daily Echo* must think we're the toast of the city.

MAY (*Dancing again*): Where does Delia get those stories?

BETTY: I suppose she talks with our parents, and let's admit it—we've never told the folks how tough the sledding has really been. I know my letters home are always bright and cheerful.

SANDRA: So are mine.

MAY: Thomas Edison has nothing on me when it comes to inventions. My letters home are full of 'em.

BETTY (*Thoughtfully, as she works at her painting*): I sometimes wonder if we ought to give it all up and go back home.

MAY (*Emphatically*): We just can't, Betty. If Springville knew the real truth about us, we'd never be able to hold up our heads again.

SANDRA: To admit that we haven't made it in the big city would be just horrible. We'd be the laughingstock of the town—just three hicks who overestimated their own talents.

BETTY: I suppose you're right. One does have one's pride.

SANDRA: You bet one does. (*There is a knock on door, and* MRS. GRIMSHAW *enters, carrying a mop and wearing an unbecoming housedress.*)

MAY (*Sweetly*): Good morning, Mrs. Grimshaw. (MRS. GRIMSHAW *walks to center and leans on mop.*)

MRS. GRIMSHAW (*Brusquely*): What's good about it? (*Looking around room*) This place looks as though a herd of buffalo has just passed through.

SANDRA: We haven't had time to clean up yet today.

MRS. GRIMSHAW: Well, I'm not here to lecture on domestic science. In fact, you girls know the reason for this little visit.

BETTY: We don't, Mrs. Grimshaw, but we're always glad to have you drop in.

MRS. GRIMSHAW: I'll bet. Let me get right to the point. I haven't seen any rent from you for two months. This isn't a charity project, you know.

MAY: We just need a little more time, Mrs. Grimshaw. We'll get the money. Something is bound to turn up.

MRS. GRIMSHAW: The only thing likely to turn up around here is the carpet. (*She gestures with the mop.*) I've been hearing that hogwash ever since you girls moved in. I have taxes to pay—or did you think the city lets me live here free because I'm so beautiful?

BETTY: You're beautiful all right, Mrs. Grimshaw.

MRS. GRIMSHAW: And don't give me any of your sarcasm, Miss Jackson. Anyway, I've come to a decision. Either you girls pay the rent by the end of the week—which gives you exactly three days—or I'll be forced to evict you.

SANDRA (*Coaxingly*): Oh, you wouldn't really do that, Mrs. Grimshaw.

MRS. GRIMSHAW: Just try me and see. I've had trouble before with girls like you—painters, singers, dancers, writers, actresses—the whole worthless lot of you. You're all deadbeats. The only tenant I ever had who plunked down her rent money right on the due date was Carolyn Collins. Now *there* was a girl with brains. Beautiful, too. She's gone right to the top—one of the best-known actresses in the country.

BETTY: Yes, she's a doll.

MRS. GRIMSHAW (*Gesturing with mop*): She was a paying doll—and that's something. Anyway, I'm not here to argue. You girls have three days. If you don't pay the rent by then—(*She bangs the mop on the floor.*)—boom! Out you go! (*She exits.*)

BETTY: Do you think she really means it?

MAY: Are you kidding? She'd evict a troop of Campfire Girls without blinking an eye., (WENDY FLEMING, *wearing a leotard, enters upstage center with an empty cup in her hand.*)

WENDY: Hi, kids. May I borrow a cup of sugar?

SANDRA: Hello, Wendy. Sure. I'll get it. (*Takes cup from* WENDY *and exits left.*)

WENDY (*Doing a few dance steps*): I met Mrs. Grimshaw on the stairs, and she had fire in her eyes. I suppose she's been reading the riot act in her own groovy way.

BETTY: We have exactly three days to pay the rent.

WENDY: If I hadn't landed a job dancing at the Kit-Kat Club, I'd be in the same boat. It's a cruel world, girls. (SANDRA *returns with cup of sugar.*)

SANDRA: Here you are, Wendy.

WENDY: Thanks, Sandra. I'm going to bake a cake, and I'll bring some up for you.

MAY: Swell. We've been eating only spaghetti for the last week. It's great stuff, but one does become disenchanted after the first hundred servings.

WENDY: Well, chins up, girls. (*She dances to upstage center door.*) Thanks again for the sugar. (*Exits dancing.*)

BETTY: She's cheerful, anyway.

SANDRA: She should be. If I had a job, I'd be doing cartwheels down Fifth Avenue. Well, back to practicing. Why, I don't know. (*She begins to sing,* BETTY *returns to her painting, and* MAY *returns to the same pose she had assumed at the beginning of the play. All look rather listless. After a moment or two, there is a knock at the door.*)

BETTY: Good heavens! Don't tell me the three days are up already! (SANDRA *goes to door upstage center and peers through the peephole. She starts with amazement, snaps the cover of the peephole shut, and turns around, pressing her back against the door as if to keep out the visitor.*)

SANDRA (*In one breath*): Oh-my-gosh! (*Pointing back at the door with her finger*) You know who that is?

BETTY *and* MAY: Who?

SANDRA (*In a whisper*): It's Delia Danforth from the *Springville Daily Echo.*

BETTY: What do we do? (MAY *frantically starts to tidy up the room.*)

MAY: We have to get this place cleaned up!

SANDRA (*Her back still against the door*): Do you think we have to let her in? Maybe she'll think we're out.

BETTY: She must have seen you open the peephole. We *have* to let her in.

MAY (*Giving the room a last inspection*): O.K., you can let her in. (SANDRA *opens the door and* DELIA DANFORTH, *beaming happily, enters.*)

DELIA (*Hugging* SANDRA): Surprise! Surprise! I'll bet I'm the last person in the world you girls expected to see! (*The girls give each other knowing glances.* DELIA *stands off and looks at* SANDRA.) Why, Sandra Lee, you're prettier than ever! This New York air must be a tonic. That, of course, and all the success you girls are having.

SANDRA (*Recovering*): How wonderful to see someone from home! (DELIA *and* SANDRA *go to center.* MAY *comes to* DELIA, *embraces her, and speaks theatrically*)

MAY: Delia, darling, you look as distinguished as ever.

BETTY (*Embracing* DELIA): Delia, you haven't changed a bit.

DELIA: Why, thank you, girls. (*She notices the easel, goes to it, and looks at the painting.*) This is superb! I think the progress you're making with your painting is just wonderful.

BETTY (*Rather uncomfortably*): Y-yes. I'm doing well, Delia. (*Guides* DELIA *to sofa*) Do sit down. (DELIA *sits.*) Tell us how you happen to be in New York.

DELIA: Well, I'm here to attend a convention of the American Association of Women Journalists. And the first thing I did after I unpacked my bags was to hop into a cab and rush over here. I just couldn't wait to see you girls. Your parents send their love. They're all fine. (*Pauses*) But I want to hear all about you—all about your triumphs.

MAY (*Exchanges glance with* BETTY, *then, to* DELIA): Triumphs? Oh, sure—triumphs.

DELIA: I suppose you've been busy on the stage, May.

MAY: It's been one mad whirl, darling. I'm in great demand.

DELIA: Of course you are. A girl with your talent was bound to succeed. What was your last play?

MAY: Well, er—

SANDRA: She was wonderful in it.

BETTY (*Helping the story along*): It was an avant-garde play, Delia. You've probably never heard of it.

DELIA: What was its title?

MAY: It was—

BETTY (*Interrupting*): May was sensational. Eleven curtain calls opening night and a line as long as eternity waiting outside the stage door to smother her with praise.

DELIA (*Impressed*): How perfectly wonderful!

MAY (*Modestly*): It was really nothing, darling.

DELIA: I'll have so much to write about for the *Springville Daily Echo* when I get back home. And, Sandra, what about your singing career?

SANDRA: My singing career? Well—

BETTY (*Quickly*): Sandra's too modest to tell you, but she's had the New York critics reaching for new superlatives.

MAY: Darling, she was positively magnificent in *Aïda*. Everyone calls her the girl with the golden throat.

SANDRA (*Going along with the gag*): Everyone has been so kind. And, Delia, Betty's doing beautifully, too. Her painting is superb. She has more commissions than she can possibly handle.

DELIA (*Beaming*): Girls, you don't know how happy this makes me feel. You're a real credit to Springville. (*There is a knock at upstage center door, and* WENDY *pirouettes onstage.*)

WENDY (*Noticing* DELIA): Oh, I didn't know you had company.

BETTY: This is Wendy Fleming, Delia. She lives downstairs. Wendy, this is Delia Danforth from our home town. (WENDY *dances to sofa and shakes* DELIA's *hand.*)

WENDY: Happy to meet you, Miss Danforth. I hate to bother you girls again, but I'm short two eggs for that blasted cake. Could I borrow some?

SANDRA: I'll get them. (*She exits left.*)

WENDY: I was just talking to Mrs. Grimshaw. I think she really means business. If you don't scrape up the mon—

MAY (*Breaking in quickly*): Darling, how is your dancing career progressing?

WENDY (*Puzzled*): Dancing career? You know as well as I do that I'm dancing at the Kit-Kat Club—if you can call that a career. (SANDRA *returns, carrying the two eggs in a dish.*)

SANDRA: Here you are, Wendy.

WENDY (*Taking dish*): Thanks. I'll be sure to bring you some generous slices of the cake. These poor kids have been eating nothing but spaghetti for a week, Miss Danforth. It's a shame that—

SANDRA (*Breaking in, taking* WENDY's *arm, and guiding her to door*): We know you want to get back to that cake, Wendy.

WENDY: I suppose so. (*At door*) I hope you find the money to pay the rent. (SANDRA *pushes* WENDY *through door and closes it.*)

MAY: Darling Wendy—she will have her little jokes.

BETTY: She loves to kid us.

DELIA: What is all this about the rent?

MAY (*Quickly*): It's just a private joke, Delia.

BETTY: Wendy is a barrel of laughs.

MAY: One long scream from the rise of the curtain to the end of the last act.

DELIA: Anyway, let's get back to you girls. I want all the information you can give me. I'm going to do a really long, detailed article about you. (*There is another knock at the door, and* MRS. GRIMSHAW, *still carrying her mop, enters.*)

MAY (*Going to* MRS. GRIMSHAW): Mrs. Grimshaw, we're very busy. We're entertaining an old friend. (MAY *tries to push* MRS. GRIMSHAW *out.* MRS. GRIMSHAW *shakes her off and brandishes the mop threateningly.*)

MRS. GRIMSHAW: Who do you think you're pushing around? Hands off! I won't take up much of your valuable time. I just want to say that I've changed my mind about that three-day deadline.

SANDRA (*Hopefully*): Oh, that's wonderful, Mrs. Grimshaw. (*Hastily changing the subject*) I'd like you to meet an old friend of ours, Delia Danforth, from Springville.

MRS. GRIMSHAW (*Nodding brusquely*): Hello. (DELIA *nods to her.*) As I was saying, I've changed my mind.

BETTY: Good for you, Mrs. Grimshaw.

MRS. GRIMSHAW: I just had a phone call from a girl who works for Bronson Brothers—she has a good job. She wants an apartment right away. In fact, she wants to move in day after tomorrow. So I've got news for you: if that rent isn't paid by tomorrow, out you go. Chew on that for a while. (*Nodding again to* DELIA) Nice to have met you. (*She exits.*)

DELIA (*Thoughtfully*): So that's the way things really are.

MAY: It was just another joke, darling. Mrs. Grimshaw is the Lucille Ball of Greenwich Village.

BETTY: She's strictly a laugh girl.

DELIA: I think I understand.

SANDRA: You do?

DELIA: Yes, girls, I think I understand what this is all

about. Let's face it. I know what it's like to be struggling in the big city. I went through it myself—before I went back to Springville. You don't have to pretend with me.

MAY: Well, we weren't exactly—

BETTY: You see, we just thought—

SANDRA: With all those stories in the paper—

DELIA: You don't have to explain to me, girls. You see, I've read some of the letters you girls sent home, and I was intrigued not by what they said but by what they didn't say. They were just like the letters I used to write home when I was in New York. Full of generalizations about how wonderful everything is—but never specific about anything.

BETTY: You mean you actually suspected things weren't exactly rosy with us?

DELIA: Yes, I did. I will admit that for a while you girls fooled me, with all this talk about avant-garde plays, *Aïda,* and commissions for paintings.

SANDRA: We're sorry we—er—exaggerated.

DELIA: But you can't go on like this. Why don't you come home?

MAY: Oh, we can't. We'd be in absolute disgrace.

SANDRA: I can just see the three of us walking down Main Street and passing Hogan's Drug Store with all the boys hanging around outside. I can just hear their wisecracks now.

BETTY: Nobody wants to be a failure. And to go back to Springville and admit failure would be terrible.

DELIA: I know. I know. You young people have pride. Well, if you won't come home, let me lend you some money to tide you over for a while.

BETTY (*Firmly*): No, Delia, we can't do that. We want to get somewhere on our own.

MAY: If we get thrown out of here, we'll just have to find another place to live.

BETTY: Even if it's a pup tent in Central Park.

MAY: And, Delia, don't tell the folks back home. After all, I really *can* act, and Sandra *can* sing, and Betty *can* paint. Something will turn up for us. Give us a chance. We'll make it yet.

DELIA (*Admiringly*): You girls certainly have courage.

MAY: We're either courageous or completely loony. But we're going to stick to our guns! (*There is a knock at door, and* MAY *goes to open it.* CAROLYN COLLINS *and* GERT DREXEL *enter.*)

CAROLYN (*Looking around room and speaking theatrically*): This is it! Gert, darling, this is the room! (*She goes to sofa and pats it fondly.*) On this sofa, I used to lie and dream big dreams about the future—stardom, minks, a Rolls Royce. (*Walks to bookcase*) And, darling, I must be photographed standing in front of this bookcase. It will give the story a divinely intellectual quality. (*Going left*) And this is the door to the darling little kitchen where I prepared the simple fare that kept body and soul together until opportunity knocked. (*Returning to center*) Ah, home again!

GERT (*Sarcastically*): Sure, Carolyn, it must be the thrill of a lifetime. Return to Tobacco Road. Good afternoon, folks. I'm Gert Drexel from the publicity department of *High Life Magazine*—the favorite periodical of Americans who would rather look at pictures than read. As you've probably guessed, this is Carolyn Collins, the toast of stage, screen, and the major TV networks.

MAY (*Somewhat overcome*): Hello, Miss Collins. We learned just a little while ago that you used to live here.

This is Delia Danforth, this is Betty Jackson, this is Sandra Lee, and I'm May Hume. (*All nod.*)

CAROLYN (*Looking around room*): Wonderful! Wonderful! Wonderful! Gert, darling, it's all *here*. The whole divine atmosphere! If *High Life* is to do my life story, this is the place where I absolutely *must* be photographed.

GERT: Sure thing, kid. We'll get enough corn in the story to stock an Iowa farm for the next century. The photographers will be here at nine tomorrow morning. We'll probably need most of the day if the thing is to be done right.

SANDRA: But, really, we don't think we can allow that.

MAY: Matters are rather uncertain here right now.

BETTY: Yes, things are pretty upset.

CAROLYN (*Imperiously*): Darling, I don't think you heard right through those pretty little ears. I must be photographed here. It's as simple as that. My public would be disappointed otherwise. I'm sure they will be absolutely thrilled to see me as I was in the dear old days when I was struggling for fame and fortune.

GERT: And you kids wouldn't want Carolyn's vast public to have nervous breakdowns, would you?

BETTY: But, you see, we'll probably have to be doing a lot of packing tomorrow. Everything will be upset. There'll be no—

CAROLYN (*Walking slowly around room*): Ah, this Greenwich Village atmosphere! It's marvelous! It's superb! Gert, darling, isn't it stupendous?

GERT: It has all the charm of the House of Usher.

CAROLYN: The House of Usher? Isn't that somewhere on Long Island? Oh, Gert, there is something absolutely special about this place. Of course, I have a beautiful home in Beverly Hills, a villa on the Riviera—but, darlings, I don't have the affection for them that I have for this wonderful old apartment. (*Runs her finger along the table*) Even the dust hasn't changed.

SANDRA: We've been so busy we haven't had much time for housecleaning.

MAY: But you see how it is, Miss Collins. You'll just have to postpone this *High Life* project.

CAROLYN: My dear child, don't talk such nonsense. Nothing will be postponed. I'll be here tomorrow morning with bells on and with a song in my heart.

GERT: We won't take no for an answer.

BETTY (*Somewhat impatiently*): Look, we're having a difficult time as it is. For your information, we may be evicted from the premises. Tomorrow we'll have to pack, to get things straightened out—

CAROLYN (*Ignoring her and walking to easel*): Of course, this easel will have to be put away. I never did any painting while I was here, and I will not deceive my public. My talent is a great one—divine, most of the critics call it—but it is for the theater. (*Going to* GERT) And Gert, darling, I'll have to have a simple wardrobe, nothing too pretentious for the pictures; something simple and wholesome to go with the setting.

GERT: I know, I know. Just a plain little Dior original.

CAROLYN: That's it, darling. And perhaps a simple little housedress, too, preferably trimmed with mink.

SANDRA: Miss Collins, I don't think you understand.

DELIA: What the girls have been trying to tell you is that it would be inconvenient for you to use the apartment tomorrow.

CAROLYN: Inconvenient? Darling, don't be dreary. It won't

be inconvenient for me at all. I'll love it. And besides, *High Life* is willing to pay.

BETTY (*Interested*): Did you say "pay"?

GERT: Sure, *High Life* will pay for the use of the hall. (*She takes a roll of money from her bag.*) I've been authorized by the geniuses who run the magazine to offer the present tenants two hundred dollars for the use of this joint tomorrow.

BETTY (*Gulping*): Was that two hundred dollars I heard?

MAY: Two hundred beautiful dollars!

SANDRA: What an interesting sum!

GERT: Now don't you kids try to hold me up for more dough. Two hundred is as high as *High Life* will go.

BETTY: We wouldn't think of holding you up, Miss Drexel.

SANDRA: We accept!

MAY: We'll be able to pay the rent and have a good sum left over.

DELIA: You were right, girls. Something did turn up.

GERT (*Counting out the money and handing it to* MAY): I don't know whether you're the treasurer of this outfit or not—but here's the cash.

MAY (*Beaming with delight as she takes money*): Thank you.

CAROLYN (*Standing near chair down right*): This is the exact spot where Otto K. Krausmeyer stood when he said to me, "Carolyn, baby, you've got it—that star quality that communicates over the footlights. You're not only beautiful, Carolyn, but you're talented, too. That's an unbeatable combination." And, darlings, he was so right.

MAY: For our money, you're the best thing that ever happened to the theater. (*She goes to upstage center door, opens it, and yells)* Mrs. Grimshaw! Will you please come up here right away? It's important!

BETTY: This will make a summit conference look like a meeting of the Cub Scouts.

CAROLYN: And how is darling Mrs. Grimshaw? She was like a mother to me, so kind, so understanding, so considerate.

SANDRA *(Ironically)*: Let's just say that the years have changed her somewhat. (MRS. GRIMSHAW *appears at door, out of breath, and mop still in hand.*)

MRS. GRIMSHAW: Well, what's up now?

CAROLYN *(Going to her)*: Mrs. Grimshaw, darling!

MRS. GRIMSHAW: Why, Carolyn Collins!

CAROLYN: I'm back in the dear old Village.

MRS. GRIMSHAW: I can tell you one thing—I wish you'd never left. Rent always paid on time. . . .

MAY: Speaking of the rent, Mrs. Grimshaw, I believe that you hinted not long ago that we owe you money.

MRS. GRIMSHAW: Hinted? I never hint about things like that. I came right out and laid it on the line.

MAY *(Counting out money into* MRS. GRIMSHAW'*s hand)*: And we're doing the same thing, Mrs. Grimshaw. Laying it right on the line. Here's what we owe you for the past two months. *(Holds bills out)*

MRS. GRIMSHAW *(Taking money and looking amazed)*: I never thought I'd live to see this day.

SANDRA: Patience pays off, Mrs. Grimshaw.

GERT *(Ironically)*: Patience and *High Life Magazine.*

DELIA: Girls, I'm so happy for you. *(There is a knock at upstage door and* BETTY *opens it. In the doorway stand* WENDY FLEMING; HETTY *and* MOLLY, *who have guitars;* LENA, *a beatnik poet, and* LUCY, *a beatnik painter.*

They hold long loaves of French bread, whole cheeses, fruit, and a coffeepot.)

BETTY: Girls! Why all the food?

HETTY (*Strumming a chord on her guitar*): Like we're going to have a real celebration, man.

MOLLY (*Also strumming a chord*): A real ball with no squares allowed.

SANDRA: You've certainly come equipped for it. I'll get a card table to put the food on. (*She exits left quickly.*)

LENA: I feel a poem coming on, like an urge to make with the words. Like a real gone poem for the occasion.

BETTY: The question is, what's the occasion? Oh, I'm sorry. The lady sitting on the sofa is Delia Danforth. And, of course, you recognize Carolyn Collins.

LUCY: Yeah, I had you pegged, Miss Collins. You've got good bones like the real thing. I'd like to paint you.

BETTY: And this is Gert Drexel of *High Life Magazine.* Delia, Miss Collins, Miss Drexel, this is Lena Columbine, a poet. (LENA *nods.*) Lucy Jenkins, a painter. (LUCY *nods.*) Molly Price and Hetty Carroll, who are folk singers. (*They nod.*) And Wendy Fleming, a dancer. (SANDRA *returns with a card table on which the guests deposit the food.*)

CAROLYN: You see, Gert, darling, it's all *here.* That Greenwich Village atmosphere.

GERT: It's here all right.

LUCY (*Reaching into pocket of her smock*): Now, for the big news. I'm in orbit. I'm way out in space. Do you know what's happened, Betty? That painting of yours, "Sunrise in Central Park," the one you exhibited at the Village Art Festival—well, it's been sold.

BETTY: Sold?

LUCY: Somebody plunked down some good solid cash for it. One hundred and fifty dollars! (*Hands money to* BETTY) On the nose.

DELIA: Betty, I'm so happy for you.

MAY: Golly, things are really beginning to happen. Maybe we'll all make it yet.

DELIA: Of course you will.

BETTY (*Dazed*): One hundred and fifty dollars! I just can't believe it.

LENA: I've just got to make with the words.

WENDY: Let's celebrate! Hetty, Molly, get going on those guitars. (HETTY *and* MOLLY *begin to play a lively song.* WENDY *begins to dance around the room.*)

CAROLYN: Oh, this is it! This is the real thing!

GERT: It's different, I'll say that for it. (CAROLYN *grabs* MRS. GRIMSHAW, *mop and all, and begins to dance with her.* WENDY *dances to sofa, grabs* DELIA's *hand, gets her to her feet, and begins to dance with her.* BETTY, SANDRA, *and* MAY, *clapping hands in time to the music, watch gleefully, their faces beaming.* MRS. GRIMSHAW *trips over her mop and almost falls.*)

CAROLYN (*Catching her*): Be careful, darling!

MAY: Yes, Mrs. Grimshaw, we don't want anything to happen to you.

LENA (*Going to center, closing her eyes, and speaking dramatically*): A poem for Betty's success. (*She recites, while the dancing and music continue.*)

This morning, cats slunk through the alley,
The sun rose on orange peels,
The milk bottles on the steps
Looked dismal as a thundercloud
And the 8:20 bus lumbered over the cobblestones.
But sing now—sing, sing, sing!

The day has changed; the sun is bright
The Muses smile on this old house.
Let joy be unconfined.

BETTY: It's lovely, Lena.

DELIA: And to think that if I'd stayed in Springville, I'd have missed all this.

WENDY (*Suddenly*): Oh, golly! My cake will be burned to a crisp! (*She rushes out at center, while the others laugh.*)

CAROLYN (*Still dancing*): Oh, darlings, it's wonderful to be home again!

SANDRA (*Happily*): It's wonderful to *have* a home again. (*The music and dancing go on. Quick curtain.*)

THE END

Production Notes

Don't Tell the Folks Back Home

Characters: 12 female.

Playing Time: 30 minutes.

Costumes: Betty wears a smock; May, slacks and sweater; Sandra, a casual cotton; and Mrs. Grimshaw, a housedress. Delia wears a frilly dress and a fruit-and-flowered hat. Carolyn wears heavy make-up and is theatrically dressed, and Gert wears a tweed suit. Wendy is dressed in a leotard; Lena, in a Japanese kimono and open-toed sandals; Lucy, in a paint-spattered smock and a beret; and the others, in typical beatnik clothing.

Properties: Mop, paintbrush, cup, dish, eggs, money, loaves of French bread, whole cheeses, fruit, coffeepot, card table.

Setting: Down right is a battered sofa, and, at center, a table on which are piled magazines, letters, pieces of sheet music. There is an easy chair down left, and a bookcase up left, in front of which stands a painter's easel. Exit at left leads to kitchen. Door upstage center leads to outside.

Lighting: No special effects.

The Tall Stranger

Characters

BAT FARR, *a villain*   *Measley Coward*
PENELOPE PRISS, *a sweet young girl*
DIANE DE KOOT, *a dance-hall girl*
MAMIE SHANKS, *proprietor of the Cactus Hotel*
POP SICKLE, *a former buffalo hunter*   *Short Stranger*
SLIPPERY ELLUM, *a stagecoach driver*
RUNNING WATER, *an Indian*
ACE HIGH, *a gambler and desperado*
MONTGOMERY BLACKSTONE, *a dude from the East*
THREE INDIAN BRAVES

SCENE 1

TIME: *A morning in the days of the Old West.*

SETTING: *The lobby of the Cactus Hotel in Muddy Creek. At right is a registration desk on which there are a bell and the hotel register. Around the lobby are chairs and a sofa.*

AT RISE: BAT FARR *is standing at center. Kneeling before him and speaking pleadingly is* PENELOPE PRISS. *Behind the desk,* MAMIE SHANKS *is shaking her head.* POP SICKLE *is standing at left of desk.* DIANE DE KOOT *is lounging in a chair.*

89

PENELOPE: Can nothing soften your heart, Mr. Bat Farr? My father is an old man; he has spent his life building the Muddy Creek Bank. And now you propose to take it away from him. Have mercy!

DIANE: You ought to be on the stage, kid. You'd wow 'em with all that sweet talk.

BAT (*Angrily*): Just hold your tongue, Diane. This business is between Miss Penelope Priss and me.

DIANE: Monkey business, if you ask me. You're not gettin' sweet on her, are you, Bat? Are those baby blue eyes softenin' you up? (PENELOPE *rises as* BAT *goes to* DIANE, *grabs her arm, and twists it*) Ouch! (*He releases her arm, and she rubs it.*)

PENELOPE: Don't hurt her, Mr. Farr, I beg you.

DIANE: You're no gentleman.

BAT: Don't give me that stuff, Diane. You wouldn't know a gentleman if you fell over one. (*He returns to center.*) I suppose I lost my temper, Miss Priss. I'm usually as kind as a mother hen.

MAMIE: Twisting women's arms isn't my idea of kindness, Bat.

BAT: Nobody asked for your opinion, Mamie Shanks. You run your hotel, and I'll—

MAMIE: You'll run the town like you've been doing— lending out money and then foreclosing mortgages on all the ranches around here. You're a dirty dog, Bat.

BAT: Smile when you say that, Mamie. If people can't pay what they owe, they have to take the consequences.

PENELOPE: Oh, Mr. Farr, have mercy on my father!

BAT (*Taking out handkerchief and wiping his eyes*): It hurts me when I have to lower the boom on the poor souls.

MAMIE: Seems funny, though. The minute you lend

money to a rancher, his cattle begin to disappear. Then when he can't pay, because he has no cattle to sell, you step in like a vulture and take over his ranch.

BAT: It's a coincidence.

PENELOPE: Won't you be fair to my father, Mr. Farr?

BAT: Why, Miss Priss, I'm as honest as the late George Washington. (POP SICKLE *cackles and slaps his thigh in merriment.* BAT *turns on him.*) As for you, you old goat, keep quiet or I'll feed you to the prairie wolves!

POP: I don't take that kind of talk from anybody. I'm Pop Sickle, I am, and in my time I was the greatest buffalo hunter and Indian fighter this country has ever seen. The Indians used to shake at the mention of my name.

BAT: With laughter, no doubt. Why keep this old wreck around here, Mamie?

MAMIE: He's been here a week, and I like him. I have a right to employ anybody I want to in my hotel.

POP (*Triumphantly*): Guess that'll hold you, Bat Farr! And don't forget, I'm a rip-roarin', gun-totin', man-killin' lion when I'm angry. (*He takes a swing at an imaginary opponent and falls flat on the floor.* BAT *laughs nastily.*)

DIANE: You tell him, Pop. I'll bet you could lick your weight in lollipops.

PENELOPE: Mr. Farr, will you please give my father more time?

BAT: Miss Priss, I hate to take over your father's bank. It really pains me.

DIANE: Yeah, he hates money. It gives him hives.

BAT: But business is business. Your father played poker with Mr. Ace High and me. Your father lost to the tune of nearly twenty thousand dollars. All he has to pay the debt with is the bank itself. So I'm taking over the bank tomorrow. That was the agreement—signed, sealed, and delivered.

PENELOPE: But what will happen to Father? Where can he turn? What can he do? (BAT *attempts to put his arm around her waist, but she eludes him.*)

BAT: Don't be frightened. I'm harmless.

DIANE: As a cobra on one of its bad days.

BAT: Miss Priss, there is a solution to your woes. As you know, I'm a power in this town. Marry me, and the world is at your feet. Then I'll be willing to forget about the bank business.

PENELOPE (*Drawing herself up*): But, Mr. Farr, I do not love you.

BAT (*With an ominous laugh*): You will when you get to know me better. (POP SICKLE *cackles again.* BAT *goes to him, grabs him by the collar, shakes him, and throws him to the floor.*)

POP (*Hiding face in hands*): You've almost made me angry. And I'm a wild and dangerous galoot when my temper's up.

PENELOPE (*Goes to* POP, *helps him to his feet, then turns to* BAT, *her eyes flashing*): Your actions have made up my mind, Mr. Bat Farr. I could never marry a man who mistreats the old and helpless.

BAT: Guess I lost my temper, Miss Priss. Ordinarily, I'm as gentle as a week-old kitten. But you may realize that I'm not such a bad catch when your father loses his bank tomorrow.

PENELOPE: Have you no heart?

MAMIE: There's hope yet, Miss Priss. (*She holds an envelope in her hand.*) This came for you today, Bat Farr.

BAT (*Taking envelope from* MAMIE *and reading the note*

aloud): "The Tall Stranger is on his way." (BAT *crumples the paper and throws it angrily to the floor.*) Drat it, that's the fourth note this week! I suppose he thinks I'll be shaking with fear. Well, Bat Farr fears no man.

DIANE: Especially old ones.

MAMIE (*With relish*): Well, if I were you, I'd do some worrying. This Tall Stranger seems to be on a crusade to clean up the towns around here. He put Filthy Mc-Nasty and his gang of crooks behind bars over in Vulture Gulch. And he did the same with Oily Grease and Killer Gatt over at Roaring Furnace. And I'll bet he has plans for you.

BAT: The man doesn't live who can put me behind bars. (SLIPPERY ELLUM *enters left excitedly.*)

MAMIE: Well, it's Slippery Ellum. What's the rush? Was your stagecoach attacked by redskins?

SLIPPERY (*Going to* BAT): I was hopin' to find you here, Bat. (*He mops his brow with a red handkerchief.*) You know you asked me to report if any strangers came here on my stagecoach. Well, I just brought one in.

BAT: Is he tall?

PENELOPE: Oh, pray heaven he may be the Tall Stranger!

MAMIE: Amen to that!

SLIPPERY: He's middlin' tall. And he's dressed like a real dude—all spit and polish. Heard him say he's one of those lawyer fellers.

DIANE (*Hopefully*): Is he good-looking?

SLIPPERY: His face wouldn't frighten children.

DIANE: That's more than I can say for yours.

BAT: Do you think he may be the Tall Stranger?

SLIPPERY: Well, I've never seen the Tall Stranger, and I don't know anybody who has. But if this dude is the Tall Stranger, I'll be mighty surprised. He's too polite in his actions, and he speaks with one of those British accents. Real la-de-da, he is.

DIANE: Looks like you can rest easy, Bat. This guy sounds like just another dude from the East.

PENELOPE: But how wonderful it would be if he were the Tall Stranger! His name has become a legend among those who fight for the right.

POP: My name was a legend once, too.

BAT: Your name will be mud if you don't shut your trap.

SLIPPERY: I need a room for the night, Mamie. The stage is stopping over. And there wasn't any water in the pitcher in my room the last time I stayed here.

MAMIE: What do you expect for fifty cents? Next you'll be wanting sheets on the bed.

SLIPPERY (*Going to door*): In this place, I'd be satisfied just to get a bed. I'd better see to the horses. (*He begins to exit and bumps into* MONTGOMERY BLACKSTONE, *who enters carrying a valise.*) Look where you're goin', dude. (*Speaking over shoulder*) This is the stranger, Bat. (SLIPPERY *exits.* MONTGOMERY *goes to registration desk and smiles at* MAMIE.)

MONTGOMERY: A very good morning to you, fair lady.

BAT: Fair lady! That's a good one.

MAMIE: I may not be Helen of Troy, but I am presentable. What can I do for you, young man?

MONTGOMERY: I should like a room in your charming establishment.

DIANE: Charming fleabag, he means. And pipe that British accent.

MONTGOMERY (*Bowing*): A relic of my Oxford days.

DIANE (*Rising and crossing to* MONTGOMERY *and regarding him with interest*): What's your name, stranger?

MONTGOMERY: My, the jolly old West is literally swarming with highly decorative females. (*He bows*.) I am Montgomery Blackstone of Boston, Massachusetts, attorney at law, and at your service.

DIANE: Pleased to meet you. (*She shakes his hand, and he winces at the power of her grip*.) If I want to sue anybody for assault and battery (*She looks meaningfully at* BAT), I'll look you up.

BAT (*To* MONTGOMERY): So you're a lawyer, are you? Let me give you a bit of free advice. Get out of Muddy Creek. We don't need any legal eagles around here.

MONTGOMERY (*Takes white handkerchief from his pocket and nonchalantly brushes an imaginary speck of dust from his sleeve. Ignoring* BAT): Shall I sign the register?

MAMIE: Sure, go ahead. (MONTGOMERY *does so.* BAT *goes to him and takes pen from his hand. Then he grabs* MONTGOMERY *by the coat collar*)

BAT: Maybe you didn't hear me, Mr. Boston, Massachusetts. I said we don't need any of your kind in these parts.

MONTGOMERY: Please unhand me, sir.

BAT (*Laughing and speaking in high falsetto*): "Please unhand me, sir." Now aren't we just too goody-goody for words!

PENELOPE: How can you be so hateful, Mr. Bat Farr? This young man has done you no harm.

MONTGOMERY: Thank you, my dear.

PENELOPE: Let him go. Why must there be violence wherever you are?

MAMIE: You have no call to say who'll stay in this hotel, Bat. I still own it.

BAT (*Releasing* MONTGOMERY): All right. Stay, Mr. Boston, Massachusetts. But if you get into trouble, you'll have only yourself to blame. (RUNNING WATER, *an Indian with a blanket around his shoulders and a feather in his headband, enters hurriedly.*)

RUNNING WATER: Ugh! There you are, Bat Farr. You heap bad man.

MONTGOMERY: Oh, I say, a genuine redskin!

BAT: Back to the wigwam, Running Water. I don't have time to talk to pesky redskins.

RUNNING WATER: Me no pesky redskin. Me Running Water. Good member of Potawatomi tribe.

PENELOPE: Why are you so angry, Running Water?

RUNNING WATER: This man, Bat Farr, he heap evil. He fill my brother, Broken Pump, with firewater last week. Then he have Broken Pump sign big X on paper. Now Bat Farr own all Broken Pump's land.

BAT: Just a normal legal procedure. I gave him a string of beads to boot. A fair price for eight hundred acres. Heh! Heh!

PENELOPE: How can you be so cruel?

RUNNING WATER: You heap big crook.

BAT: Watch your language, redskin. I'm a kind man, but there's a limit even to my patience.

MONTGOMERY: Oh, I say, this is all so frightfully interesting. It sounds as though I have my first jolly case in Muddy Creek. Running Water, I am a lawyer. I'll be happy to talk with your brother. I'll look at that peculiar paper he signed, and see what I can do to get back his land.

RUNNING WATER: Ugh! You good paleface. We be blood brothers if you get back land. I find nice squaw for you, too.

MONTGOMERY: That's awfully good of you, old boy, but I think I can do without the squaw.

BAT: You can do without the case. Keep your legal nose out of my business.

PENELOPE: Oh, Mr. Blackstone, I need an attorney, too. I am Penelope Priss. This man (*Pointing to* BAT) intends to take over my father's bank in a most underhanded manner.

MONTGOMERY (*Bowing*): At your service, Miss Priss. I must say, Mr. Farr, you are a busy man. What is your hobby—robbing the poor and helpless?

BAT: Smile when you say that, stranger.

MONTGOMERY (*Grinning*): How's this for size, old boy?

BAT: So you're a joker, too. Well, Mr. Boston, Massachusetts, before this day is over, you won't be smiling so cheerfully. I'm a gentle man, but I can be tried just so far. I advise you to watch your step. A little bird tells me that your days are numbered.

MONTGOMERY (*To* PENELOPE): Is there somewhere we can go for a jolly old chat? (*To* RUNNING WATER) Running Water, you had better come, too.

PENELOPE: I would be happy to talk with you and Running Water in my own home.

POP (*Chuckling*): All homes should have running water in them. (*He cackles and slaps his thigh.*)

MONTGOMERY: Splendid. Shall we depart, then?

POP: I'll take your valise up to your room, stranger.

MONTGOMERY: Thank you. (*He takes* PENELOPE'*s arm and motions to* RUNNING WATER.) Let us be on our way. (MONTGOMERY, PENELOPE, *and* RUNNING WATER *exit.*)

DIANE: Say, he's a cool one. And kind of cute.

BAT (*Laughing nastily*): He'll be stretched out cold before long. I'll get some of the boys after him.

MAMIE: You don't mean you're going to have Ace High make trouble for him?

BAT: That's what I pay Ace for—to make trouble. (*He laughs nastily and twirls his mustache.*)

DIANE: And he's the nastiest man in the West—outside of you, of course, Bat.

POP: And speaking of the devil, look who's coming. (ACE HIGH *enters. He has a six-shooter at his belt, wears a large hat, and looks tough.*)

ACE: I was just lookin' for you, Bat. I just took a thousand clams from old Joe Turpentine in a friendly little poker game.

BAT: Splendid. Did you get him to sign the usual paper?

ACE (*Smiling coldly*): His ranch will be yours within the week.

BAT: You're a prince of a fellow, Ace.

ACE: I aim to please. Say, who's the dude I just saw with Running Water and that Priss filly?

BAT: A nosy legal eagle from Boston. Looks as though he might give us trouble. (*Laughing*) You know what to do.

ACE: Sure. First, I'll get him in a little game of cards—

BAT (*Smiling*): Then you accuse him of cheating—

ACE: And then (*He touches his gun*)—the end. (POP *takes valise and goes toward left. As he passes* ACE, ACE *trips him, and* POP *sprawls on the floor.*)

POP: Ace High, you're flirting with danger. You know who you're fooling with?

ACE: Yes, a tall-tale teller who claims he used to be a buffalo hunter. The nearest you ever got to a buffalo was probably Buffalo, New York. (POP *rises and picks up valise.* ACE *gives* POP *a hard shove, which sends* POP *through doorway.* ACE *laughs loudly.*)

MAMIE: You're a brave one, Ace High. Too bad there

aren't any little children around here so you could tangle with them, too.

ACE: Save your talk for Sunday school, Mamie. (*To* BAT) I'll arrange that little game. (*He pats his gun.*) Haven't had any good clean fun for a long while. (ACE *and* BAT *laugh nastily, and* BAT *claps* ACE *on the shoulder as the curtain falls.*)

*　　*　　*　　*　　*

SCENE 2

TIME: *An hour later.*

SETTING: *The same.*

AT RISE: MAMIE SHANKS *is sweeping the floor with a battered broom. She is singing "Oh, Susannah!" in a somewhat raucous and off-key voice.* POP SICKLE, *grinning broadly and looking pleased with himself, enters.*)

POP: You ought to be in opery, Mamie. You have a voice like a nightingale.

MAMIE (*Taking a swipe at him with the broom*): None of your wisecracks, Pop Sickle. Just where have you been for the last hour?

POP (*Mysteriously*): On a little errand, Mamie. (*He slaps his thigh.*) Oh, there'll be plenty of fireworks around here before long.

MAMIE: How come? It's not the Fourth of July.

POP: You'll see. Ace High is on his way here. So's that lawyer feller.

MAMIE: Say, that reminds me. Bring in one of those small tables from the kitchen. Ace says he needs it for a little game. (*She goes behind desk.*) I hate to have that skunk on the premises with his crooked gambling, but if I say no, he'll shoot the place as full of holes as a piece of Swiss cheese.

POP (*Vehemently*): In the old days, I'd have taken care of him, all right. I'd have cracked him on the jaw (POP *swings*), and then I'd have taken my trusty six-shooter and drilled him.

MAMIE: Quit dreaming, Pop, and get that table. (POP *exits left, still swinging at his imaginary opponent.* ACE HIGH *enters.*)

ACE: That dude returned yet? And where's that table I wanted? When I tell you to do something, I mean it. Nobody refuses Ace High anything and stays healthy.

MAMIE: We all know what a tough hombre you are, Ace. Pop's getting the table. (POP *enters, carrying a small table. He sets it down between two chairs.*)

POP: Fixin' for a little game, Ace?

ACE (*Laughing nastily*): You'll see, you old coot. A certain stranger is goin' to get the last surprise of his life. (MONTGOMERY BLACKSTONE *enters. As he comes to center,* ACE *takes a pack of cards from his pocket.*) Sit down, dude. We're goin' to have a little game.

MONTGOMERY: Frightfully sorry, old boy, but Mother always told me not to gamble. She always said that card playing was invented by the beastly old devil.

ACE (*Drawing his gun*): Your ma ever see one of these, dude? (*He pats gun.*) They're great things to make even mamas change their minds.

MONTGOMERY: Oh, I say, are you threatening me?

ACE: I'm not exactly askin' you for the next dance. Sit down at that table.

MONTGOMERY: You seem to have the upper hand with that dreadful-looking weapon. I do wish you'd be careful. It might go off.

ACE (*Laughing*): That's the general idea, chump.

MONTGOMERY: Well, if you insist. (*He sits down, and so does* ACE. ACE *places the gun beside him on the table.*)

ACE: Let's decide on the stakes. (*He reaches into his pocket, takes out money, and places it on table.*) Let's say ten dollars for a start.

MONTGOMERY: That's a frightfully large sum of money. And really, old boy, I don't know any card games. But wait a moment—I do know one jolly little game that's oodles of fun. I saw two men playing it on the stage-coach coming in.

ACE (*Suspiciously*): Yeah? What is it—tiddledywinks?

MONTGOMERY: I say, you do have a sense of humor, don't you? No, it was a simple affair, almost as simple as you, old boy.

ACE (*Touching gun*): Watch your language, dude.

MONTGOMERY: Frightfully sorry. No offense meant. As I recall it, it went like this. Each player merely cuts the cards—and high card wins.

ACE: Oh, that one. That's almost as old as Mamie.

MAMIE: Never mind my age, Ace High. (POP SICKLE *chuckles.*)

ACE: Cut the cacklin', you old rooster. All right, dude. I'll play high card with you. But let me see the color of your money.

MONTGOMERY (*Takes money from pocket and places it on table*): You may cut first. Mother always taught me to be courteous.

ACE (*Nastily*): Your ma was a real sweet kid, dude. (*He shuffles pack, places it on table, and then cuts. He looks at card.*) King of hearts. (*He is about to show it to* MONTGOMERY, *who pushes* ACE'S *hand away quickly.*)

MONTGOMERY: No, I don't want to see it. I trust you.

ACE (*Puzzled*): You kiddin'?

MONTGOMERY: Not at all, old thing. (*He puts* ACE's *card back in pack without looking at it, then takes pack, puts it on table, and cuts. He looks quickly at card.*) Ace of diamonds. Well, old boy, I guess I win that one. (*He takes* ACE's *money and puts card back in pack.*)

ACE: Hey, not so fast, dude! I didn't see that card!

MONTGOMERY: My, you are a suspicious character, aren't you? Did I ask to see yours? I trusted you implicitly. But if you insist. . . (*He takes pack, looks through it, finds ace of diamonds, and holds it up for* ACE's *inspection.*) See, old boy, here it is. The ace of diamonds. All open and aboveboard. (ACE *looks bewildered for a moment. Then he jumps angrily to his feet just as* BAT FARR *and* DIANE DE KOOT *enter.*)

ACE: Why, you snivelin', crawlin', no-good worm! You expect me to let you get away with that?

MONTGOMERY (*Innocently*): With what? Oh, I say, I like this game! Let's have another go at it, shall we?

BAT: What's wrong, Ace?

ACE: This guy's a crook. (*He takes his gun from table.*) He's trying to fleece me out of ten bucks.

BAT (*Shaking his head*): Tsk, tsk! How I hate a dishonest man. Anybody who would rob a fellow creature is lower than the scurviest reptile.

DIANE (*Shaking her head*): Now I've heard everything.

ACE: There's only one thing to do with a snake like this.

BAT: I catch your drift, Ace. I catch your drift. (*He takes handkerchief from pocket and wipes his eyes.*) The sight will pain me. But a man must pay for his sins. (ACE *levels his gun at* MONTGOMERY *just as* PENELOPE PRISS *enters. She stops in her tracks and stares with horror at the scene.*)

ACE (*Smiling*): Do you have any last message for your dear old ma, dude? The one who doesn't favor gambling?

PENELOPE (*Rushing to* MONTGOMERY *and standing in front of him*): Don't do it, Ace High! He is a harmless young man, good and true!

BAT (*Rushing to her, grasping her arm, and tearing her away from* MONTGOMERY): Don't interfere with the course of justice, Miss Penelope Priss. This man is a miserable cheater. And he must pay—that's the code of the West. I hate to see it done, but do my personal feelings count? I must sacrifice them in the cause of justice.

PENELOPE (*Struggling*): Oh, you are odious, Bat Farr!

ACE (*Leveling gun at* MONTGOMERY): This is it, dude. (POP SICKLE *creeps up behind* ACE, *and suddenly grabs his leg.* ACE *falls to the floor.* MONTGOMERY *grabs the gun.*)

MAMIE (*Amazed*): You been drinkin' firewater, Pop?

POP (*Smiling*): I told you I'm a tiger when I'm riled up.

DIANE: And I guess you weren't kidding.

ACE (*Begins to stir on the floor*): Get the number of the stagecoach that hit me. (*He rises painfully and slowly to his feet.*)

MONTGOMERY (*Pointing gun at him*): Just sit quietly at that table, old boy.

ACE (*Rubbing neck*): Says who?

POP (*In a commanding voice*): Sit, Ace! Or I'll smack you into kingdom come. (ACE *sits.*)

BAT (*Going furtively towards door*): Well, I must be off. I have business to attend to.

MONTGOMERY: You sit, too, Bat. I have a tale to tell.

BAT: But—(POP *goes to* BAT, *and with an amazing show of strength, grabs him by the collar, and plops him into a chair.*)

DIANE (*Admiringly*): Why, that old geezer must have muscles on his muscles! (RUNNING WATER *enters suddenly and surveys the scene with satisfaction. He is carrying a tomahawk.*)

RUNNING WATER (*Going toward* BAT): Me scalp him now. His hair look good in wigwam.

BAT (*Frightened*): It's all a mistake. You've all misjudged me. I'm as gentle as the spring rain.

MONTGOMERY: I say, Running Water, I don't think you really ought to give this miserable fellow a haircut right now. We had better let his barber and the law take care of him.

RUNNING WATER (*Reluctantly*): Too bad. Law sometimes slow. But tomahawk fast. (*He brandishes tomahawk, and* BAT *cowers in terror.*)

MONTGOMERY: Please, Running Water.

RUNNING WATER: All right, boss. You blood brother to Running Water. He like you heap much.

MONTGOMERY: Thank you, old fellow. I'm immensely flattered. And now I owe you two thugs an explanation. I might say that dear Pop Sickle had already informed me of your intentions, Ace High.

ACE (*Angrily*): Why, you filthy rattlesnake.

POP: Sticks and stones may break my bones, but names will never harm me.

MONTGOMERY: Consequently, I knew just how to deal with you in our little card game. Furthermore, Mr. Bat Farr, I have investigated your shady dealings with the lovely Miss Priss and the somewhat impetuous Running Water and his brother.

DIANE (*With admiration*): My, doesn't he know how to use the King's English!

MONTGOMERY: Your dealings, Bat Farr, have been dishonest. First of all, none of the papers you have signed and persuaded others to sign are legal; this goes for your evil tricks on Miss Priss's father and on Running Water's brother, Broken Pump. The papers are not legal because the name Bat Farr is on them.

BAT: My name is Bat Farr.

MONTGOMERY: Not at all. Your real name is Measley Coward.

DIANE: What an appropriate moniker that is!

MONTGOMERY: I have been tracing your dealings for a long time. Your name has never been legally changed. Therefore, everything you have signed is worthless.

PENELOPE: Then Father can keep his bank!

RUNNING WATER: And Broken Pump—he keep land!

MONTGOMERY: Exactly. And that is not all. (*He picks up the pack of cards from table.*) This jolly little deck of cards used by you and Ace High in the poker games with your unfortunate victims, Bat Farr, is a crooked deck. (*He holds up one of the cards.*) Each of these cards is marked.

BAT: Why, I'm shocked, Ace. I had no idea you were using a marked deck. I'm an honest man. I—

ACE: You slimy coyote. You marked the cards for me yourself.

MAMIE: Oh, you're a great pair, all right.

PENELOPE: Mr. Montgomery Blackstone—you—you must be the Tall Stranger!

MONTGOMERY: Miss Priss, I cannot tell a lie. I am, indeed, the Tall Stranger.

PENELOPE: Oh, how thrilling!

DIANE: Who would have thought it!

POP: Get ready for a shock, folks. I'm the Tall Stranger's assistant. Some call me the Short Stranger.

MAMIE: What! An old goat like you!

POP: I may be a goat—but I'm not old. (*Dramatically, he removes his wig and beard and stands before them, a young man.*)

DIANE: Why, he's cute!

MAMIE: He's a young feller!

MONTGOMERY (*Dropping British accent*): It's all easily explained. The person you know as Pop Sickle is really my cousin, Ferdinand Blackstone. You will note that he has been here for a week—getting the lay of the land, so to speak.

PENELOPE: Why, Mr. Blackstone, you're not British at all!

MONTGOMERY: No, ma'am, it was only an act. I'm one hundred per cent American, just like my cousin Ferdinand here. I put on the accent so no one would suspect he had done this preliminary spadework for me.

POP: I found out plenty in the week I was here.

MONTGOMERY: Measley Coward, alias Bat Farr, and Ace High, I arrest you.

BAT: You can't arrest us. You have no official capacity. I'll take the case to the Supreme Court.

RUNNING WATER (*Brandishing tomahawk*): You shut mouth!

MONTGOMERY (*Taking a paper from his pocket*): You're wrong, Bat Farr. Listen to this. (*Reading aloud from paper*) "The White House, Washington, D. C. This will certify that Mr. Montgomery Blackstone has been appointed by me as a special federal marshal. He has full power to investigate and to prosecute the evil and corruption that have crept into certain towns of the West. He has full power to arrest. He is to receive the co-operation of all law officials. Signed, Chester A. Arthur, President."

PENELOPE: How wonderful! But what will you do now, Mr. Tall Stranger? Are there other towns that need your help?

MONTGOMERY: No, my mission has ended. Muddy Creek was my last assignment.

PENELOPE: Then is there a chance—could you—would you stay?

MONTGOMERY: Miss Priss, I was hoping you'd ask. I shall, indeed, stay. And I hope, Miss Priss, that I have your permission to call on you frequently—object, eventual matrimony, after I have established my law practice.

PENELOPE (*Looking radiantly happy*): I would be honored, Mr. Blackstone.

DIANE (*Going to* POP): And how about you, Ferdy? Why not stay around these parts, too? You could run for sheriff. I'd be glad to act as your campaign manager.

BAT (*Scornfully*): You're nothing but a dance-hall girl.

POP: Don't scorn dance-hall girls, Bat Farr. Everybody knows that all dance-hall girls of the West have hearts of gold. Miss Diane de Koot, I've always known that beneath your tough exterior there beats a womanly heart. I accept your offer. Anyway, I want to stay here with my cousin. Blood is thicker than water—even running water.

MAMIE: Well, well, love comes to Muddy Creek—and high time, too.

PENELOPE (*Happily*): Love and law and order! Oh, what a wonderful day this has been! (MONTGOMERY *goes to* PENELOPE *and embraces her. During this short lapse of time,* BAT *and* ACE *jump up and try to escape.* RUNNING WATER *utters a shrill war whoop, and suddenly* THREE INDIAN BRAVES, *brandishing tomahawks, rush in and stop* BAT *and* ACE *at the door.*)

MONTGOMERY (*Laughing*): I wouldn't advise you boys to try making a run for it. I brought along some of Running Water's friends. (RUNNING WATER *and the* INDIAN BRAVES *whoop loudly.*)

BAT (*Cowering*): It's all a mistake. No one really understands me.

ACE: Same here.

MONTGOMERY: Just take these two galoots to the town jail, men. We'll deal with them in the courts.

RUNNING WATER: Ugh! We take 'em quick. Plenty bad men.

BAT: You're not leaving us in the hands of these wild redskins?

MONTGOMERY: As you yourself so appropriately remarked —it's the code of the West. (RUNNING WATER *and* INDIAN BRAVES *grab* BAT *and* ACE *and rush them through the door.*)

MAMIE: Muddy Creek has now become a real community.

POP (*Taking* DIANE'*s hand*): A place for tenderness and love.

MONTGOMERY (*Taking* PENELOPE'*s hand*): Where the future is bright and unclouded. (*Quick curtain*)

THE END

Production Notes

The Tall Stranger

Characters: 9 male; 3 female.

Playing Time: 30 minutes.

Costumes: Typical clothing of the Old West. Bat is dressed as the traditional villain. Ace wears cowboy suit. Diane wears a fancy dance-hall dress. Running Water and Indian Braves wear Indian costumes, with blankets and feathers. Montgomery wears dude's clothing—dress clothing of the period. Pop wears Western clothing, with white wig and beard which he later removes. Penelope wears a long, gingham dress and Mamie a long, dark dress.

Properties: Envelope, note, valise, white handkerchief, six-shooter, broom, deck of cards, handkerchief, tomahawks, paper, bell, pencil, hotel register, card table.

Setting: The lobby of the Cactus Hotel. At right is a registration desk. Around the lobby are chairs and a sofa. Exits up center and left lead outside and to the rest of the hotel.

Lighting: No special effects.

See You in the Funnies

Characters

TYLER BRAYTON, *28, creator of Ambitious Aloysius*
SUE BLAKE, *his secretary*
BRENDA CARTWRIGHT, *his fiancée*
KAREN HALL, *17*
BILL PRATT, *Karen's boy friend*
THE AMBITIOUS ALOYSIUS FAN CLUB, *ten boys and girls*
PROFESSOR WENTWORTH KING
EDGAR ALLAN SCHMIDT, *an avant-garde poet*

TIME: *Afternoon.*
SETTING: *Tyler Brayton's studio. A large drawing table and two chairs are at center. At right are a sofa and a desk with papers and telephone on it. An easy chair is at left.*
AT RISE: TYLER BRAYTON *is seated at drawing board,* SUE BLAKE *is at her desk, and* BRENDA CARTWRIGHT *is seated in easy chair, reading.*

TYLER (*Sighing unhappily*): Gosh, I don't know what's the matter with me. I've been staring at this drawing board for an hour, and it just stares back. I can't seem to come up with an idea. (*He throws drawing pencil ex-*

asperatedly onto table, rises, and begins to pace the floor.)

BRENDA (*Looking up from her book*): You're just proving that I'm absolutely right, Tyler. Drawing a comic strip like "Ambitious Aloysius" just isn't important enough work for a man of your ability. It's as though Einstein had devoted himself to multiplying two by two. Or as though Shakespeare had spent his time writing nursery rhymes.

TYLER: You may be right, Brenda. Something *is* wrong with me.

BRENDA: It's your subconscious in revolt.

SUE (*Looking up from desk*): I don't see why you think "Ambitious Aloysius" is unimportant, Brenda. It brings plenty of enjoyment to lots of people.

BRENDA (*Very sarcastically*): People with pointed heads, perhaps. Don't tell me you really enjoy reading "Ambitious Aloysius," Sue.

SUE (*Loyally*): Of course I do. "Ambitious Aloysius" is funny, realistic, and perceptive. (BRENDA *shakes her head.* TYLER *comes up behind her, and puts his hand on her shoulders.*)

TYLER: I think I know what's wrong with me, Brenda. If you'd marry me, I'll bet I'd be able to work again. Not knowing where I stand is what worries me. After all, we've been engaged for three months. (BRENDA *takes his hand, squeezes it, and then releases it quickly.*)

BRENDA: Look, Tyler, we've been through all this before. When we became engaged, I understood that you would eventually give up "Ambitious Aloysius." I just will not marry a man unless I feel that he is making a worthwhile contribution to society.

SUE: You're too intellectual, Brenda.

BRENDA: I can't help it if I was born with a mind. (*She returns to her book.*) Now here is somebody (*She holds up book*) who is really contributing something to his time. Edgar Allan Schmidt, the poet. He's magnificent.

SUE: I can't make heads or tails of what he writes.

BRENDA: He's deep. You'd better stick to "Ambitious Aloysius," Sue. As for Tyler, I know he has the talent to write a good novel or an outstanding play.

TYLER (*Returning to drawing board and looking glumly at it*): I wish I had your confidence, Brenda. I tried a novel once. It was rejected by nine publishers. (KAREN HALL *and* BILL PRATT *enter right.*)

KAREN: Hi, Uncle Tyler. Why aren't you hard at work today? After all, "Ambitious Aloysius" has to go on.

BILL: And on and on. All the kids I know love it.

BRENDA (*Contemptuously*): Kids!

BILL: Well, they help pay Tyler's grocery bills.

KAREN: And I wouldn't be visiting with Uncle Tyler unless there were plenty of groceries.

BILL: That's no lie. Karen has the appetite of a bird—an eagle.

KAREN: Well, Mr. Bill Pratt, I'd rather have an eagle's appetite than an eagle's brain.

SUE: Come on, now, let's not bring personalities into this.

BRENDA (*Wearily*): For all our sakes, let's have no more of this silly teen-age talk. (*She rises, putting book down on chair.*) Tyler, how about a walk in the garden? I need fresh air—and so do you.

TYLER (*Staring down gloomily at drawing board*): All right. I'm certainly not accomplishing anything here. I suspect I never will.

SUE (*Holding up letter*): Will you sign this letter to Professor King before you go out, Tyler?

TYLER (*Takes a sketch from drawing board, looks at it, shakes his head, and tosses it back on board*): Yes, I will.

BRENDA: I didn't know that you corresponded with professors, Tyler.

KAREN: I saw Professor King's letter. He loves "Ambitious Aloysius."

BRENDA: The man must be mad. He should be investigated by the American Association of University Professors. He's obviously not fit to instruct the young.

TYLER (*Going slowly to* SUE's *desk*): I'll sign that letter to the Professor, Sue. (*He does so. Then he sighs*) And I'll sign that other letter I wrote this morning.

SUE: Oh, no, Tyler! You shouldn't!

TYLER (*Firmly*): Yes, I should. I'm in a rut. Brenda's right. Let's have that letter.

BRENDA (*Coming to* SUE's *desk*): What is this mysterious letter, Tyler?

TYLER: It's my resignation. I've written to tell the syndicate that I shall discontinue "Ambitious Aloysius" on the first of next month.

KAREN: Uncle Tyler, you can't do that!

BILL: It would be a crime!

BRENDA (*Triumphantly*): It would be a crime if he didn't. Put your John Hancock on that letter, Tyler. This is the happiest day of the year!

SUE: Tyler, please think this over carefully—

TYLER (*Firmly*): I've thought. Let's have the letter. (*Reluctantly,* SUE *hands him the letter. He signs it with a flourish.*) There. (*He puts letter down on* SUE's *desk.*)

BRENDA: It's like the signing of the Declaration of Independence. (*She hugs* TYLER) You're free! Farewell to that infantile "Ambitious Aloysius." Come on, Tyler. (*She takes his hand*) That fresh air will seem even

fresher now. (*She and* TYLER *go toward right. At door,*
BRENDA *looks back and casts a triumphant look at* SUE.
TYLER *and* BRENDA *exit.*)

BILL: Phew! She's certainly done her nasty work today.

KAREN: She does her nasty work every day. She makes
Uncle Tyler feel like an insect under a rock. Why he
wants to marry her is the greatest mystery of the age.

SUE: Let's be fair. She's very attractive.

KAREN: So was Helen of Troy—and look at all the trouble she caused. And so are you, Sue. I know you're carrying a torch for Uncle Tyler.

BILL: Look—Sue's blushing. Very becoming, too.

SUE (*Embarrassed*): Let's stop this nonsense. How I feel
about Tyler is unimportant. How he feels about Brenda
is important. (*Sighing sadly*) This letter of Tyler's is
the kiss of death for the plans we made yesterday. (*Looking at watch*) And it's too late now to do anything about
canceling them.

KAREN (*Sitting on* SUE's *desk*): Golly. All the kids in the
Ambitious Aloysius Fan Club were simply thrilled
when Bill and I called them yesterday. They promised
to be here today at one o'clock sharp.

SUE: That's when the Professor is coming, too.

BILL: And everyone's going to be singing the praises of
Ambitious Aloysius—because they think the syndicate
has threatened to drop the comic strip.

KAREN: And, instead, it's Tyler who's dropping it. (*Shaking her head*) I never thought our little white lie could
land us in such a mess. All we wanted to do was have
the Professor and the Fan Club convince Brenda that
"Ambitious Aloysius" is important, so she'd let Tyler
work in peace.

SUE: But Tyler has signed the letter.

BILL (*Hopefully*): You don't have to mail the thing. Not right away, anyway. (SUE *rises and walks slowly to center.*)

SUE: I'm afraid the damage is done. Tyler has made up his mind, and nothing on earth is going to change Brenda's opinion of "Ambitious Aloysius." (*Looking at watch*) It's almost one o'clock. This little convention here today will probably be one of the disasters of all time. (*The three look downcast as* BRENDA *and* TYLER *enter at right.*)

BRENDA: It's chillier in the garden than we thought it would be. (*Looking at watch*) Oh, Tyler, I'd almost forgotten. I asked Edgar Allan Schmidt to drop by this afternoon. And I'm glad I did. Now that you've made your big decision, you can profit from a talk with him. He's so intellectual. He may be able even to inspire you to try something really important.

KAREN (*Alarmed*): Edgar Allan Schmidt!

BRENDA (*Picking up book from easy chair*): He wrote this book, *Days of Anxiety.* It's wonderful poetry. He tears down the false values of American civilization.

BILL: Never heard of him.

BRENDA (*Coldly*): I'm not surprised. You look strictly like an Ian Fleming fan to me. I wouldn't expect you to be familiar with a writer of Edgar Allan's substance.

SUE (*Worried*): What time is Mr. Schmidt coming, Brenda?

BRENDA: He promised to come at one. It's nearly that now.

KAREN: Ouch!

BRENDA: What's wrong with you, Karen?

KAREN: N-nothing. I just felt a little twinge. Must be neuralgia.

TYLER (*Worried*): I hope I can converse intelligently with Mr. Schmidt. He's a bit out of my league.

BRENDA: Where's your self-confidence, Tyler? It'll do you good to rise above the level of "Ambitious Aloysius." (*The doorbell rings.* TYLER *goes to right and exits. After a moment, he returns, followed by* EDGAR ALLAN SCHMIDT. SCHMIDT *has long hair, wears beatnik clothes and horn-rimmed glasses.*) Hello, Edgar Allan. How nice of you to come. I suppose Tyler has introduced himself. (*Nodding toward* SUE) This is Sue Blake, Tyler's secretary.

SUE: Hello.

BRENDA (*Nodding toward* KAREN): And this is Karen Hall, Tyler's niece.

KAREN: How do you do?

BRENDA (*Nodding toward* BILL): And this is Bill Pratt.

BILL: Nice to meet you. (SCHMIDT *nods wearily, then slouches over to drawing table and looks at* TYLER's *sketches.*)

SCHMIDT: How utterly bourgeois! We have here an example of the lowest common denominator of American civilization—the bird-brained comic strip.

BILL: Hey, wait a minute! "Ambitious Aloysius" is good stuff.

SCHMIDT: Stuff it may be; good it is not. It is merely a symptom of the growing childishness and shallowness of the American mind.

BRENDA (*Admiringly*): That's just what I've been telling Tyler, Edgar Allan. And I think I've finally convinced him.

KAREN (*Angrily*): I don't think it's very good manners to come into Uncle Tyler's studio and then start to tear him to pieces.

BILL: It's not the sort of thing Amy Vanderbilt would approve of.

BRENDA: Oh, be quiet. Edgar Allan is a genius. He's above Amy Vanderbilt.

SCHMIDT: I am above anything bourgeois and common.

TYLER (*Uncomfortably*): Why don't you sit down, Mr. Schmidt? You look tired.

SCHMIDT (*Slouching over to sofa and sitting*): I am tired. this dull, materialistic, unintelligent world is enough to fatigue anyone. I have a poem that expresses my feelings exactly. (*He closes his eyes and recites in a dull voice*)

> The hills of avarice stretch long
> Beyond the garbage pail,
> Beyond the sewer.
> Is there no vein of iron
> To catch the hawk in his temple?

BRENDA: Wonderful!

SUE: Just what does it mean, Brenda?

BRENDA: Well—well, it's very clear. (*Quickly*) You tell her, Edgar Allan.

SCHMIDT (*Scratching the back of his neck and speaking wearily*): For a poet to explain anything is unnecessary.

TYLER (*Rather timidly*): Still, it is a little obscure, Mr. Schmidt.

SCHMIDT: Only to the untrained mind.

BILL: Come on, Brenda, explain it to us.

BRENDA: You heard what Edgar Allan said. Why spoil a thing of beauty by taking it apart?

SCHMIDT: My poetry is not for the market place. (*The doorbell rings.* TYLER *again exits right. There is the sound of excited voices offstage. Then* TYLER *enters, followed by the members of* THE AMBITIOUS ALOYSIUS

FAN CLUB. *The boys wear girls' aprons, and the girls wear boys' caps.* SCHMIDT *looks at them in amazement and shakes his head wearily.*)

KAREN: Hi, kids.

FAN CLUB (*Ad lib*): Hi, Karen. Hi, Bill. (*Etc.*)

1ST GIRL (*To* TYLER): Mr. Brayton, we're here on a vital mission.

SCHMIDT: I thought it must be Halloween.

1ST BOY: We think it's a shame that the syndicate wants to drop "Ambitious Aloysius." (*There is a chorus of agreement.*)

TYLER (*Surprised*): The syndicate wants to *what?* This is news to me. In fact, I am dropping "Ambitious Aloysius" but not at the syndicate's request.

BRENDA: And that's the best decision you've ever made.

SCHMIDT: There may yet be hope for this tired old American society.

2ND BOY: But you can't do that, Mr. Brayton.

2ND GIRL: "Ambitious Aloysius" has become part of our lives.

3RD BOY: Sure. That's why we're dressed the way we are. We're having "See How the Other Half Lives Week" at school—just the way Ambitious Aloysius wants it.

3RD GIRL: He always says that the way to understanding is to be aware of other people's problems. When you had him persuade the citizens of Zanyville to exchange roles for a week and have the men do women's work and the women do men's work, we thought it was a super idea.

4TH BOY: So *we've* been doing it all week.

4TH GIRL: You really understand teen-agers, Mr. Brayton.

5TH GIRL: I wish we could say the same for our parents.

TYLER (*Melting*): You kids are very kind.

5TH BOY: You just can't drop "Ambitious Aloysius." We'll send a petition to the syndicate.

1ST GIRL: We can get thousands of signatures.

1ST BOY: They'll learn that America's teen-agers are a force to be reckoned with. (*They all begin to talk excitedly.*)

2ND GIRL: After all, this "See How the Other Half Lives Week" is becoming a national institution.

ALL (*Ad lib*): That's right! We'll show them! Right! (*Etc.*)

TYLER (*Holding up hand for silence*): I appreciate what you want to do. But (*He looks toward* BRENDA), I have made a decision.

2ND BOY: We're not giving up, Mr. Brayton. (*To* FAN CLUB) Let's give him the song, kids. (*The doorbell rings.*)

SUE: I'll get it, Tyler. You stay and listen to the song. (*She exits right.*)

2ND BOY: (*Ready to conduct the singing*): All right, gang. Let's have some pear-shaped tones. Just sing along with "Ambitious Aloysius."

BOYS (*Singing to the tune of the chorus of "The Battle Hymn of the Republic"*):
Oh, Ambitious Aloysius!
Now we have to do the dishes,
But our cooking is delicious,
We know how the other half lives.
(*SUE and* PROFESSOR KING *appear in doorway right and stand listening.*)

GIRLS (*Singing to same tune*):
Oh, Ambitious Aloysius!
Now it's girls who wear the "britches,"

And we've learned just what the pitch is—
We've seen how the other half lives.

ENTIRE FAN CLUB (*Singing to same tune*):
Oh, Ambitious Aloysius!
Though you may be just fictitious,
You have cured our prejudices,
We've learned how the other half lives.

SCHMIDT (*Disgustedly*): Doggerel! And a most unfortunate lack of lyric sentiment.

PROFESSOR (*Coming to center*): I disagree heartily, young man. That song expresses what I think is sincere admiration for a scintillating and perceptive piece of work.

SUE: This is Professor Wentworth King, Tyler. You remember—he sent you a letter telling you how he admires "Ambitious Aloysius."

TYLER (*Shaking hands with the* PROFESSOR): Your letter was very kind, Professor. (*As he turns toward others*) Let me introduce you to the others. This is Miss Cartwright, my fiancée. Edgar Allan Schmidt, the poet. My niece, Karen. Her friend, Bill Pratt. And these young people are members of the Ambitious Aloysius Fan Club. (*All greet the* PROFESSOR.)

PROFESSOR: How do you do? (*Turning back to* TYLER) I am alarmed to hear from Miss Blake that you wish to give up your work.

TYLER: I have given much thought to my decision to desert the world of comic strips, Professor.

PROFESSOR: You know, Mr. Brayton, I feel you are making a grave mistake in, as you say, deserting the world of comic strips. You have many friends on college campuses. To abandon "Ambitious Aloysius" would be, in my opinion and the opinion of many, virtually a national catastrophe. For example (*He nods toward* FAN

CLUB), I note that these young people are observing "See How the Other Half Lives Week." So are the students at my own college. You see how influential you have become. (*Chorus of agreement from* CLUB.)

BRENDA: But, Professor King, Tyler has realized that he can rise above "Ambitious Aloysius." He has the talent to devote himself to more serious matters.

PROFESSOR: More serious matters? Since when has bringing enjoyment to young and old not been a serious matter?

TYLER: What Brenda means, Professor King, is that "Ambitious Aloysius" doesn't have any real significance.

BILL: It does too!

SCHMIDT: It's inane. It's an obvious symptom of a rattle-brained, unthinking civilization.

PROFESSOR (*Looking at him with interest*): Those are strong words, Mr.—Schmidt, isn't it? You are, I believe, a poet?

BRENDA (*Impatiently*): Of course he's a poet. One of the best of our time.

PROFESSOR: Forgive me, but even though I am a professor of English, I must confess I am unacquainted with Mr. Schmidt's work.

BRENDA: That's easily remedied. Recite the poem we just heard, Edgar Allan. I think you'll agree, Professor, after hearing it, that Edgar Allan is a writer of significance. Please recite the poem, Edgar Allan.

SCHMIDT (*Wearily*): If you insist. (*Closes eyes and recites*)
> The hills of avarice stretch long
> Beyond the garbage pail,
> Beyond the sewer.
> Is there no vein of iron
> To catch the hawk in his temple?

1ST BOY: Say, that's real crazy stuff!

1ST GIRL: Real beat. (*The* PROFESSOR *looks puzzled.*)

BRENDA: You see, Professor King, Edgar Allan has caught the spiritual sickness of our era.

PROFESSOR: He has? Well, perhaps, but Mr. Schmidt's poem somewhat befuddles me.

BILL: You have company there.

KAREN: Company galore.

PROFESSOR: First of all, Mr. Schmidt, you are guilty of a peculiarly mixed metaphor. I don't quite see how a vein of iron can capture a hawk—even a hawk in a temple.

SCHMIDT: I don't believe in explaining my symbols. They just come to me.

BRENDA: The whole thing is crystal clear.

PROFESSOR: Splendid. Then let's have it explained.

BRENDA: Tell him, Edgar Allan.

SCHMIDT: I never attempt to clarify the obvious.

SUE: Brenda, please tell us what the poem means. (*Ironically*) This suspense is killing me.

BRENDA (*Looking to* SCHMIDT *for help*): Well, well—it's apparent, I think.

PROFESSOR: There's no need to go on with this act. If I may speak frankly, I don't think that the poem has an ounce of meaning for any reader of normal intelligence.

SUE: That's just what I think.

PROFESSOR: I gather, though, not from your poem, but from your remarks, that you're against materialism and conformity. Mr. Brayton here, in "Ambitious Aloysius," has said the same thing—only clearly—in several of his installments. I am thinking, Mr. Brayton, of the time Aloysius' Uncle Gravelthroat and his Aunt Sabrina were going into debt so they could keep up with their neighbors, the Astorbilts. Ambitious Aloysius showed them that they were adhering to false values, and your message came through most lucidly—"crystal clear," as Miss Cartwright would say.

SCHMIDT (*Coming to life for the first time*): Is that so? That's the trouble with you college professors—you look down your noses at us serious young writers. You won't listen to what we say.

PROFESSOR (*Smiling*): My dear young man, I just can't make out what it is you're trying to say.

SCHMIDT: Is it my fault if I'm too deep for you? (*Rising*) Maybe "Ambitious Aloysius" and all such infantile junk is more your style, Professor. You may as well get on the bandwagon of mediocrity.

TYLER: Now, Mr. Schmidt, please—

SCHMIDT: I can't help it if I'm profound.

PROFESSOR: You're laboring under a delusion, Mr. Schmidt.

BRENDA: What a thoroughly nasty thing to say!

PROFESSOR: You seem to think that obscurity gives writing significance. It doesn't. Most of the world's great writers are clear—even though some may also be profound.

SCHMIDT (*Sarcastically*): And I suppose by great writers you mean Brayton here and his brilliant "Ambitious Aloysius," because Brayton's message is as obvious as a conk on the head with a lead pipe.

SUE (*Loyally*): Stop picking on Tyler! He's worth ten of you!

BRENDA: Sue, control yourself. Edgar Allan is a guest here.

KAREN: We didn't invite him.

PROFESSOR: I did not say that Mr. Brayton ranks with Shakespeare or Tolstoy. But I do say this. When anything gives as much genuine pleasure as "Ambitious Aloysius," then it is important.

SCHMIDT: For young meat-heads maybe. (*There are angry reactions from* FAN CLUB.)

PROFESSOR: You're forgetting something, Mr. Schmidt. It takes a very special sort of talent to write for the young —and even more talent to appeal to both young and adult readers—as "Ambitious Aloysius" does.

SCHMIDT (*Disgusted*): Nuts! (*Angrily going to drawing table*) This is what I think of such kid stuff. (*He takes a sketch from the table and deliberately tears it into pieces.*) Put that in your pipe and smoke it!

TYLER: Hey, that's my property you're tearing to bits! (*Advancing toward* SCHMIDT)

BRENDA: Tyler, watch your temper!

1ST BOY (*Hopefully*): You want us to throw this guy out on his ear, Mr. Brayton?

TYLER: I'll admit that the suggestion is a tempting one. (*Firmly*) But maybe it's about time I began to stand up for myself. (*He advances again toward* SCHMIDT.)

SCHMIDT: Remember, Brayton, I'm wearing glasses!

BRENDA: Tyler, don't you dare to touch Edgar Allan! Be a man! Accept criticism when someone offers it!

BILL: Sock him, Tyler!

TYLER: I'm a man of peace, Schmidt, but I'm telling you that I'm just about fed up with your insults. First of all, you have the bad manners to come here and to make very nasty comments about my work. Well, you're entitled to your opinion, and I will admit that my work hasn't been exactly first-class lately. But I still resent your manner and your condescending attitude.

SUE: You tell him, Tyler!

KAREN: Uncle Tyler, I'm proud of you.

TYLER: Let's get down to brass tacks. You want to know what I think about your poetry, Schmidt? I think it's phony. I think it's a lot of pretentious mumbo jumbo that doesn't mean anything.

BRENDA: Tyler, I'm shocked! How can you speak that way to a genius like Edgar Allan?

TYLER: If being a genius means writing unadulterated, incomprehensible tripe, then he's a genius. All I can say is—thank heaven, I'm normal.

BRENDA: To be great is to be misunderstood.

TYLER: And let me say a word or two to you, Brenda. I don't think you know what Schmidt's poetry means either. You sound as phony as he does.

BRENDA: Tyler Brayton, this is the end! I will not stay here to be insulted!

TYLER: Maybe that's just as well. I've had my eyes opened here this afternoon. First by these kids (*He nods toward the* FAN CLUB) and then by Professor King. After all, every man ought to devote himself to what he can do best. For me, that seems to be "Ambitious Aloysius." And, by golly, I'm deciding right now to go on with it, doing the best I know how. (*There are cheers from the* FAN CLUB)

SUE: Good for you, Tyler.

PROFESSOR: Sensible words, Mr. Brayton.

BRENDA (*Very angry*): Tyler, think carefully. Do you really intend to devote yourself to something insignificant? Are you going to stay in the "Ambitious Aloysius" rut?

SUE (*Sarcastically*): Would you rather see him do something significant like Mr. Schmidt's "crystal clear" poetry?

BRENDA: Don't be catty, Sue. Just because Edgar Allan is miles above you intellectually, that's no reason to be offensive. (*Demandingly*) Well, Tyler, what are you going to do?

TYLER (*Firmly*): Brenda, I've made up my mind. It's "Ambitious Aloysius" for me. Let people like Schmidt try to capture the spiritual sickness of our era.

BRENDA (*Dramatically*): Then this is it. (*She removes engagement ring from her finger, goes to drawing table, and throws ring onto it.*) There's your ring. It's appropriate that it should lie there on the drawing table. (TYLER, *expressionless, looks down at ring.*) Well, aren't you going to say anything?

TYLER: I've said all I have to say.

BRENDA: You're just going to let me walk out of your life?

TYLER: No, wait a minute, Brenda. There is something else. Be honest with me now—no posing, no pseudo-intellectual nonsense. Do you or do you not know what Schmidt's poem means?

BRENDA (*Quickly and defensively*): Of course I do!

TYLER: Then tell me. Prove I've been wrong about you.

KAREN: This is your big chance, Brenda.

BRENDA: Well—well—(*Quickly and irritably*) No, I will not lower myself to reply to such a silly question.

TYLER (*Shrugs shoulders and smiles rather sadly*): Then goodbye, Brenda—and thanks for making everything "crystal clear". (BRENDA *stares unbelievingly at him for a moment.*)

BRENDA: All right, Mr. "Ambitious Aloysius." Come, Edgar Allan. There must be some people somewhere who appreciate the finer things of life. (BRENDA *and* SCHMIDT, *who is slouching as usual, go toward right. At door,* SCHMIDT *turns and looks back.*)

SCHMIDT: Well, Brayton, we'll leave you to the kids and

the moss-backed college professor. They're just about your speed. (TYLER, *fists clenched, makes a move toward* SCHMIDT, *who lifts his arms protectively and exits rapidly.*)

PROFESSOR (*Wiping brow*): I certainly did not intend to precipitate such a scene, Mr. Brayton. I apologize. That's the first engagement I have ever been the cause of breaking.

TYLER (*Returning to center*): You needn't apologize, Professor. There comes a time in every man's life when he has to open his eyes wide to the truth. You've helped to do that for me. (*Turning to* FAN CLUB) And so have you kids. I'm grateful to all of you.

1ST BOY: This is really "See How the Other Half Lives Week," Mr. Brayton. "Ambitious Aloysius" was right. We understand some of *your* problems now.

1ST GIRL: We sure do.

TYLER (*Going to drawing table*): You know, all this seems to have cleared the air—and my head as well. I've just had a gem of an idea for an "Ambitious Aloysius" installment. (*Sits at table and takes up pencil.*)

SUE: That's wonderful, Tyler. We'll let you work in peace. Perhaps you kids had better be running along now. And thanks for coming. I'll see that Mr. Brayton sends each of you an autographed "Ambitious Aloysius" panel. Just leave your names and addresses with Karen and Bill.

FAN CLUB (*Ad lib*): That'll be swell. Terrific! Thanks a lot! (*Etc.*)

2ND GIRL: Let's get going then.

KAREN: Bill and I can take your addresses outside. (*She and* BILL *pick up pads and pencils from* SUE'S *desk.*)

FAN CLUB (*Ad lib*): So long, Mr. Brayton. Keep up the

good work with "Ambitious Aloysius." We'll be waiting for that new installment. (*Etc.*) (FAN CLUB *members exit, with* KAREN *and* BILL.)

PROFESSOR: I also will leave you to your work, Mr. Brayton. And, incidentally, I'd like to have an "Ambitious Aloysius" panel, too.

TYLER: I'll certainly see to that, Professor. You're obviously a powerful friend to have on one's side. (PROFESSOR *goes to drawing table, shakes hands with* TYLER, *and then with* SUE.)

PROFESSOR (*Going toward right*): I shall look forward to many more delightful sessions with "Ambitious Aloysius." Goodbye, Mr. Brayton. Goodbye, Miss Blake.

TYLER: Goodbye, Professor.

SUE: Goodbye, Professor King. (PROFESSOR *exits right.* SUE *goes to her desk, sits, and begins to examine some papers. From offstage, the* FAN CLUB *begins to sing the "Ambitious Aloysius" song. The singing continues during the following dialogue.*)

TYLER (*Working at table and smiling*): Not to coin a phrase, they're playing our song.

SUE (*Looking up and speaking timidly*): Tyler, I must confess something. Bill, Karen, and I engineered the visits of the Fan Club and the Professor. We wanted to convince Brenda that "Ambitious Aloysius" is significant.

TYLER (*Grinning*): I suspected that the recent mob scene was something more than mere coincidence. Anyway, you convinced *me* instead. (*Turning to* SUE) You know, Sue, there's an old saying that a man never sees the treasure in his own garden. (SUE *looks up hopefully.*) The way you stood up for me today was wonderful.

SUE: It's the least a girl can do for her boss.

TYLER: What you did was above and beyond the call of duty. (*He goes back to his drawing.* SUE *looks at him for a moment.*)

SUE: Tyler, this is "See How the Other Half Lives Week." I think we ought to change places. (*She rises.*) You sit at my desk. (TYLER *looks puzzled but follows her instructions.* SUE *now speaks in deep voice.*) All right, Miss Blake. What is it we do with letters that are either unwelcome or not useful?

TYLER: We file them in the wastebasket, Mr. Brayton.

SUE: Splendid. It seems to me I wrote a silly letter this morning to the syndicate. You may file it away, Miss Blake. (TYLER *takes his letter to syndicate from desk, tears it into pieces, and throws it into wastebasket.*) Ahem. Now, Miss Blake, are you doing anything for dinner tonight?

TYLER: Yes, Mr. Brayton—I'm going to dine with you. (*They both laugh, then look serious. Offstage singing fades and stops.* TYLER *rises.*) Sue.

SUE: Tyler. (*He comes to center and takes her hand just as* BILL *and* KAREN *enter at right.*)

KAREN: Oops! Excuse us.

BILL: We'll go out and come in again. (TYLER, *embarrassed, returns to drawing table and sits.*)

TYLER: Back to work for me—at least until dinner.

BILL (*Grinning*): Nice work if you can get it. (*The "Ambitious Aloysius" song is heard again from offstage.*)

KAREN: The kids are really going all out.

BILL: They're right in the groove.

TYLER: (*Happily*): I think we're all in the groove today. (*He makes quick strokes with his pencil.*) This panel is already going like a house afire. (*He looks up and grins.*) Who knows—maybe someday people will think

I'm as big a genius as Edgar Allan Schmidt. (*All laugh and gather around* TYLER *at drawing board. Offstage singing rises to crescendo as the curtain falls.*)

THE END

Production Notes

See You in the Funnies

Characters: 4 male; 3 female; 10 boys and girls for Fan Club.

Playing Time: 40 minutes.

Costumes: Edgar Allan Schmidt wears beatnik clothes, has long hair and wears horn-rimmed glasses. Others wear appropriate everyday dress. Boys in the Fan Club add girls' aprons to their costumes; girls add boys' caps. Brenda and Sue have wristwatches; Brenda wears an engagement ring.

Properties: Sketch paper, note pads, pencils, pen, drawing pencil, book.

Setting: Tyler Brayton's studio. A large drawing board with sketches and drawing pencil on it, and two chairs are at center. At right are a sofa and a desk with papers, note pads, pen, pencils, letter, and telephone on it. A wastebasket is beside the desk. An easy chair is at left.

Lighting: No special effects.

Sound: Doorbell, as indicated in text.

Shades of Shakespeare

Characters

PENELOPE LANSING, *a young American girl*
MRS. LUDLOW, *the housekeeper*
HUBERT ROSSITER, *a stuffy young Englishman*
IRENE ROSSITER, *his attractive sister*
DAN CARSON, *an American student from Penelope's home town*
OBADIAH JUDSON, *a young Elizabethan gentleman*
MEG APPLEBY, *a pretty Elizabethan girl*

SCENE 1

TIME: *A morning in the present.*
SETTING: *The living room of an attractive cottage on the outskirts of Stratford-on-Avon, England.*
AT RISE: PENELOPE *is sitting on sofa, writing on a note pad.* MRS. LUDLOW *is dusting the furniture.*

PENELOPE (*Thoughtfully*): Let's see, now—eggs, coffee, perhaps a small chicken, potatoes, peas, and onions.
MRS. LUDLOW (*As she dusts table*): Don't forget tea, Miss Lansing. There's nothing like a cup of tea to brighten the day.
PENELOPE: Gosh, I was forgetting. I'm not quite used to

132

English customs yet, Mrs. Ludlow. But you'll have to be patient with me. After all, I've been here for only two weeks.

MRS. LUDLOW: Your Aunt Eleanor—ah, what a good soul she was—was very partial to tea. Always had her cup in the morning, she did, and one in the afternoon, and another before retiring. (*Sighing*) I miss her, Miss Lansing.

PENELOPE: I'm sure you do, Mrs. Ludlow. She was a wonderful woman. And, frankly, I never dreamed that she would leave me this lovely cottage.

MRS. LUDLOW: Generosity was her middle name, miss. She always said that she wanted you to be able to spend your summers here in England. Many's the time I heard her say that Americans hurry about too much, that they ought to learn how to be still and relax, so to speak. Ah, yes, miss, she loved this house—all except for one thing, of course.

PENELOPE (*Grinning*): Now, Mrs. Ludlow, you're not going to tell me about that ghost, Obadiah, are you?

MRS. LUDLOW: Ah, now, you may smile, Miss Lansing, but things have happened around here that nobody can explain. Ask anyone in Stratford. Nearly frightened your poor Aunt Eleanor out of her wits on more than one occasion, I can tell you. You see, she saw him several times.

PENELOPE: Saw Obadiah, you mean?

MRS. LUDLOW: Saw him just as plain as I'm seeing you now. And we all know in Stratford that he's haunted this house for more than three hundred years.

PENELOPE (*Laughing*): Really, Mrs. Ludlow, this *is* the twentieth century.

MRS. LUDLOW: The century makes no difference to Obadiah. He haunts whenever the urge comes on him.

PENELOPE: Well, he obviously hasn't had the urge lately. (*Writing again on pad, tears off sheet, rises, and hands paper to* MRS. LUDLOW) There you are. Could you get these items from the greengrocer's?

MRS. LUDLOW: Certainly. Miss Hall's on Henley Street would be best, I think. I'll be on my way at once. (*She goes toward door up center.*)

PENELOPE: By the way, Mrs. Ludlow, did you ever see this ghost, Obadiah?

MRS. LUDLOW: Not in the flesh—that is, if ghosts do have flesh. But I give you my word, Miss Lansing—and Daisy Ludlow was never one to lie—that I once came into this room and saw that rocking chair (*She points to it.*) rocking merrily all by itself. It was Obadiah. *That* I'm certain of.

PENELOPE (*Laughing*): Or the wind.

MRS. LUDLOW: This cottage is strongly built, and there isn't a crack for the wind to blow through. (*Firmly*) It was Obadiah. (*She opens door and almost collides with* HUBERT ROSSITER *and his sister,* IRENE.) Oh, good morning, Mr. Rossiter. Good morning, Miss Rossiter.

IRENE: Hello, Mrs. Ludlow.

HUBERT: Splendid day, Mrs. Ludlow.

MRS. LUDLOW: If you'll excuse me, I've a bit of shopping to do.

HUBERT: But, of course, Mrs. Ludlow.

MRS. LUDLOW: I'll be back shortly, miss. (*She exits.*)

PENELOPE: How nice to see you both! I want to thank you for the brace of pheasants you sent me.

IRENE (*Sitting in chair at right*): English hospitality, Penelope. People think we're rather cold fish, but we're not.

HUBERT (*Sitting at left*): Indeed, we're not. Jolly good

hearts, that's what we have. Especially when our neighbor is as attractive as you are, Penelope.

PENELOPE: Why, thank you, Hubert.

HUBERT: Not at all, old girl. Only speaking the truth and that sort of thing. (PENELOPE *sits on sofa.* HUBERT *joins her.*) Wanted to ask you if you'd like to attend the County Ball with me next Tuesday night. Always a cheerful little affair.

PENELOPE: I'd love to.

IRENE: I warn you, Penelope, Hubert is an atrocious dancer. He's ruined more girls' feet than ill-fitting shoes ever have.

HUBERT: Oh, I say, Irene, I'm not as bad as all that. I've had a truly enormous number of compliments on my waltzing. I whirl around the floor like a blooming ballet dancer. Everybody in dear old Stratford says I'm as graceful as a gazelle.

IRENE (*Chuckling*): Any self-respecting gazelle would resent that.

HUBERT: One's sister never gives one credit for one's talents.

IRENE: One's sister knows her brother too well. But to change the subject, Penelope, how is Mrs. Ludlow treating you?

PENELOPE: She's a treasure—cooks like a dream and cleans like a wizard. No wonder Aunt Eleanor was so fond of her. (*Smiling*) She does seem obsessed, though, with the idea that this lovely old house is haunted.

HUBERT: Oh, heaven help us! Don't tell me she's been blathering about Obadiah, the Elizabethan spook.

PENELOPE: She's quite convinced that Obadiah haunts the premises.

HUBERT: I'm a man of fact, old girl. I don't believe in these old wives' tales.

IRENE: Don't forget, Hubert, what Stratford's most distinguished citizen of all time once said—"There are more things in heaven and earth . . . than are dreamt of in your philosophy."

HUBERT: Don't quote Shakespeare to me, Irene. I will not be a party to ghostly tales told by a blooming lot of village idiots. (*Knock on front door is heard.* PENELOPE *rises and opens door.*)

PENELOPE (*Surprised and pleased*): Dan Carson! How nice! (DAN, *a good-looking boy in his early twenties, enters.*)

DAN: Penny! Long time no see.

PENELOPE: Mother wrote that you might be looking me up, but I didn't expect you to turn up in Stratford so soon.

DAN: I guess I did get a bit homesick—eager to see a friendly face from home, you know. So I thought I'd spend a few days here. Besides, Oxford isn't very far from here. (*Noticing* IRENE *and* HUBERT) Oh, I didn't know you had guests.

HUBERT: Think nothing of it, old man.

PENELOPE: Dan, I'd like you to meet Irene Rossiter and her brother, Hubert—good neighbors of mine. (DAN *shakes hands with them both.*) Dan and I were in college together. He's a Rhodes Scholar now at Oxford.

HUBERT: Splendid. Americans should be allowed a taste of genuine university life.

IRENE: Hubert, you're being stuffy again.

DAN: Well, there are a great many opportunities for education here. In fact, I've already started on some research here at the Shakespeare Institute. I'm staying nearby at the Welcombe Hotel, so I can keep an eye on you, Penny, and see how you're managing.

PENELOPE (*Flirtatiously, with a side glance at* HUBERT): I'm managing beautifully, thanks.

DAN: And I thought you might like to have dinner with me tonight. I could call for you about seven.

PENELOPE: I'd love to. It will be like old times.

HUBERT (*Coughing*): Penelope will be having a busy social life. I am taking her to the County Ball next Tuesday.

DAN (*Displeased*): Oh?

IRENE: My brother dances like a happy blend of Dumbo the Elephant and King Kong.

DAN (*Laughing*): Then he must be a sight to behold. Really, Penelope, you must be careful. You young girls bruise easily.

HUBERT: Oh, come now, old man, don't believe everything Irene says. She's been needling me since we were children. (*The rocking chair begins to rock slowly.* PENELOPE *stares with a look of surprise and horror.*)

PENELOPE (*Passing her hand before her eyes and looking again; startled*): Oh!

IRENE: Is something wrong, Penelope?

PENELOPE (*Pointing to rocker*): Look! It's rocking!

HUBERT: What's rocking, old thing?

PENELOPE: What usually rocks? The rocker, of course! (HUBERT, IRENE, *and* DAN *stare at the rocker.*)

IRENE: It's perfectly still.

PENELOPE (*Almost hysterically*): It's not! It's moving! Just the way Mrs. Ludlow said it did!

DAN: Perhaps you're not well, Penelope.

PENELOPE: I'm perfectly well. (*The chair rocks faster.*) Look, it's rocking furiously!

HUBERT: Oh, I say, old girl, it must be something you ate for breakfast. Have to watch out for kippers, you know. They're sometimes frightfully hard on the digestion.

PENELOPE: I didn't have kippers. All I had was tea and a rock bun.

IRENE (*Taking* PENELOPE's *arm and leading her to sofa*): Why don't you lie down for a while, Penelope? You're obviously overwrought.

HUBERT: We'd better have Dr. Thornbright in for a look at her.

PENELOPE (*Sitting on sofa*): I don't want any Dr. Thornbright. There's nothing wrong with me—and that rocker is still moving. (*The rocking stops.*) Oh, it's stopped now.

HUBERT: Of course it has, old girl. Everything will be all right now. Just lie back and have a jolly little nap. What's happened to you is probably a simple case of auto-suggestion. That old coot, Mrs. Ludlow, spoke to you the chair moving, and she made an impression on your mind. Lie back now. (*Trying to make* PENELOPE *lie down*) Easy does it.

PENELOPE (*Sitting up*): Please! Stop treating me as though I were a baby.

DAN: You know, Rossiter, Penelope may have seen something. I've known her for years, and she's not given to imagining things.

PENELOPE: It was Obadiah.

DAN: Who in the world is Obadiah?

PENELOPE: A ghost that haunts this house.

DAN: Hm-m-m, a ghost. Well, Rossiter, there's a lot of work being done in psychic research and extrasensory perception.

HUBERT: Extrasensory nonsense!

IRENE: Hubert, you're being stuffy again.

HUBERT: Well, really, old girl, let's all try to use a bit of jolly old common sense. We're not in the Dark Ages anymore. (*To* PENELOPE) I'm sure you'll calm down after a while, old thing. (*She lies down.*) Perhaps it's been a bit of a strain getting settled here. (HUBERT *looks at watch; to* IRENE) Irene, we're due at the Collingwoods' in five minutes. Ought to get on, you know.

IRENE: Right. (*Solicitously*) I'm sure you'll be all right, Penelope. And don't worry. We'll drop around later to see how you are.

HUBERT: And don't forget the ball. That will take your mind off spooks. (HUBERT *and* IRENE *go to door;* HUBERT *turns.*) Pleasant to have met you, old man.

DAN: Nice to have met you both.

IRENE: And take care, Penelope. Have a good nap. (IRENE *and* HUBERT *exit.*)

DAN: That Hubert's not my type.

PENELOPE: He's really quite pleasant, although "veddy English."

DAN: I have to get back to the Institute myself. No rest for us dedicated scholars, you know. Is there anything you need before I leave?

PENELOPE: No, but thanks for asking, Dan. Mrs. Ludlow will be back soon. (*She sits up.*) Thanks for coming to my defense. (*Rising*) But, Dan, I did see that chair rock.

DAN: Penelope, I'm all for you. If you say it rocked, it rocked.

PENELOPE: I don't want you to think that I've lost my mind.

DAN: I don't. (*He goes to door.*) See you at seven. Maybe over a good chop or two, we can untangle the mystery. 'Bye until then.

PENELOPE: Goodbye, Dan. (DAN *exits. After he leaves,* PENELOPE *goes to rocker, looks at it fixedly, and shakes her head. Suddenly, it begins to rock again. She stifles a shriek, steps back, her hands over her mouth, and is startled by the sound of the closet door opening, up left.* OBADIAH JUDSON *stands in closet doorway. He wears Elizabethan doublet and hose. He has a small beard.* PENELOPE, *staring at him in disbelief and horror, backs toward sofa and sinks onto it.*)

OBADIAH (*Bowing*): Obadiah Judson at your service, Mistress Penelope.

PENELOPE: Oh, no! This isn't real! I'm dreaming!

OBADIAH (*Going to table and running his finger along it*): Now, by the bones of St. George and the dragon, there's a goodly amount of dust here. (*He holds up his finger.*) Mark it. You had best have a word with Mrs. Ludlow.

PENELOPE (*Angrily*): I'll thank you not to criticize our housekeeping habits.

OBADIAH (*Approaching the sofa*): A fiery lass, indeed. Anger becomes you.

PENELOPE: I suppose it was you who were doing tricks with that chair.

OBADIAH (*Smiling*): A man—even though he be a ghost— has to pass the time with a few jests and japes.

PENELOPE: Well, it wasn't very fair of you. You might have arranged it so that the others could see the chair rock, too. Everybody thinks I'm a lunatic.

OBADIAH (*Bowing*): My humble apologies. But you should know full well that we ghosts usually can appear to only one person—except on special occasions—and only one person can be aware of our little jokes. I did manage once to convince Mrs. Ludlow. What a joke that was!

PENELOPE: Joke! You have a warped sense of humor. (OBADIAH *sits on sofa beside* PENELOPE, *and she moves away from him.*)

OBADIAH: Oh, come now, lass, if you had been haunting this cottage for more than three hundred years, I'm doubly sure you would wish to create a few moments of mirth. Your Aunt Eleanor understood.

PENELOPE: Do you mean to tell me you've actually haunted this house since the seventeenth century?

OBADIAH: Obadiah Judson is a friend of truth. Of course, I have. And thereby hangs a tale.

PENELOPE: And I suppose you're going to tell it. (*Uncomfortably*) Well, if you are, I wish you wouldn't sit there. You make me nervous.

OBADIAH (*Rising*): By St. George and the dragon, you're not a very hospitable lass, are you? (*He paces the floor slowly.*) You've heard tell of Will Shakespeare, I suppose.

PENELOPE: Of course.

OBADIAH: It was Will and his acting company that did me in. We were preparing to give a performance of *Hamlet,* and it came time to parcel out the roles. There were just enough parts to go around. Headstrong youth that I was, I declared that I'd play the ghost of Hamlet's father, or nothing at all. But another was chosen to play the part.

PENELOPE: So what did you do?

OBADIAH: As I said, I was stubborn in those days, and I left the company in a fury. But that was only the beginning of my trouble. It seems that years after, when my time came to go to the hereafter, I met up again with the spirits of Will Shakespeare and his company. And nary a one would so much as speak with me, so angry were they still.

PENELOPE: But that doesn't explain why you're here.

OBADIAH: But it does, lass. You see, the actors said as I'd turned my back on them on earth, I'd have to do the same in the hereafter. And so, I was doomed to live as a wandering spirit, haunting this cottage where I was born. Now that you're here, it's not so bad, however. You're the comeliest owner this house has ever had. And we shall be together for a long time. (MRS. LUDLOW *appears at door, carrying a bag of groceries.* PENELOPE *does not see her, as she stands, listening in bewilderment.*)

PENELOPE: Now that's a bright forecast for the future. I don't want to share this cottage with a ghost.

OBADIAH: But I am a most presentable ghost, am I not?

PENELOPE: Well, for a ghost, I suppose you are.

MRS. LUDLOW: Obadiah is here!

PENELOPE (*Seeing her for the first time; rising*): Oh, Mrs. Ludlow! Yes, he's here, all right. (MRS. LUDLOW *walks to center, looking about her.*)

MRS. LUDLOW: Where is he?

PENELOPE: He's standing right here by the sofa. (OBADIAH *goes to table at center, lifts a magazine from it, and throws magazine into the air.* MRS. LUDLOW *screams, drops the bag of groceries, and falls to the floor in a faint.* PENELOPE *rushes to her.*) Now see what you've done!

OBADIAH: A ghost must have a bit of fun and frolic.

PENELOPE: Oh, you're impossible.

OBADIAH (*Wistfully*): I wish I were. (*He goes to* PENELOPE, *as she is leaning over* MRS. LUDLOW, *and he tentatively touches* PENELOPE's *hair.*) But then again, mayhap I don't. (*Quick curtain*)

*　　*　　*　　*　　*

Scene 2

Time: *Seven o'clock on the following Tuesday night.*
Setting: *The same as Scene 1.*
At Rise: Obadiah *is stretched out on the sofa watching* Penelope, *who stands at center, modeling her ball gown.*

Penelope: Do you like my dress, Obadiah?

Obadiah (*Fervently*): 'Tis beauty truly blent.

Penelope: That line sounds familiar.

Obadiah: It is. It's from one of Will Shakespeare's plays.

Penelope (*Fussing with her hair*): Hubert and Irene should be here soon. I imagine the ball will be lots of fun.

Obadiah (*Gloomily*): You seem very happy to be leaving me all alone in the house.

Penelope: Now, Obadiah, don't be a spoilsport.

Obadiah: A spoilsport, mayhap. But we have become great friends, have we not, in the last few days? (*Sitting up*) Many's the fine talk we've had there by the fire.

Penelope: And most interesting talks, too. Stratford must have been wonderful when you lived here. I love your stories about it.

Obadiah: We could have another talk tonight. But you will go to the ball with this fellow, Hubert? And you abandoned me the other night to go to dinner with that American fellow, Dan. I am a neglected ghost.

Penelope (*Smiling*): Now, Obadiah, I can't be here all the time.

Obadiah: Why not? Mistress Penelope, you have brought light and joy into what was the dull life of a poor ghost. (*He rises and goes to her.*) Your skin is pink—like the roses that used to grow in my garden here in Stratford. Would I could offer you a bouquet of those roses to match your complexion.

PENELOPE: That's very sweet of you, Obadiah.

OBADIAH (*Rather petulantly*): But pray tell, what am I to do with myself while you're away dancing?

PENELOPE: You won't be alone. Mrs. Ludlow will be here.

OBADIAH: Oh, a pox on Mrs. Ludlow. You know full well that she can't see or hear me. A man might as well talk to a post or a stone.

PENELOPE: Really, Obadiah, you must stop feeling sorry for yourself. (MRS. LUDLOW *enters left.*)

MRS. LUDLOW: He's still here, isn't he, miss?

PENELOPE: Yes, he is. He's standing right beside me, Mrs. Ludlow.

MRS. LUDLOW: Gracious, he's all over the place these days.

OBADIAH: Why shouldn't I be? I've been in this house since 1616.

PENELOPE: Don't be irritable, Obadiah.

MRS. LUDLOW: Did he say something?

PENELOPE: Yes. He's a little out of sorts tonight.

MRS. LUDLOW: Well, so am I, miss. It's a bit creepy, it is, having a ghost on the premises all the time.

PENELOPE (*Examining her dress*): Mrs. Ludlow, do you think you could tighten this button for me? It seems a little loose.

MRS. LUDLOW: Of course, miss. Come into the sewing room, and I'll take care of it. (*She goes to left, followed by* PENELOPE.)

OBADIAH: I'll come, too.

PENELOPE: Oh, no, you won't, Obadiah. This is a private matter. Behave like a gentleman.

MRS. LUDLOW (*Exasperatedly*): What's he want now?

PENELOPE: Nothing important. (OBADIAH *sticks his tongue out at* MRS. LUDLOW.) Behave yourself, Obadiah! (MRS. LUDLOW *and* PENELOPE *exit.* OBADIAH *looks gloomy as he returns to sofa and sits. He begins to whistle "Greensleeves" pensively. Suddenly, there is the sound of the closet door opening.* OBADIAH *looks startled and jumps to his feet as* MEG APPLEBY, *dressed in Elizabethan costume, emerges excitedly from the closet.*)

OBADIAH (*Astonished*): Meg! Meg Appleby! (MEG *rushes to him and embraces him. He moves away.*)

MEG: Why, Obadiah Judson, you don't seem happy to see me—and after more than three hundred years!

OBADIAH: Of course, I'm happy to see you, Meg. But it is a bit of a surprise.

MEG: Oh, Obadiah, I have glad tidings for you! You can come back to us!

OBADIAH: Come back?

MEG: Is it not glorious news?

OBADIAH (*Rather gloomily*): Aye, mayhap it is.

MEG: Mayhap? Do you forget, Obadiah Judson, that we were betrothed? It is not every lass who would wait for you for more than three hundred years.

OBADIAH: You're a good lass, Meg. I always said so.

MEG: You said more than that in the garden on the night we became promised to each other.

OBADIAH: And now you tell me that I may come back. How is that, Meg?

MEG: Will Shakespeare's acting company is putting on a play.

OBADIAH: And what, pray tell, have I to do with this play?

MEG: They're going to perform *Hamlet,* and they need you to play the ghost of Hamlet's father. Isn't that splendid news?

OBADIAH: Aye, splendid.

MEG: So you can return with me now. (PENELOPE *appears in doorway left and looks startled as she hears* OBADIAH *talking.*)

OBADIAH: Not so fast, Meg. I have business here that must be concluded.

MEG (*Perplexed*): Business?

OBADIAH: Aye, business.

MEG (*Catching sight of* PENELOPE): Aha! (*Nodding toward* PENELOPE) So *she* is your business, as you call it.

PENELOPE: Obadiah, why are you talking to yourself?

OBADIAH: I'm not, Mistress Penelope. There is another here.

PENELOPE (*Coming to center*): Another? You mean another ghost?

OBADIAH: You might call her that.

PENELOPE: Her?

OBADIAH: She is an old friend from my Stratford days.

MEG (*Angrily*): Old friend! I like that, Obadiah Judson!

OBADIAH: Pray be calm, Meg.

MEG: I shall return to my home (*Pointing*) up there, Obadiah Judson. And you can come with me—or not— as you will. (*With a toss of her head,* MEG *goes angrily toward closet.*)

OBADIAH: Now, Meg, I shall explain all.

MEG (*Sarcastically*): I'll wager you will. (*She exits hurriedly into closet and slams door.* PENELOPE *hears the door slam and jumps. She goes to sofa.*)

PENELOPE: Whoever that female ghost is, she seems angry. What is this all about, Obadiah?

OBADIAH: I shall be honest with you, Mistress Penelope. The girl was Meg Appleby, whom I once knew well. She came with news. Will Shakespeare's company has relented, removed from me the curse of haunting, and I can go (*He looks toward ceiling.*) up there.

PENELOPE: That's wonderful news, Obadiah.

OBADIAH: Is it? (PENELOPE *sits by him on the sofa.*) I am not certain now that I desire to return.

PENELOPE: But why not?

OBADIAH: Need you ask? I am happy here now with you in this house. I was never happier on earth, I assure you.

PENELOPE (*Gently*): I am complimented, Obadiah. But have you really thought seriously about the situation?

OBADIAH: Seriously?

PENELOPE: You and I belong to different worlds. And then, too, you must not forget that I shall be here in Stratford only during the summer.

OBADIAH: Then summer will be a gracious season for me.

PENELOPE (*Still gently and seriously*): And, Obadiah, I will not always be here—even in the summer. Someday, for example, I may be married.

OBADIAH: Oh, no—

PENELOPE: And you must not forget that I will not live forever—even if I remain an old maid. I do not have your advantages. I certainly will not be here for three hundred years. (*The door up center opens, and* DAN, HUBERT, *and* IRENE, *all in formal evening dress, enter. They stand in doorway, listening.*) So you see, Obadiah, it is best that you take advantage of Will Shakespeare's kindness. Otherwise you are doomed to lonely days here. It is better for you and me.

OBADIAH (*Sadly*): Mayhap you are right. I had not looked at matters in that manner. (*He rises.*)

HUBERT: Oh, I say, don't tell me the same old ghostly hanky-panky is going on here.

PENELOPE: Please, Hubert, don't interrupt my conversation with Obadiah. It's very important.

HUBERT: Obadiah! By Jove, I thought you had put all that beastly nonsense behind you.

IRENE: Control yourself, Hubert.

HUBERT: Well, how would you feel if you came to take a girl to a deucedly fine ball, and you found her in intimate conversation with a blooming ghost? At least, so she says.

IRENE: I don't imagine the situation will ever occur—at least not in the conventional circles in which I travel.

DAN (*Going to* PENELOPE): Is he really here, Penelope?

PENELOPE: Of course, he is. But what are you doing here, Dan?

DAN: Irene's escort for tonight had a fall from his horse. I'm a sort of replacement.

OBADIAH: Mistress Penelope, have nothing to do with this Hubert fellow. Dan seems more fitted for you.

PENELOPE: You may be right, Obadiah.

HUBERT: Come now, old girl, you must get your nerves under control.

PENELOPE (*Pleading*): Obadiah, can't you do me one last favor? Please make Hubert see that you are really here —and that I'm not a raving maniac.

OBADIAH: I'll try, Mistress Penelope—as I would try anything for you. Let us see now. What would convince this churlish fellow?

PENELOPE: You might rock the chair.

HUBERT: Great grief, are we back to chair-rocking again?

OBADIAH: No, that is too childish. This requires somewhat of a spectacle. (*Thoughtfully*) Mayhap I can do something that I have done only once before. I feel a new strength in me. Once on the morning of May 6, 1703,

I was able to appear to two persons at the same time. That's a feat we ghosts can accomplish only rarely. We call it double ectoplasmic manifestation.

PENELOPE: Oh, please try, Obadiah! (HUBERT *looks angry.* DAN *is staring at* PENELOPE *with interest.* IRENE *looks at* PENELOPE *rather skeptically, but with compassion.*)

OBADIAH (*Closing eyes*): I must concentrate. Ah, I feel the strength pulsing through my veins. Now, watch well. (*He goes behind* HUBERT *and touches him on the shoulder. There is no reaction from* HUBERT. OBADIAH *closes his eyes again, his face grim with concentration. Then* OBADIAH *gives* HUBERT *a resounding slap on the back.*)

HUBERT: Ouch! I say, what was that? (HUBERT *turns around, looks intently, and then his face assumes a look of great horror.*) Help! It's a ghost! It's Obadiah!

OBADIAH (*Bowing*): Obadiah Judson, at your service, Hubert—but not for long. (HUBERT *backs away toward sofa.*)

HUBERT: Don't touch me! Don't come near me!

IRENE: Hubert, have you gone off your rocker?

HUBERT: And don't mention rockers! (OBADIAH *advances on* HUBERT, *who falls in terror onto the sofa.* OBADIAH *holds out his hand.*)

OBADIAH: Pray, shake my hand, brother Hubert. (HUBERT *shrieks and faints.*)

PENELOPE: That's enough, Obadiah! (IRENE *and* DAN *rush to* HUBERT *and try to revive him.*)

OBADIAH: Yes, it is enough. (MRS. LUDLOW *rushes in from left.*)

MRS. LUDLOW: Oh, miss, what was that scream? (*She catches sight of* HUBERT *lying, eyes closed, on the sofa, with* IRENE *and* DAN *standing over him.* DAN *is loosen-*

ing Hubert's *collar, and* Irene *is chafing his wrists.*)
Oh, it's Mr. Hubert. Is it his heart?

Penelope: No, it isn't his heart. (Hubert *begins to come to.*)

Hubert (*Looking wild-eyed about the room*): Has that blooming ghost gone?

Mrs. Ludlow: So it was Obadiah. I might have known.

Irene: Sit up now, Hubert. I'll have to take you home. You're in no condition to go to the ball.

Hubert: I saw him, I tell you.

Irene (*Obviously humoring him*): Of course you did, Hubert. We'll get you home, and you'll feel much better after a cup of strong tea. Dan, perhaps you had better take Penelope to the ball. If I find it's safe to leave Hubert alone, I may join you both later.

Dan: A pleasure, Irene. (Dan *helps* Hubert *to his feet.*)

Obadiah: And now, Mistress Penelope, I had best go.

Penelope: Yes. That is best. And thank you, Obadiah. (Obadiah *goes to closet, and turns back toward others.*)

Obadiah: And my thanks to you for a wondrous few days. (*Opens closet door*) I'm coming, Meg! (*He exits.*)

Penelope (*Rather sadly*): Farewell, Obadiah. (Irene *leads* Hubert *to up center door. At door, they turn.*)

Irene: I'm frightfully sorry about all this.

Hubert: I saw the beastly fellow, I tell you. A horribly grotesque creature!

Penelope (*Loyally*): He's not grotesque at all. In fact, he's rather a dear.

Obadiah (*From offstage*): Thank you, Mistress Penelope.

Penelope: You're welcome, Obadiah.

Irene: Come, Hubert, you're only working yourself up to a nervous breakdown. (Irene *and* Hubert *exit.*)

MRS. LUDLOW: My, there are things going on around here that leave me in a puzzlement.

DAN: That makes two of us, Mrs. Ludlow.

PENELOPE: But Obadiah was here, Dan—really here.

DAN: Penelope, I've told you before that I believe you. I don't know why, but I do.

PENELOPE: Oh, if only you could be convinced the way Hubert was.

DAN (*Hastily*): No, thanks. I don't want to get an attack of the screaming meemies. (*The closet door suddenly opens wide, and a bouquet of roses comes flying through it.*)

MRS. LUDLOW: Bless my soul! What's that? (PENELOPE *picks up bouquet, which she cradles in her arms.*)

DAN (*Amazed*): Penelope, I'm convinced! (*He goes to her.*) Those are beautiful flowers.

MRS. LUDLOW: That they are. Look just like those that grow in a good many Stratford gardens.

PENELOPE: Of course they do. (*Smiling*) Thank you, Obadiah! It's a heavenly bouquet—in more ways than one. (*She takes* DAN's *arm.*) Well, Dan, shall we go to the ball? (*Quick curtain.*)

THE END

Production Notes

SHADES OF SHAKESPEARE

Characters: 3 male; 4 female.

Playing Time: 40 minutes.

Costumes: Obadiah and Meg wear Elizabethan costumes. Obadiah has a small beard. Others wear modern everyday dress. Hubert has a watch. In Scene 2, Dan, Irene, Hubert, and Penelope wears formal evening dress.

Properties: Feather duster, note pad, pencil, bag of groceries, bouquet of roses.

Setting: The living room of an attractive cottage on the outskirts of Stratford-on-Avon, England. The front door is up center; door to rest of house is at left. A closet is up left, and there is a fireplace in left wall. A table with magazines on it, a rocking chair, a sofa, a bookcase, chairs, etc., complete the furnishings. NOTE: There may be a string attached to rocking chair so that it can be manipulated from offstage.

Lighting: No special effects.

Sophia the Seamstress

Characters

NATHANIEL H. NASTY, *owner of Nasty's Dress Factory*
SOPHIA SWEETBLOSSOM, *a beautiful seamstress*
LETTIE LA RUE, *a fragile seamstress*
PEARL PEACH, *a hungry seamstress*
MIRANDA MILDEW, *a dumb seamstress*
SAMSON HAMHOCK, *a member of the State Senate*
WILHELMINA CRACKTHORP, *Nasty's middle-aged secretary*
MRS. QUENCH, *a suffragette*
MR. SWEETBLOSSOM, *Sophia's elderly father*
MRS. SWEETBLOSSOM, *Sophia's elderly mother*
RONALD FANCY, *the handsome, wealthy hero*

SCENE 1

TIME: *The turn of the century.*
SETTING: *A workroom in Nathaniel H. Nasty's Dress Factory.*
AT RISE: SOPHIA SWEETBLOSSOM, LETTIE LA RUE, PEARL PEACH, *and* MIRANDA MILDEW *are sitting at four small tables, sewing dresses.* NATHANIEL H. NASTY *stands at center, beating a stick on a block of wood in rapid rhythm; the girls are sewing in time to his beat.*

153

NASTY (*Loudly and nastily*): Now, my *dear* ladies, this is
the rhythm I want. Don't slow down. (*He increases the
rate of his beat, and the girls work frantically to keep
up with him.*)

PEARL (*Trying in vain to thread needle*): Gee, Mr. Nasty,
I'm hungry.

NASTY (*Still beating and going to her table*): What's
wrong with you, Pearl Peach? You had lunch six hours
ago—a nice, juicy apple core and a crust of bread. (*He
shakes his head.*) I don't know what the world is coming
to. It's a world of gluttons, that's what it is.

LETTIE: I'm feelin' faint, Mr. Nasty.

NASTY (*Going to her table*): Faint? Nonsense. A 15-hour
work day never hurt anybody. And where else can you
get $1.75 for a 75-hour week? You don't know when
you're well off, Lettie La Rue.

MIRANDA: All I got last week was $1.50, Mr. Nasty. I
counted it.

NASTY (*Going to her table*): Are you insinuating, Miranda
Mildew, that I, Nathaniel H. Nasty, would cheat my employees? I am an honest man. I am a kind man.

MIRANDA: You gave me a dollar bill and two quarters.

NASTY (*Triumphantly*): And are you aware, you stupid
girl, that the dollar is now worth $1.25 on the open
market?

MIRANDA: What's an open market?

PEARL: One that's not closed, dumbbell.

MIRANDA: Oh, I didn't know that. Sorry, Mr. Nasty.

NASTY: You should be. Now let's get some speed into our
sewing. One-two. One-two. One-two. (*He increases the
rate of his beat. Suddenly,* LETTIE LA RUE *stops and
falls forward, her face on the table.*) Drat the girl. Play-

acting again. (*All the girls stop sewing.* SOPHIA *rises quickly, goes to* LETTIE, *and lifts her head.*)

SOPHIA: Lettie is in need of water. She is ill.

NASTY: Water, Sophia Sweetblossom? With the water rates as high as they are? You girls will ruin me.

SOPHIA: I implore you, Mr. Nasty, to show some charity. And I remind you that a true gentleman should always display consideration for others.

MIRANDA: That's a lovely thought, Sophia.

SOPHIA: Thank you, Miranda.

PEARL: I wish I knew a true gentleman.

MIRANDA: Don't we all!

SOPHIA (*Pleadingly*): Mr. Nasty, please.

NASTY (*Ogling her*): Well, my little wren, since *you* ask it, I will comply. You girls may take Lettie to the pump in the next room. (*Goes to left and calls*) Wilhelmina, prime the pump!

SOPHIA: Thank you. (*All the girls help* LETTIE *as they exit left.*)

NASTY: My kind heart will be the ruination of me. (*After a moment,* WILHELMINA CRACKTHORP *enters.*) Well, Wilhelmina?

WILHELMINA: There's a young fellow in hunting clothes who wants to see you. His name is Ronald Fancy.

NASTY: Ronald Fancy? Ah, yes, the young millionaire who made his fortune in the city and has now retired to a country life. Show him in. (WILHELMINA *exits briefly and returns, followed by* RONALD FANCY, *dressed in boots and hunting jacket and carrying a shotgun.*) Ah, Mr. Fancy. (*Shakes* RONALD's *hand*) An honor, sir.

RONALD: Forgive my appearing in hunting clothes, Mr. Nasty, but I intend to avail myself of some sport after I leave here. WILHELMINA *exits.*

NASTY: Excellent. And to what do I owe the honor of your visit?

RONALD: As you know, Mr. Nasty, I have retired, young as I am, from the world of business. Yet the Coal and Smoke Railroad, of which I have been a director, has asked me to do one last bit of business for them. They have informed me that you own a farm—I believe it is the Sweetblossom farm, although I do not know its location. The railroad, as you know, wishes to purchase part of the property.

NASTY (*Rubbing his hands*): Splendid! Splendid!

RONALD (*Taking paper from pocket*): I have here a deed of sale.

NASTY: Well-er, Mr. Fancy, I—I do not yet have all rights to the property. But I shall—in the near future.

RONALD (*Suspiciously*): You do not own the property? Really, Mr. Nasty, this is most unusual. You gave the railroad directors reason to believe that you did. (*Drawing himself up*) Sir, I hope there is nothing shady about all this.

NASTY: My dear Mr. Fancy, honesty is my middle name. It is merely that the transaction is still being negotiated. See me in two days, and all will be well.

RONALD (*Still suspiciously*): Very well. By the way, I could not help noting, sir, the four young lady employees of yours. They appear worn and bedraggled—with the exception of one who is as lovely as a rose.

NASTY: Worn? Bedraggled? Not at all. I treat those girls as though they were my own daughters.

RONALD: What is the name of the lovely rose?

NASTY: I am sorry, Mr. Fancy, but I cannot give you that information. I protect those girls always.

RONALD: Really, Mr. Nasty, your conduct strikes me as most unusual. I have a suspicion that you may be hiding something.

NASTY: My dear Mr. Fancy, I am merely a man of honor and integrity. I have promised those girls' parents that I would shield them from the vicissitudes of the world.

RONALD: As you will, Mr. Nasty. But now I must leave. (*Looking around him*) In the big city, textiles were among my major interests. I have often thought of founding a dress factory—as a sort of hobby.

NASTY: Don't do it, Mr. Fancy. There is no money in it. One headache after another.

RONALD: And yet you seem prosperous.

NASTY: I face the world with a smile that hides a broken heart.

RONALD: Mr. Nasty, I have a feeling that you are not all that you seem. Good day, sir. I shall communicate with you in two days' time. (*He starts left.*)

NASTY: I shall count the hours. (RONALD *exits.*) Heh. Heh. Has an eye on Sophia Sweetblossom, has he? I'll put a stop to that. The Sweetblossom farm will be mine, or my name is not Nathaniel H. Nasty. (*The girls enter at left.*)

MIRANDA: Gee, what a handsome young man!

PEARL: A regular Prince Charming.

NASTY: Feeling better now, Lettie La Rue?

LETTIE: Yes. I don't know what happened to me, but suddenly everything went black.

NASTY: Well, now let's get back to work. (WILHELMINA *enters at left.*)

WILHELMINA: I have news for you, Nathaniel. State Senator Samson Hamhock and that Mrs. Quench—you know, the one who's working for women's rights—are on their way here. They're investigating labor conditions.

NASTY: The dratted busybodies! But I'll be ready for them. And if you little canaries peep one word of complaint while they're here, you'll be out of jobs.

PEARL: Oh, no, Mr. Nasty, not that! I have all I can do to keep body and soul together on $1.75 a week.

NASTY: Just remember—things could be worse on nothing a week.

SOPHIA: Oh, Mr. Nasty, that was an unkind remark, not worthy of a true gentleman.

NASTY (*Going to her and chucking her under the chin*): For you, my dear, I would be a gentleman to my fingertips. Ah, you're a sweet one! And we could be loving partners for life. (*He starts to put his arm around her.*)

SOPHIA (*Politely pushing his arm away*): Sir, I resent your familiarity.

WILHELMINA: Yes, act your age, Nathaniel. (*She goes toward left.*) The Senator and Mrs. Quench will be here at any moment. Get your mind on that.

NASTY: Ah, how I am misjudged. I attempt a kindly little act of affection, and I am unjustly condemned for it by my devoted secretary.

WILHELMINA (*Acidly*): Save the blarney for the Senator and that amazon. (*She exits left.*)

NASTY (*With false sweetness*): Quite recovered now, Lettie La Rue?

LETTIE: Yes, I think so.

NASTY: Splendid. Splendid. And I have a little surprise for you, Lettie. Your salary this week will be different.

LETTIE (*Happily*): Oh, Mr. Nasty, how wonderful!

NASTY: Yes, indeed. I'm deducting ten cents to pay for the glass of water.

MIRANDA: That's not fair, Mr. Nasty.

NASTY: Don't you believe it. Now everyone back to work, or you'll all be candidates for the bread line. (SOPHIA *returns wearily to her table.* LETTIE *gets her needle ready, and* NASTY *begins to beat once more on the block of wood. After a moment,* WILHELMINA *enters.*)

WILHELMINA: Get ready, Nathaniel. Senator Hamhock and Mrs. Quench are here. (*She exits.*)

NASTY: Meddlesome intruders! But I'll cook their goose! And remember my words of advice, girls—one complaint and (*He claps his hands together.*) out in the cold. Now let's take a little rest period.

PEARL: About time.

NASTY: Silence, Pearl Peach. (SENATOR SAMSON HAMHOCK *and* MRS. QUENCH *enter.*)

SENATOR: Mr. Nathaniel H. Nasty, I presume.

NASTY (*In an oily manner*): Ah, sir, what an honor to have you visit our humble but happy little factory. This is, indeed, a day of days.

MRS. QUENCH: I believe you know why we're here, Mr. Nasty. We're investigating labor conditions in this area. And I, personally, want to be sure that these girls are being treated properly. Equal rights for women—that's the ticket.

NASTY (*Bowing*): Ah, Mrs. Quench, you voice my thoughts exactly. (*He goes to* LETTIE.) Miss Lettie La Rue, are you feeling better? You look somewhat uncomfortable. (*He pats her shoulder.*) Perhaps your back is tired. Well, I know just the thing for that. (*He goes to left.*) Wilhelmina! Fetch a pillow. (*Returns to center*)

Ah, nothing is too good for the employees of the Nasty Dress Factory. (WILHELMINA *enters with a pillow.*) Thank you, my dear. (NASTY *takes pillow and places it tenderly behind* LETTIE's *back.*) There. Isn't that better?

LETTIE: Much better.

SENATOR (*Wiping his eyes*): You're good to these girls, Nasty. It brings a tear to my eye.

MRS. QUENCH: He should be good to them. A girl is the equal of any man.

NASTY (*Taking watch from pocket and looking at it*): My, how the hours fly. It is time for tea. Wilhelmina, fetch the tea and cakes for the girls.

SENATOR (*Astounded*): The girls have tea every day?

NASTY (*Innocently*): Why, bless my soul, my good man— of course. Do not all the factories you visit serve tea every afternoon?

MRS. QUENCH: None that I've seen, Mr. Nasty. You're a man in a million. (WILHELMINA *sighs and exits left.*)

NASTY (*Modestly*): I have a kind heart, Mrs. Quench. I learned consideration for others at my mother's knee.

SENATOR (*Again wiping eyes*): Nasty, you are a prince. I learned the same thing from my dear old mother.

NASTY (*Shaking the* SENATOR's *hand*): Every day is Mother's Day with me. Ah, yes, Senator, a mother is a man's best friend.

MRS. QUENCH: A mother is the equal of any father.

NASTY: My sentiments exactly, Mrs. Quench. We are kindred spirits. (WILHELMINA *enters with a tray on which are cups of tea and cakes. She deposits a cup of tea and one or two cakes on each girl's table.* PEARL *crams a cake into her mouth and chews wolfishly.*)

SENATOR: Great Scott, girl, you must be hungry.

PEARL (*With mouth full*): It's six hours since—

NASTY (*Coughing warningly*): Pearl has a great appetite. Why, this morning she ate heartily of wheat cakes, bacon, eggs, oatmeal, and coffee. I always serve a late breakfast to the girls.

MIRANDA: Very late.

SENATOR (*Again wiping eyes*): Nasty, I shall break down completely if I stay any longer. You are too good—too good.

MRS. QUENCH: You're a credit to American industry, Mr. Nasty.

NASTY (*Humbly*): I try to be. I try to light my own little candle in the world's darkness.

SENATOR: You can be assured that in my report on the Nasty Dress Factory I shall have nothing but words of praise. And I might add, Nasty, that the word of State Senator Samson Hamhock goes a long way.

NASTY: I respect your reputation, my dear Senator. You are a gem among statesmen.

MRS. QUENCH: And there'll come a day when we women will be state senators, too. A female state senator will be equal to any male senator.

NASTY (*Gallantly*): A woman of your great charm, Mrs. Quench, is already equal to anybody. (MRS. QUENCH *slaps* NASTY *heartily on the back and sends him into a fit of coughing*)

MRS. QUENCH: Nasty, you're a real gentleman!

NASTY (*Recovering*): Thank you. My mother raised me to be one.

SENATOR: Now, Mrs. Quench, we must go. We still have to visit the Crunchy Biscuit Company and the Bulging Bustle Corporation.

MRS. QUENCH (*Going toward left*): Yes, that we do.

SENATOR: Goodbye, Nasty. This has been a heartwarming experience. (*Wiping eyes*) I haven't been so touched since I saw that great play, "Over the Hills to the Poor Farm."

NASTY: Goodbye, Senator. Goodbye, Mrs. Quench. (SENATOR *and* MRS. QUENCH *exit*. NASTY *rubs his hands together gleefully*.) The idiots! The nincompoops! The busybodies! Wilhelmina, take away the tea.

PEARL: But, I'm not finished yet.

NASTY: Take one more bite or one more sip, and you'll be finished for good. (WILHELMINA *goes to the tables and collects the tea things*. PEARL *makes a last effort to take another bite of cake*. NASTY *slaps her hand*.) Greed, girl, greed. One of the seven deadly sins. (WILHELMINA *exits*.)

SOPHIA: For shame, sir!

MIRANDA: It's time to go home. Five o'clock.

NASTY (*Looking at watch*): So it is. We've lost time because of those infernal nuisances, Senator Hamhock and Mrs. Quench. (*Smiling and stroking mustache*) But that's easily remedied. We'll begin tomorrow at five a.m. instead of six.

LETTIE (*Weakly*): But, Mr. Nasty, even the birds aren't up at five.

NASTY: Well, you little birds will be.

SOPHIA: It does seem to be a somewhat early hour.

PEARL: It's practically the middle of the night.

NASTY: And one other small item of interest. I'm taking twenty cents from your wages this week for that scrumptious tea. It's only fair. I can't be expected to be the soul of generosity all the time. My soft heart is my worst enemy.

LETTIE: Gracious, that's thirty cents I've lost already.

SOPHIA (*Sighing*): Well, girls, come. It is time to go. (*She takes a small basket from under her table.*) I must stop in the woods on my way home to gather berries. Alas, they are probably all my sweet mother and dear father will have to eat tonight. (*The girls rise and move wearily toward left.*)

NASTY: One moment, my dear Sophia Sweetblossom, I would have a word with you. (*The other girls exit, and* SOPHIA *returns to center.*)

SOPHIA: Yes, Mr. Nasty.

NASTY: You may call me Nathaniel.

SOPHIA: I'd rather not.

NASTY (*Chucking her under the chin*): Come, come now. Is this the way to act toward a kindhearted gentleman who wishes only to be your benefactor? Have you thought about what we discussed yesterday, my little country flower? I am offering you my hand in marriage. Think of it. You will become Mrs. Nathaniel H. Nasty. I know that your mother and father are old. I know there is a heavy mortgage on your little home.

SOPHIA: How true. Alas, how true! Our troubles seem to accumulate endlessly. And it's so hard for me to care for my dear parents on $1.75 a week.

NASTY: $1.55 this week, my dear. Don't forget the tea. But as Mrs. Nathaniel H. Nasty, you will live in the lap of luxury. I will pay off the mortgage on your home. I will take care of your mother and father.

SOPHIA: Oh, sir, you put me in a difficult position. You see, I do not love you.

NASTY: Only because you do not know me well. (*With a sly laugh*) To know me is to love me!

SOPHIA: I do want to make life easier for my dear father and sweet mother. But I must have time to decide.

NASTY: My dear, I must press for an answer. I shall visit your home tonight. Then and there you must give me your decision.

SOPHIA: I shall think about it. I am prepared to make sacrifices for my beloved parents.

NASTY (*Attempting to put his arm around her*): Ah, you're a sweet one. (*She eludes him and goes quickly to door.*)

SOPHIA: I must gather my berries before night falls.

NASTY (*Blowing her a kiss*): Until tonight then, my sweet little petunia. (SOPHIA *exits.* NASTY *comes downstage, twirls his mustache, takes handkerchief from pocket, and wipes his eyes. He addresses the audience.*) Forgive me, my good friends, but I am overcome by my own generosity. Heh. Heh. Is Sophia not a sweet morsel? I am certain she will agree tonight to marry me—who can resist my charm? (*Twirls mustache*) Heh. Heh. But kind as I am, I must think also of yours truly, Nathaniel H. Nasty. Little Sophia does not know that the railroad wishes to purchase her property and at a good price. Even though that dismal fop, Ronald Fancy, seems suspicious, I shall marry Sophia, pay off the mortgage, get the property, and sell it. I'll show that dandy, Ronald Fancy. And as for her dear father and sweet mother— heh, heh—I shall soon send them over the hills to the poor farm. I hate to do it. (*Wipes his eyes*) I am a warmhearted man. Heh. Heh. But business is business. So, dear friends, I know you will be cheering for my success. Thank you. Thank you. (*He laughs nastily and twirls his mustache.*)

CURTAIN

* * * * *

Scene 2

Time: *Fifteen minutes later.*

Setting: *The woods near* Sophia's *home.* (*This scene may be played before the curtain, if desired.*)

At Rise: Sophia *enters from right, carrying basket.*

Sophia: Alas, it is growing dark, and I have managed to find only three berries. Ah, well, that will be one each for Mother, Father, and me. (*Sound of dogs barking is heard.*) The hounds again. I have seen three of them, and how lovely they were! They were barking loudly, and their ears seemed to sweep the ground before them. (*Sound of footsteps is heard.*) But hark. I hear footsteps. (Ronald Fancy, *dressed as in Scene 1 and carrying his gun, enters at left. He catches sight of* Sophia, *who shrinks in fear.*)

Ronald: Do not be alarmed, pretty maiden. I would not hurt a hair of your lovely head. I am merely looking for my dogs.

Sophia (*Pointing to right*): Your dogs went in that direction. And how beautiful they are. I love dogs!

Ronald (*Clasping hand dramatically to forehead*): But this is miraculous! So young and tender a girl, and yet filled with love for our canine friends. Mother always said to me, "Ronald, be certain that any young lady in whom you become interested is a lover of dogs. That is the acid test." Ah, how wise Mother was. But tell me, what brings you to these woods?

Sophia: Alas, sir, I am poor, and have come here to gather berries.

Ronald (*Gallantly*): You may be poor in wealth, but not in beauty.

SOPHIA: It is good of you to say so, sir. My family is poor because my dear father cannot work. In his youth, he was a sea captain, but he has rheumatism. And my sweet mother must look after him. Thus, I am a seamstress in Mr. Nasty's dress factory.

RONALD (*Thoughtfully*): Nasty's dress factory. . . . (*Suddenly*) But of course! I knew I had seen your lovely countenance before. I visited Mr. Nasty just this morning, and you were the sweet creature I saw at the factory. (*Bowing*) I am Ronald Fancy, at your service.

SOPHIA (*Curtsying*): How do you do, sir? I recognize you now, although I had only a fleeting glimpse of you at the factory. How remarkable that I should meet you again, and in these woods.

RONALD: Not so, fair child. You see, I live nearby. Disgusted by the hubbub and sordid life of the metropolis, I have come here, seeking a country existence of peace and serenity. I have purchased the mansion on the other side of the woods.

SOPHIA: Oh, it is a magnificent house, sir.

RONALD: It is, indeed. But I can well afford it. I made my fortune in the detestable city, and I shall now devote my life to doing good. But about Mr. Nasty—I had a feeling, from my conversation with him, that he is not absolutely trustworthy.

SOPHIA: It is not for me to say, sir. Sometimes I have a suspicion that he is not an entirely good man. But he has asked for my hand in marriage.

RONALD: Great heavens! Not that! Perhaps that is why he would not tell me your name.

SOPHIA: You see, sir, I must protect the welfare of my sweet mother and good father. Mr. Nasty promises to care for them in their old age.

RONALD (*Fervently*): You are a gem of womanhood. (*Dogs bark offstage*) Hark, there are my hounds.

SOPHIA: I must hurry home with these berries. Mr. Nasty will be visiting our humble abode tonight. (*She goes toward left.*) Good night, sir.

RONALD: But what is your name?

SOPHIA: Sophia Sweetblossom, sir. (*She exits, accidentally dropping her handkerchief.*)

RONALD: Sweetblossom! Aha! Now I see that my suspicions of Nasty were well founded. But what a fair flower Sophia is! And she loves dogs. More than anything else, I want to save her from marrying Nasty—a fate worse than death. (*Putting hand to forehead*) But, alas, I neglected to ask her where she lives. (*Seeing handkerchief and picking it up*) Her handkerchief! She must have dropped it. (*Clutching it to him*) At least I shall have this cherished memento of the fair Sophia!

CURTAIN

*   *   *   *   *

SCENE 3

TIME: *Three hours later.*

SETTING: *The Sweetblossom home.*

AT RISE: MR. SWEETBLOSSOM, *wearing sea captain's hat, is rocking in his chair.* MRS. SWEETBLOSSOM *is seated at table.*

MR. SWEETBLOSSOM (*Rocking and rubbing his leg*): Drat this rheumatiz. It's plaguing me something fierce. Must be a storm a-brewing. Heaven help the poor sailors on a night like this. I'm hungry, too.

MRS. SWEETBLOSSOM: My berry was good, but, somehow

or other, a berry does not stick to the ribs. And, alas, there is nothing else in the larder.

MR. SWEETBLOSSOM: Well, shiver my timbers, Sophia does the best she can. But it's hard to provide on $1.75 a week.

MRS. SWEETBLOSSOM: And with prices the way they are. Why, butter is up to eleven cents a pound.

MR. SWEETBLOSSOM: Avast, but dear Sophia is taking a long time to dress.

MRS. SWEETBLOSSOM: She wants to look her best. As she told us at dinner, Nathaniel H. Nasty will be here to-night to ask for her hand in marriage. He promises to take care of us in our old age.

MR. SWEETBLOSSOM: He's as generous a man as you'll find this side of starboard.

MRS. SWEETBLOSSOM: And yet, dear Sophia does not seem very enthusiastic about him.

MR. SWEETBLOSSOM: What's wrong with the girl? Nasty is as fine a figure of a man as ever paced the quarterdeck.

MRS. SWEETBLOSSOM: We shall hope for the best. Sophia will be wearing her new dress—the one she made from a sugar sack and an old umbrella. My, that girl is clever.

MR. SWEETBLOSSOM: We are blessed with such a daughter.
  (SOPHIA *appears at right*.)

MRS. SWEETBLOSSOM: You make a pretty picture, Sophia.

SOPHIA: Thank you, dear Mother.

MR. SWEETBLOSSOM: A picture pretty enough for a sailor's calendar.

SOPHIA: Thank you, good Father.

MRS. SWEETBLOSSOM: Tell me, Sophia, have you decided to accept Mr. Nasty?

SOPHIA (*Sighing*): Yes, Mother. The mortgage must be paid, and you and dear Father provided for. And yet—

and yet I sometimes feel that all is not well. I sometimes suspect that Mr. Nasty may not be as kindly as he pretends to be. (*There is a knock at front door.*)

MRS. SWEETBLOSSOM: That must be Mr. Nasty. (SOPHIA *goes to door and opens it.* NASTY *enters and hands her a bouquet of flowers.*)

NASTY: How I wish that these flowers could match your beauty, my dear.

MR. SWEETBLOSSOM: Ahoy there, Mr. Nasty. (*Rubs his ankle*) Drat this rheumatiz. (NASTY *kisses* SOPHIA's *hand. Then he goes to* MRS. SWEETBLOSSOM *and kisses her on forehead.*)

NASTY: I take the liberty of bestowing an affectionate caress on the charming woman whom I hope I shall soon have the right to call Mother.

MRS. SWEETBLOSSOM: Oh, Mr. Nasty, how kind of you. (*He goes to* MR. SWEETBLOSSOM *and shakes his hand.*)

NASTY: Father. (*He takes out his handkerchief and wipes his eyes.*) Forgive me, but I am a man of sentiment. These emotional scenes quite overcome me.

MR. SWEETBLOSSOM: You're shipshape, that's what you are, Mr. Nasty.

NASTY: Quite right, Father Sweetblossom. Indeed, I am. (*Goes to* SOPHIA) And now, my little meadow lark, say the word that will make me the happiest dress manufacturer in the nation.

SOPHIA: Sir, I have thought and thought about the matter, and I have come to my decision. Sir, to rescue my sweet mother and dear father from the penury in which they live, I will be your wife.

NASTY: You will never regret it, my dear. And now, of course, a little kiss to seal the bargain. (*He is about to kiss her when there is a knock at the door.* SOPHIA, *much relieved, rushes to door and opens it. Standing in the doorway is* RONALD FANCY. *With him are* LETTIE LA RUE, PEARL PEACH, *and* MIRANDA MILDEW.)

SOPHIA: Why, Mr. Fancy! How did you ever find me?

RONALD (*Taking handkerchief from his pocket and handing it to* SOPHIA): This is yours, I believe, Miss Sweetblossom. Through its scent, one of my loyal hounds, the admirable Lysander, was able to find your residence for me. I beg your forgiveness for bursting in like this, but I could not forget our recent meeting. My heart has been racing ever since. I knew that I must see you again. And so I brought these girls with me—

SOPHIA: Pearl, Lettie, and Miranda—come in.

NASTY: Have you girls forgotten you're to be at work tomorrow at five a.m.? What are you doing here?

MIRANDA (*Sticking out her tongue*): Fiddle-dee-dee to you, Mr. Nasty!

PEARL: You can keep your job, Nathaniel H. Nasty.

LETTIE: I'll never faint in the Nasty Dress Factory again.

NASTY: What's this? Do you girls realize what you're saying? It will be the poor farm for all of you.

RONALD: Not so fast, Nathaniel H. Nasty! You are nothing but a scoundrel and a cad. You have mistreated these poor working girls; you've deceived Senator Hamhock and Mrs. Quench; and you have tried to trick this lovely flower, Miss Sophia Sweetblossom, into marrying you—

NASTY: There must be some mistake. I am the soul of honor and righteousness.

RONALD: Honor? Why, you don't know the meaning of the word, sir. You did not tell the Sweetblossoms, who trusted you, that I had made an offer on behalf of the Coal and Smoke Railroad to buy their property, and they could live in comfort for the rest of their lives. I repeat, sir, you are a cad!

SOPHIA: Why, Mr. Nasty, you never told me about the railroad.

NASTY: Just an oversight, my dear. (*Smiling ingratiatingly*) It slipped my mind.

RONALD: You can't deceive us any longer, Mr. Nasty. I have been doing a little investigating tonight, and I am appalled by what these girls told me about the conditions in your factory.

NASTY (*Blustering*): What?

RONALD: And I have reported the information to Senator Hamhock, who has, in turn, informed Mrs. Quench. Mrs. Quench was most upset. She vowed, and I quote her, to give you "a good taste" of her walking stick. In fact, she threatened to appear here tonight.

NASTY: But this is absurd. I am a kindhearted man, beloved by all who know me.

PEARL: Not by me.

MIRANDA: Me either.

NASTY: You girls are fired!

MIRANDA: We've already resigned.

NASTY: And just how are you girls going to earn a living? It will be most unpleasant to starve to death. Heh. Heh.

RONALD: I have taken care of that. You may recall my mentioning that I might like to own a dress factory. Well, I am starting my own—to be known as Fancy Frocks. Miss La Rue, Miss Peach, and Miss Mildew will work for me. Moreover, I shall pay them a living wage. In fact, I intend to go as high as six or seven dollars a week.

SOPHIA: Oh, Mr. Fancy, you are one of nature's noblemen!

RONALD: Ah, Miss Sweetblossom, how beautifully you express your thoughts!

NASTY (*Coming close to* SOPHIA): Well, now, my little wren, these small misunderstandings need make no difference between us. (*He attempts to take her hand.*) You are my betrothed.

RONALD: Unhand her, sir. This fair flower is not for a serpent such as you.

MRS. SWEETBLOSSOM (*Worried*): Easy, Mr. Fancy. Mr. Nasty is a rich man.

RONALD: So am I.

MR. SWEETBLOSSOM: You are? Well, full speed ahead then, mates. How much are you worth, young man?

RONALD: In the neighborhood of six million dollars.

MR. SWEETBLOSSOM: Shiver my timbers, but that's a wonderful neighborhood to be in!

MRS. SWEETBLOSSOM: Bless you, my boy. I see that you are a prince of good fellows.

NASTY: Chicken feed. Chicken feed. (*He again attempts to take* SOPHIA's *hand.* RONALD *grabs* NASTY's *arm, pushes him, and* NASTY *falls to the floor.*)

MIRANDA: Now, that's a funny sight!

PEARL: No bones broken—I hope. Ha. Ha.

LETTIE: Get him a glass of water—and charge him for it.

NASTY (*Rising to his feet and glaring*): This will not go unchallenged, Mr. Ronald Fancy. No man insults Nathaniel H. Nasty.

RONALD (*Drawing himself up proudly*): Nasty, I do not fear you. Your evil ways are at an end.

SOPHIA: Bad deeds will always be punished severely.

MR. SWEETBLOSSOM: That's my daughter who said that. (*Rubs his arm*) Drat this rheumatiz.

RONALD: Take my advice, Nasty. Leave this humble

abode at once. Senator Hamhock will communicate with you tomorrow. You will be forced to answer some embarrassing questions.

NASTY: Curses! Foiled again! (*He goes toward front door. LETTIE, PEARL, and MIRANDA giggle at him.*) Female hyenas!

MIRANDA: Cheer up, Mr. Nasty. Wilhelmina Crackthorp is fond of you.

NASTY (*Smiling*): Ah, so she is. She will testify in my behalf. She will tell of my generosity and warm heart. She will sing my praises.

RONALD (*Triumphantly*): There you are wrong, Nathaniel H. Nasty. I have talked with Miss Crackthorp, and I am happy to report that she has seen the error of her ways. She has vowed to lead a righteous life from now on. In fact, she will be a secretary for Fancy Frocks.

NASTY: A pox on you, Ronald Fancy! (*MRS. QUENCH suddenly rushes in at front door and collides with NASTY. She is carrying a stout walking stick.*)

MRS. QUENCH: Ah, there you are, you dreadful rogue! Thought you had pulled the wool over my eyes, did you? Trying to make me believe you think girls are equal to anybody! (*She strikes at him with her stick.*) I'll show you that at least one woman is equal to anybody—namely me. (*NASTY holds his arms up to shield his head.*)

NASTY (*Nervously*): There has been a misunderstanding. I can explain. (*MRS. QUENCH hits him with her stick. He exits, yelling "Police!", with MRS. QUENCH in pursuit.*)

RONALD (*Laughing*): Nathaniel H. Nasty is in good hands.

SOPHIA: I sometimes suspect that he is not really a pleasant person.

RONALD: And now, Miss Sweetblossom, I come to the most important purpose of my visit. Miss Sweetblossom, ever since I met you, the vision of your fair face has constantly been before me. Forgive me if I seem somewhat brash. But Mother always told me that there are times when one must not be backward about being forward. Therefore, I must ask the question that is burning in my soul. Miss Sweetblossom, I know that our acquaintance has been brief, but could you—would you—will you be my wife?

MIRANDA: Oh, how romantic!

SOPHIA: This is indeed an honor for me, a poor but honest seamstress.

RONALD (*Eagerly*): You mean—

SOPHIA: You have saved me from a fate worse than death. Of course I will be yours, Mr. Fancy.

RONALD: Call me Ronald.

SOPHIA: I will be yours, Ronald.

RONALD: Oh, joyful night!

SOPHIA: My hero! (RONALD *embraces her*.)

RONALD: And your dear mother and father will have enough money from the sale of this house to the railroad to live in comfort for the rest of their years.

MR. SWEETBLOSSOM (*Jumping up from rocker and doing a jig*): Ahoy there, mates, we're in for a spell of fair weather!

SOPHIA: Why, Father, your rheumatism is better.

MR. SWEETBLOSSOM: Why, so it is.

RONALD: This is a miraculous night, indeed. And now I must be off to make plans for the morrow—and for our wedding, Sophia, which will be as soon as possible.

MRS. SWEETBLOSSOM (*In businesslike tone*): Today's Wednesday. How about Friday?

RONALD: A superb suggestion, Mrs. Sweetblossom.

MRS. SWEETBLOSSOM (*Demurely*): I have Sophia's happiness at heart.

MIRANDA: We had better go, too, girls. (MIRANDA, LETTIE, *and* PEARL *go toward front door*.)

LETTIE: Such a wonderful night! And I haven't felt faint once.

PEARL: Three cheers for Fancy Frocks! (LETTIE, PEARL, *and* MIRANDA *exit*.)

MR. SWEETBLOSSOM (*Again doing a jig*): We've come into port, mates—safely and happily.

RONALD (*Going to door*): Farewell, sweet Sophia, until the morrow. (*He blows her a kiss*.)

SOPHIA: Farewell, my hero. (*He exits*.) Oh, I am the most fortunate girl in the world! (*Curtain*)

THE END

Production Notes

Characters: 4 male; 7 female.

Playing Time: 40 minutes.

Costumes: Appropriate dress of the turn of the century. Mr. Nasty has a mustache, and carries a pocket watch and a handkerchief. Ronald wears boots and hunting clothes. Mrs. Quench wears rather mannish tweeds and a man's hat. In Scene 3, she carried a walking stick. Mr. Sweetblossom wears sea captain's hat; in Scene 2, Sophia has a handkerchief.

Properties: Needles, thread, etc., for factory workroom, pillow, tray with cakes and cups of tea, gun, bouquet of flowers, stick and block of wood.

Setting: Scene 1 takes place in a workroom in Nathaniel H. Nasty's Dress Factory. There are four small work tables, with chairs; there is a small basket under Sophia's table. Exit is at left. Scene 2 is set in the woods near Sophia's home and may be played before the curtain, if desired. Scene 3 is the Sweetblossom's shabby but tidy home. At center is a rough wooden table with three chairs. A rocking chair and battered sofa complete the furnishings. Door up center leads to outside. Exit right leads to rest of house.

Lighting: No special effects.

Sound: Dogs barking, footsteps, as indicated in text.

Collector's Item

Characters

MRS. COLLINS
MR. COLLINS
RALPH COLLINS, *their seventeen-year-old son*
MIRIAM COLLINS, *their sixteen-year-old daughter*
THAYER GROVE, *museum director and art expert*
ELSA CRINGLE, *an art dealer*
UNCLE NORTON, *Mr. Collins' elder brother*

SCENE 1

TIME: *A Saturday morning.*

SETTING: *The living room of the Collins household, a comfortable but somewhat shabby room. At upper left on the floor are several cartons, an open trunk, and a number of boxes.*

AT RISE: MRS. COLLINS *is standing behind table, holding an unframed painting and looking at it thoughtfully. She places it on table, walks to window at up center, and looks out. Suddenly she becomes very excited, rushes to door at left, and calls.*

MRS. COLLINS: Sam! Miriam! Ralph! Mr. Grove has just driven up in front of the house! There's a lady with him. Hurry down! (*She hurries to window and looks out.* MR. COLLINS *and* RALPH *enter left, carrying a trunk. They are followed in by* MIRIAM, *out of breath, toting a large carton.*)

MR. COLLINS: Let's put this trunk over there with the others.

RALPH: Gosh, it sure is heavy. Grandfather Collins must have collected lead.

MIRIAM (*Placing carton on floor*): But he collected paintings, too, bless him! (MR. COLLINS *and* RALPH *set trunk on floor.*)

RALPH (*Wiping brow*): Phew! I thought I was in top condition after football season, but this is hard work.

MIRIAM: Work and you have always been almost complete strangers, Ralph.

RALPH: Oh, you're a real card, Miriam. There must be a spot for you somewhere on TV. (*The doorbell rings.* MRS. COLLINS *goes quickly to door, up center, and opens it.*)

MRS. COLLINS: Good morning, Mr. Grove. We've been expecting you. (THAYER GROVE, *wearing horn-rimmed spectacles and a Vandyke beard, enters, followed by* ELSA CRINGLE, *who is overdressed and walks slinkily.*)

GROVE: Good morning, Mrs. Collins. May I present Miss Elsa Cringle, an art dealer for whom I have the greatest respect.

ELSA (*Kittenishly*): Oh, Thayer, you always manage to say the appropriate thing. Isn't he a dear? But, of course, how could he be anything else with his Boston and Harvard background? As the French say, "Ça va sans dire." Breeding is so important. I am enchanted to meet you, Mr. and Mrs. Collins.

MRS. COLLINS: It's a pleasure to have you here, Miss

Cringle. This is my daughter, Miriam. (MIRIAM *nods.*)
And my son, Ralph. (RALPH *bows.*)

MR. COLLINS: When you sent the painting back to us this
morning, my heart sank, Mr. Grove. I felt that it was
probably not a genuine Romney Gregg, after all.

MRS. COLLINS: But then when you phoned just after the
painting was delivered, and said you were coming over
with good news for us—well, I can tell you, our spirits
soared.

RALPH: Into outer space!

GROVE: You must forgive me for not saying more on the
phone, but I wanted to give you the glad tidings in
person. I won't keep you in suspense any longer. (*Dramatically*) Mr. Collins, the painting, "Still Life at Sunset" (*He goes to table, takes painting, and holds it before
him.*), which you found in your father's trunk in the
attic, is unquestionably a genuine Romney Gregg.

MR. COLLINS (*Sinking onto sofa*): Well! Just let me get my
breath a moment!

ELSA: How perfectly wonderful it is to be present on this
historic occasion! I feel just the way I did when I was
visiting Mrs. Pemberton-Norwood on the day she was
named to the "Ten Best-Dressed Women in the World"
list. She and I, of course, are intimate friends.

MIRIAM: Then the painting is really valuable.

GROVE (*Smiling*): That's an understatement.

ELSA: Let me tell you something about Romney Gregg.
Naturally, as an art dealer, I keep well informed on
such matters. Mrs. Gordon Hallscomb-Peregrine—her
husband is president of three banks—tells me that I'm
really a walking encyclopedia. She's so kind. Anyway,
Romney Gregg was born in 1850—

GROVE: Er—I hate to interrupt, Elsa, but I think he was born in 1848.

ELSA: Oh, well, Thayer, what's a couple of years among friends? And he died in 1871.

MR. COLLINS: My, he had a short life, didn't he?

ELSA: Ah, yes. He died penniless in Paris, poor thing. He never had the advantages of either birth or money—and these are so important.

GROVE (*Dryly*): He had one advantage, though—genius.

ELSA: He was a sort of primitive painter, rather like a male Grandma Moses. Unfortunately he wasn't taken seriously in his time. But during the last ten years, he has been rediscovered by the art world. And now his paintings are highly valued.

MRS. COLLINS (*Hesitantly*): Just how valuable do you think the painting is, Mr. Grove?

GROVE: Get ready for a shock. At a conservative estimate, I'd say that "Still Life at Sunset" is worth anywhere from twenty to twenty-five thousand dollars.

RALPH (*Sinking into chair at left of table*): Wow! That's a lot of money!

ELSA: Now, as Thayer can tell you, I have access to the very best homes in this area, homes where great art is used to bring beauty into daily life. Naturally, my position in the community can be of great advantage to you. To put the matter frankly, if you tried to sell the painting yourself, you probably would not know exactly how to begin. That's why Thayer phoned me to come here with him this morning. He agrees that I can obtain the absolutely top price for your Romney Gregg.

MR. COLLINS: Twenty to twenty-five thousand dollars sounds like a very respectable sum to me. I may as well be frank with you both. We were planning to sell this house because I must raise ten thousand dollars at once if I am to save my business. We were going to move into a small apartment. In fact, it was in the process of preparing to move that we went through some of my father's things in the attic.

ELSA (*Gushing*): Mr. Collins, that necessary ten thousand dollars and much more is practically in your pocket right now. With a little pushing (*She makes a pushing motion with her hands.*), I think I can get you thirty thousand—minus, of course, my customary commission of ten percent.

MIRIAM (*Calculating quickly*): So we'd get twenty-seven thousand dollars.

ELSA: Ah, you have a mathematical brain, Miriam. You know, only last week while I was lunching at the Weston-Gilberts—Mr. Weston-Gilbert is chairman of the board of several large corporations and a great friend of mine —I said, "You simply must have something for that spot on your wall, and I know just the thing." Of course, I didn't then, but I do now. "Still Life at Sunset" was just made for that spot on the Weston-Gilberts' drawing-room wall.

RALPH: Gosh! I can see myself driving a snazzy sports car now. I'll be the hit of the campus at college next year.

MIRIAM: And won't I look divine in a new fur coat!

MRS. COLLINS: What do you think, Mr. Grove?

GROVE: Elsa is a woman of her word. She'll get you the price she says.

ELSA: Of course I will. As my dear friend, Miss Harriman-Stanhope—she inherited the Stanhope millions—always says about me, "Elsa's promises are as solid as the Rock of Gibraltar." She's a lovely woman. I'll set the wheels in motion at once. In fact, the wheels will be whizzing away like mad.

MR. COLLIN: I can't tell you how much this means to us. (*Turning to* MRS. COLLINS) Do you realize, dear—we won't have to sell the house? And we'll be able to keep the business going and even improve it!

MRS. COLLINS: It's a miracle.

GROVE: I'm delighted by your stroke of good fortune.

ELSA: And so am I. We had better be on our way, Thayer. I want to contact Mrs. Weston-Gilbert as soon as possible.

MR. COLLINS: I appreciate your kindness, Mr. Grove. And thank you, too, Miss Cringle.

GROVE: Not at all.

ELSA (*Going toward up center*): Mrs. Weston-Gilbert will be in seventh heaven when I tell her about the painting. She's so aesthetic. You'll be hearing from me. Good-bye for now.

GROVE: Good morning, all. (ELSA *and* GROVE *exit up center.*)

MRS. COLLINS: It's just unbelievable!

MIRIAM (*Ecstatically*): Grandfather Collins, I love you! (*She begins to dance around the room.*) Can't you just see me in that fur coat—a luscious Russian sable or a soft Canadian mink—

RALPH: You sound like the United Nations. But picture me behind the wheel of that shiny, flashy sports car. The girls will flock around like flies.

MRS. COLLINS (*Looking at watch*): Sam, I'd completely forgotten. You're supposed to pick up Norton at the station.

MR. COLLINS: That's right. I was so excited not to be

selling the house that it slipped my mind entirely. I'll drive down at once. It's a good thing the station is only a couple of minutes away. (*He goes toward up center and turns.*) Won't that brother of mine be astounded? He's a sedate fellow, but I'll bet this news will have him dancing like a schoolboy. (*He exits up center.*)

MRS. COLLINS: It's so wonderful to see your father happy for a change. He's been so plagued by business worries. This certainly came at just the right time for us.

RALPH: His worries are over now.

MIRIAM: And, best of all, we won't have to leave this beautiful old house.

MRS. COLLINS: I'd better make myself presentable for Norton. Incidentally, it might be a good idea to wait until he arrives before we begin going through those trunks and cartons. He knows a good deal about Grandfather Collins' effects. (*She exits right.*)

RALPH (*Lying down on sofa with hands locked behind his head, and staring dreamily at the ceiling*): The meaning of all this is just beginning to hit me. We were going to have to scrimp and save until Dad got on his feet again and then, all of a sudden—bingo, we have it made!

MIRIAM: And I saw myself looking like Miss Hand-Me-Down for the next few years. But now, I'll be Miss Fashion Plate of Renfield High. (*She goes to one of trunks and opens it.*) There's plenty of good old junk here. Maybe we'll find a Rembrandt.

RALPH: Don't be greedy. And you heard what Mother said. We're not to touch anything until Uncle Norton arrives.

MIRIAM: There's a book in here that looks like a diary.

RALPH: Hands off! (MR. COLLINS *and* UNCLE NORTON *enter up center.* MR. COLLINS *looks thoroughly dejected.*

UNCLE NORTON *carries a suitcase which he puts down at center.*)

MR. COLLINS: Norton had started to walk from the station. He was almost here when I picked him up.

MIRIAM: Hi, Uncle Norton. (*She goes to him and hugs him.*)

RALPH (*Going to NORTON and shaking hands*): Welcome to Millionaire's Alley, Uncle Norton.

MR. COLLINS (*Gloomily*): That's a laugh.

MIRIAM: What's wrong, Dad? (MRS. COLLINS *enters hurriedly at right.*)

MRS. COLLINS: I thought I heard voices. How are you, Norton? (*She embraces him.*)

NORTON: Fine, Helen. (*He goes to table, lifts painting, looks searchingly at it, and nods his head.*) But I seem to be the bearer of bad tidings.

MRS. COLLINS: What do you mean?

MR. COLLINS: Norton has just dropped a bombshell in our midst. He says that our painting isn't a Romney Gregg, after all.

RALPH: What!

MIRIAM: Oh, no!

MRS. COLLINS: But, Norton, you must be mistaken. We have it on the authority of Thayer Grove—who is an art expert and a museum director of long experience—that this is a genuine Romney Gregg.

NORTON (*Looking at painting again, then placing it on table*): Look, Helen, I don't like this any more than you do. I don't relish the role of wet blanket. But I know that this painting isn't genuine, because I painted it myself.

MRS. COLLINS (*Bewildered*): You what?

MR. COLLINS: You remember that Norton lived in Paris for a year after he graduated from college.

MRS. COLLINS: Yes, but what has that to do with anything?

NORTON: Let me explain. As you know, I used to paint, just as a hobby, when I was younger. One time, Jack Wainwright and I—you remember Jack; we shared a room in Paris—well, Jack and I thought we'd have a little fun. There was an art shop down the street owned by a friend of ours. The shop had a Romney Gregg painting on display, "Still Life at Sunset."

MIRIAM: That's it on the table.

NORTON: No, it isn't. You see, Jack and I made a bet. Each of us decided to copy the Gregg painting to see if we could pass off our copies as genuine—just for fun—to Roland Carpentier, an art critic we knew. Naturally, if Roland fell for the joke, we'd tell him the truth. Jack and I wagered five hundred francs on whose painting would be declared genuine. Well, Roland was a good art critic; he almost fell for my copy but finally decided against it. Neither of us fooled him. I must have packed my copy in my trunk and sent it home. But there seems to be no question that Father put it in the attic where you found it. I signed the painting "Romney Gregg." And I'm afraid that this painting on the table is merely my copy. (*He sighs.*) I'm genuinely sorry.

RALPH (*Sinking dejectedly onto sofa*): Goodbye, sports car!

MIRIAM: And fur coat.

MRS. COLLINS: This is terrible news!

NORTON: Of course it is. I feel like one of the three Fates. But I had to tell you the truth.

MR. COLLINS: It was all too good to be true, anyway.

RALPH (*Struck by an idea*): Say, all this doesn't really have to make any difference! (*Jumps up excitedly from sofa*) If Thayer Grove says the painting is genuine, we can make money on it anyway!

MIRIAM (*Brightening*): Twenty-seven thousand dollars!

NORTON (*Surprised and unbelieving*): You mean—by selling the painting under false pretenses?

RALPH: Why not? Gosh, Uncle Norton, this money would mean a lot to us now, and nobody would know the difference.

NORTON: *You* would. Aren't integrity and honesty still important to a man?

RALPH: But things are different nowadays.

NORTON: Different? Has integrity gone out of fashion?

RALPH (*Rather bitterly*): The older generation always has the stock answers. They've lived their lives, but they won't let us live ours.

MRS. COLLINS (*Angrily*): That's enough from you, Ralph.

MR. COLLINS (*Also angrily*): I'm shocked. I thought that your mother and I had taught you children better.

MIRIAM: Nobody ever taught us that we ought to let twenty-seven thousand dollars slip through our fingers.

MRS. COLLINS: Nobody ever taught you to steal twenty-seven thousand dollars, either.

RALPH: It wouldn't be stealing. For Pete's sake, I've never stolen anything. But if we have a painting that the art experts say is genuine, what's the harm in going along with the verdict?

MIRIAM: I agree with Ralph.

MRS. COLLINS: Then you ought to be ashamed of yourself. Do you think this is easy for your father and me? You know the financial trouble he's in. Don't you think we would have welcomed the money, too? It would save our business and our house. He needs new clothes, a new car. But we've always tried to save for you children, and gone without many things so that your future might be secure.

MR. COLLINS: Helen, don't be so upset.

MRS. COLLINS: Well, I am upset. We've sacrificed, and all of a sudden we discover that our children have a pretty shaky moral code, in addition to thinking only of themselves. One is obsessed about a sports car; the other can't wait to show herself off in an expensive fur coat. It's enough to upset anyone. (*Goes right, wiping her eyes and speaking shakily*) I don't even want to think about it. (*She exits.* RALPH *and* MIRIAM *look somewhat crestfallen.*)

MR. COLLINS: I'll take your bag to your room, Norton.

NORTON (*Uncomfortably*): Thank you. I'll come along. (*He looks first at* RALPH, *then at* MIRIAM, *shakes his head, and follows* MR. COLLINS *out.*)

MIRIAM (*Going to up center window and looking out thoughtfully*): I've never heard Mother so angry before.

RALPH: She and Dad just don't understand.

MIRIAM: I know. The whole thing is awful.

RALPH: Miriam, do you think there could be some mistake about the painting? I mean, maybe Uncle Norton is wrong.

MIRIAM: That's wishful thinking, Ralph.

RALPH (*Dejectedly*): I guess it is. (*He goes slowly toward right.*) Twenty-seven thousand dollars up the chimney (*He snaps his fingers*) just like that! (*He shakes his head sadly as he exits.* MIRIAM *stares gloomily before her as the curtain falls.*)

*   *   *   *   *

Scene 2

TIME: *The next morning.*

SETTING: *Same as Scene 1.*

AT RISE: THAYER GROVE *and* ELSA CRINGLE *are standing behind table.* GROVE *is examining the painting with a magnifying glass.* MR. *and* MRS. COLLINS *are standing at right;* NORTON *is at left.*

GROVE: I've gone over this painting again and again, and I could swear that it's a genuine Romney Gregg. Wouldn't you say so, Elsa?

ELSA: Dear me, Thayer, I just don't know what to think. All I know is that Mrs. Weston-Gilbert was absolutely thrilled when I called her last night about the painting. "Elsa," she said, "you're a friend in need." I shudder to think what she'll say now. I do hope I haven't done myself any harm with so prominent a woman. Friendship is so important.

GROVE (*Dryly*): And then there's the little matter of your three-thousand-dollar commission, Elsa.

ELSA: Well, yes, there is that. (*Looking closely at painting*) I've handled at least five Romney Greggs over the past ten years, and I must say that this looks like his work to me.

NORTON: I feel flattered. (*Wryly*) Evidently, I copied Gregg's style well, Mr. Grove.

GROVE: You surely did, if this is a copy.

NORTON (*Firmly*): Oh, it's a copy all right.

MRS. COLLINS: We'll just put it back in the trunk where we found it, unless you want it, Norton, for sentimental reasons.

NORTON (*Determinedly*): No, I'm sorry I ever painted it. It's caused enough trouble.

GROVE (*Shaking his head*): I still can't understand it. (RALPH *enters at left.*)

MRS. COLLINS (*Rather coldly*): Good morning, Ralph. Sleep well? Or did your conscience bother you?

RALPH (*Gloomily*): I didn't sleep much.

MR. COLLINS: Is Miriam awake yet?

RALPH: I heard her moving around in her room. She ought to be down soon. (*Notices others*) Hi, Uncle Norton. Good morning, Mr. Grove, Miss Cringle. (ELSA *smiles at him.*)

GROVE: Good morning, Ralph. Mr. and Mrs. Collins, I owe you a heartfelt apology. I'm genuinely sorry that I raised false hopes.

MR. COLLINS: No apology needed, Mr. Grove. We all make mistakes.

ELSA: What bothers me most is that I've never known Thayer to be mistaken on art matters. Why, it's almost like finding an error in the *Encyclopaedia Britannica*, or a wrong name in the Social Register.

GROVE (*Smiling ruefully*): Perhaps I'm getting old, Elsa. In any event, I must be going. And, again, I'm sorry. (MIRIAM *enters excitedly at left, carrying a small notebook.*)

MIRIAM (*Rushing to center*): I've found something perfectly wonderful! (*She waves notebook in air.*) This is Grandfather Collins' diary!

MRS. COLLINS (*Wearily*): It can wait, Miriam.

MIRIAM (*Impatiently*): But it can't wait. It's the most important thing that has happened in years! We do own a genuine Romney Gregg!

GROVE: What!

ELSA: Why, if that's true, I won't have to disappoint Mrs. Weston-Gilbert after all.

MR. COLLINS (*Rather irritably*): Now, Miriam, you know we've been through all that.

MRS. COLLINS: And I've had just about enough genuine Romney Greggs.

MIRIAM: But you don't understand. I couldn't sleep last night so I came down and rummaged through one of the trunks. Right near the top was this diary. I began to read it in bed, but I fell asleep. Then, just a little while ago, I woke up and started looking through it again— and I discovered the most amazing thing!

RALPH (*Bitterly*): Did Grandfather Collins bury a million dollars' worth of diamonds in the back yard?

MIRIAM: Laugh if you want to, Ralph Collins, but listen to this. (*She opens diary and begins to read aloud.*) "October 8, 1930: Norton, who has always had a most peculiar sense of humor (inherited perhaps from his mother), has shipped home, among other things from Paris, his own copy of a painting by an artist named Romney Gregg."

NORTON: You see, that clinches it, Mr. Grove. That painting is my work.

MIRIAM: But it doesn't clinch it at all. Listen. "Although I suspect that the copy may not be a good one (I have never placed much faith in Norton's artistic ability)—"

NORTON: That sounds like Dad. He could always cut a man down to size.

MIRIAM: "I would dearly love to see the original. There is something about the painting—even in Norton's copy —that fascinates me. I must write to my friend, Robert Baylor, in Paris to see if he can discover something about

Romney Gregg and perhaps purchase for me a painting or two by this interesting artist."

GROVE: Mr. Collins had good taste, anyway.

MRS. COLLINS: All this is interesting, Miriam, but it still leaves us in the same situation.

MIRIAM: But I haven't finished yet. Listen to this entry. "March 18, 1931: I have heard from Baylor in Paris. He has located a Romney Gregg painting for me, and, surprisingly enough, it is the original of Norton's copy, 'Still Life at Sunset.' The price is only one hundred dollars in American money, and he will ship it here." (*The others simultaneously give expressions of excitement and astonishment, but* MIRIAM *holds up her hand imperiously for silence.*) Please let me finish. This is the most important entry of all. "July 2, 1931: I have now been forced to sell almost my entire art collection because of the financial disaster which struck my company —the embezzlement of funds by a trusted employee. I have been unable, however, to find a buyer for one of the paintings—Romney Gregg's 'Still Life at Sunset.' Ah, well, I shall keep it as a sentimental reminder of all the beauty I once owned. My attorneys have told me that I am not legally responsible for my financial losses and thus not actually required to pay my creditors. However, there is a greater law than mere man-made legalities. I consider myself the guardian of the honor of the Collins name. To leave that name unspoiled and unsullied to my descendants is more important than mere material wealth."

ELSA: How perfectly beautiful! Birth and breeding really tell, don't they?

MR. COLLINS: That sounds like Dad. He had more integrity than any man I've ever known.

NORTON: Strange that Dad never mentioned the genuine Romney Gregg, though. But, of course, Sam, you and I were away from home during most of that period, and he died shortly after.

GROVE (*Unable to contain his excitement*): But this is remarkable! Don't you see that it is quite possible this painting here is the original and that your copy (*He nods at* NORTON) may very possibly be among those relics. (*He points toward the trunks and cartons.*) This makes me very happy. In fact, it restores my faith in myself. It may prove that I wasn't wrong, after all.

MRS. COLLINS (*Very excitedly*): Well, let's look! (MR. *and* MRS. COLLINS, RALPH, MIRIAM, *and* NORTON *rush to trunks and cartons and begin to go through them frantically. They work for a couple of moments, rapidly throwing aside old papers, clothes, knickknacks, and the like.*)

ELSA: Oh, Thayer, how perfectly marvelous! I'll be able to regard you again as the Great White Father of the art world.

RALPH (*Shouting*): I've got it! (*He removes a painting from a trunk.*) "Still Life at Sunset." (*The others crowd around him.* GROVE *takes the painting, goes to table quickly, and begins to examine it through the magnifying glass.*)

GROVE: Hm-m. Of course. Romney Gregg never painted with as heavy a brush stroke as this. And the color of this blue vase is not quite in Gregg's style. What do you think, Elsa? (*He hands her the magnifying glass.*)

ELSA: I've got so many goose pimples at this point that I'm not sure I can think at all. (*Looking through glass*) It's not a bad copy, but, my dears, it's perfectly obvious that it's not the real thing. (*She smiles at* NORTON.) Not that I mean to offend you; after all, feelings are so important.

NORTON (*Returning the smile*): No offense taken.

GROVE: There's no question about it. (*He takes copy from table and places it on chair.*) It's a copy all right. And this (*He holds up the other painting.*) is the genuine article. My congratulations, Mr. and Mrs. Collins. You own a Romney Gregg after all.

ELSA: Oh, this is a deliriously happy day. Mrs. Weston-Gilbert will be in ecstasy. I'll get those wheels whirring once more.

MR. COLLINS (*Resignedly*): By all means, Miss Cringle. Get the wheels whirring. (*Looking pointedly at* RALPH) My son intends to get the wheels whirring on an expensive sports car so that he can be the envy of the college campus. (*Looking at* MIRIAM) And my daughter's life can be complete at last with a fur coat to make her acceptable in the best of circles. As for me, of course, there is the minor matter of ten thousand dollars that will save my business and this house.

ELSA: Why, Miriam will be able to look like a fashion model. As for Ralph, he can buy a car with a gold steering wheel. A dear friend of mine—Jerome Montgomery, the famous importer—has one.

GROVE: Perhaps you might like me to take this genuine painting to the Museum. It might be safer there until Elsa completes the sale, and (*Smiling*) we certainly don't want another mix-up between the genuine work and the copy.

MRS. COLLINS: Heaven forbid! Take it, by all means.

ELSA: As for me, I promise more good news by tomorrow.

And my word, as all my friends can tell you, is my bond. I'll be on my way now. (*Goes up center*) You'll be hearing from me. (ELSA *exits up center.*)

GROVE (*Taking up the genuine painting*): I'll guard this with my life. (*Going up center*) And I'm glad that matters have turned out so well.

MRS. COLLINS: Thank you for all your trouble, Mr. Grove.

GROVE: No trouble at all. To restore a genuine Romney Gregg to the world of art is an honor and a pleasure. Good morning. (GROVE *exits.*)

NORTON (*Looking at* RALPH): How do you feel, Ralph? At peace with the world once more? (*Looking at* MIRIAM) And you, Miriam, how does a girl react when all her dreams come true a second time? (RALPH *and* MIRIAM *glance uncomfortably at each other.* RALPH *walks to center and hesitates for a moment.*)

RALPH: You know something: I'm ashamed of myself.

MRS. COLLINS: You should be.

RALPH: I got to thinking about things last night, especially about what you said yesterday, Mother. About how you and Dad have had to scrimp and save. And there I was going along as if I were the only one in the world, as if you and Dad didn't have real troubles of your own— there I was talking a lot of kid stuff about getting behind the wheel of a fancy sports job and just showing off.

MR. COLLINS: Let's forget it, Ralph. It's—

RALPH (*Firmly*): No, I won't forget it. I don't want that sports car. It's what Mr. Glenn, my English teacher, would call a symbol of selfishness. (*Smiling sadly*) After all, I won't need a sports car at college. I'll be better off concentrating on my studies. What I mean is that I hope both of you will use all the money for the business and for your own needs.

NORTON: Now you're talking like a Collins, boy.

RALPH: It's about time I did. Because, most of all, I'm ashamed of even considering doing something dishonest. What Miriam just read from Grandfather Collins' diary really floored me.

NORTON: Floored you?

RALPH: I mean his saying that he regarded himself as the guardian of the honor of the Collins name and that he wanted to leave it honorable for his descendants.

NORTON (*Nodding*): Shakespeare said the same thing, Ralph, in *Othello*. "Who steals my purse steals trash. . . . But he that filches from me my good name robs me of that which not enriches him, and makes me poor indeed."

MIRIAM: Shakespeare was right. And my feelings are the same as Ralph's. I've talked a lot of nonsense about that fur coat. I've been selfish, too. And I'm ashamed that I ever even thought of trying to sell a phony painting.

MR. COLLINS: These feelings are all to the good, I'm sure. But let's not get too serious this morning; I feel as though I've been put through a wringer. In fact, what we all need is some exercise. Ralph, you can begin by helping me carry all this stuff back to the attic.

RALPH (*Smiling*): Right, Dad.

MRS. COLLINS: And, Miriam, while the men are flexing their muscles, how about helping with the dishes?

RALPH: There's one other thing, though. You know, I think we ought to give a cheer for Grandfather Collins. Miriam's a cheerleader; she could lead us. (*Very seriously*) We've inherited something more important than a painting from him.

NORTON: Right you are, boy. But after what we've been through this morning, I don't think we're really up to a cheering session. Instead let's just give a salute as tribute to Grandfather Collins. (*He salutes.*) To Grandfather Collins! Bless him.

ALL: To Grandfather Collins! (*All look serious for a moment. Then they laugh happily. MR. and MRS. COLLINS exchange pleased smiles. MRS. COLLINS pats RALPH on shoulder as she and MIRIAM exit left. RALPH and MR. COLLINS begin to carry one of trunks toward right, followed by NORTON with a carton. All are smiling happily as the curtain falls.*)

THE END

Production Notes

COLLECTOR'S ITEM

Characters: 4 male; 3 female.

Playing Time: 30 minutes.

Costumes: Mr. and Mrs. Collins and Norton wear casual, everyday dress. Mrs. Collins has a wrist watch. Ralph and Miriam are dressed simply and neatly, in clothes appropriate for clearing out the attic. Thayer Grove is dressed elegantly, wears horn-rimmed glasses and has a Vandyke beard. Elsa Cringle is overdressed, with flashy, colorful clothes and heavy costume jewelry.

Properties: Cartons, trunks and boxes full of assorted items, two paintings, suitcase for Norton, magnifying glass, small notebook.

Setting: The living room of the Collins home, a comfortable but somewhat shabby room. At center a door leads to the front porch. There are windows on either side of this door. Doors at right and left lead to other parts of the house. Down right is a comfortable somewhat worn sofa. At center is a table with chairs on each side. An easy chair is down left. At upper left on the floor are several cartons and boxes, and an open trunk.

Lighting: No special effects.

Sound: Doorbell.

Beauty and the Ballot

Characters

STELLA STARLIGHT, *the eighteen-year-old heroine*
AUNT EMMA, *a crusading suffragette*
LUCY HOLLER, *another suffragette*
JOSIAH STARLIGHT, *Stella's domineering father*
GUDGEON FALCRON, *Stella's stuffy suitor*
JENNY STARLIGHT, *Stella's younger sister*
FOXY FALCRON, *the mayor of Fairview*
RICHARD ALLDARE, *Stella's real love*
FIVE SUFFRAGETTES

TIME: *An evening in November, 1890.*
SETTING: *The living room of the Starlight home in Fairview.*
AT RISE: AUNT EMMA *and* LUCY HOLLER *enter up center. Each wears a placard. On* AUNT EMMA's *are the words:* VOTES FOR WOMEN. *On* LUCY's: TELL YOUR HUSBAND TO VOTE FOR RICHARD ALLDARE.

AUNT EMMA (*Limping to sofa and sighing deeply as she sits*): Lucy, I can walk no farther. I have gone my last mile for today.

LUCY: Ah, Emma—we may be footsore on this Election Day, but for what a glorious cause! (*She joins* EMMA *on sofa.*) It will be truly shameful if young and handsome Richard Alldare does not defeat that wily Foxy Falcron for mayor of this once fair city of Fairview. If women only had the vote, we would put Richard in office by a landslide.

AUNT EMMA: Mark my words, Lucy Holler, the day will come when members of the fair sex will make themselves felt at the polls. Then fakers like the unspeakable Foxy Falcron will get their comeuppance. (STELLA STARLIGHT *enters at left. She looks dejected.*)

STELLA (*Gloomily*): Good evening, Aunt Emma. Good evening, Miss Holler.

AUNT EMMA: Well, I must say, Stella, you are not your usual sunny self. Are you having the same old trouble, dear?

STELLA: Yes, the ax has fallen at long and miserable last. Father has set next Saturday as the date of my marriage to Gudgeon Falcron. How dreadful it is to contemplate. But I must go through with it. If I do not, Foxy Falcron has threatened to fire Father from the office of City Treasurer and send him to the poorhouse. But think of having Foxy Falcron for a father-in-law. I know that beneath his affable exterior, there beats an evil heart.

LUCY: Truer words were never spoken. And Gudgeon is no prize, either.

STELLA: Oh, I have really nothing against Gudgeon, except that he is as dull as any human being could be and still be breathing. But you know how Father is—as immovable as the Rock of Gibraltar. (*She sits in easy chair.*)

AUNT EMMA: My esteemed brother has the mistaken idea that men are all-knowing and that women are incapable of thought.

LUCY (*Loudly*): Equal rights—that's what we want! Equal rights! Women are as capable as men! (JOSIAH STARLIGHT *enters up center, followed by* GUDGEON FALCRON.)

STARLIGHT: Please, Miss Holler! Such vociferous outbursts are unnecessary. They are not ladylike.

GUDGEON: That's right, Mr. Starlight.

AUNT EMMA: Well, Gudgeon Falcron—a regular little Sir Echo, as usual.

STARLIGHT: I'll thank you not to insult my guests, Emma.

GUDGEON: Right. It's not ladylike. (*Goes to stand near* STELLA) Good evening, Stella.

STELLA (*Gloomily*): Hello, Gudgeon.

STARLIGHT (*Observing placards with distaste*): I suppose you two women have been marching through the streets of Fairview with those nonsensical placards on display. I never thought a sister of mine would ever stoop to such conduct.

AUNT EMMA: And yet we find such conduct is effective.

STARLIGHT: I have heard horrifying reports of your proceedings. John Handler told me that his wife, at the prodding of you two ladies, has threatened to stop cooking his meals if he does not vote for that young upstart, Richard Alldare.

GUDGEON: And she's not the only one. Half the wives in town are trying to blackmail their husbands. It's just terrible. (*Rather worried*) I hope you won't attempt anything so unbecoming after we're married, Stella.

STARLIGHT: Bank on it, my boy, she won't. Stella has been carefully brought up to realize that a woman's place is in the home, and that she should obey her husband in all things.

LUCY: Humph. Just remember, Josiah Starlight, women do not intend to be kept down forever. There will come a day—and it is not far off—when we shall achieve full equality.

AUNT EMMA: Most of the women in town have regularly attended our meetings during the past month. That is why they are exerting pressure on their husbands. The women know a vote for Richard Alldare is a vote for honesty and integrity in city government.

STARLIGHT: Do not mention Alldare's name to me. That audacious scamp has had the unmitigated gall to hope to marry my daughter and the brashness to run for office against my old friend, Foxy Falcron, a statesman of the first rank.

LUCY: Just because Foxy has let you be City Treasurer all these years, Josiah, you want him in office forever. Well, it's time for a change and the women of Fairview are solidly behind Richard Alldare.

STARLIGHT: I do not intend to argue with a woman. (JENNY STARLIGHT, *a lively girl of fifteen, enters up center, completely out of breath.*)

JENNY: Oh, Stella, they're counting the ballots now at City Hall. I listened as you asked me to.

STELLA (*Getting up, excitedly*): Is Richard winning?

JENNY: He seems to be running second.

STARLIGHT: Daughter, what nonsense is this?

STELLA: I asked Jenny to check on the voting, Father.

JENNY (*Quickly*): And I must return to my post. (*She exits.*)

STARLIGHT: Jenny! Drat it! A man can find no peace, even

in his own home. I am expecting my friend Foxy Falcron at any moment. He wishes to discuss with me certain appointments he will make tonight, after the election results are announced. (*Taking watch from pocket*) We expect the ballots to be counted by nine o'clock. It is now eight-thirty.

AUNT EMMA: If that old faker is going to poison the premises, Lucy and I will make ourselves scarce. We will go to City Hall and join Jenny to learn how the voting has gone.

STARLIGHT: There is no necessity for such a journey. The vote can go only one way—complete victory for Foxy Falcron.

LUCY: If I were a betting woman, I would make you a wager on that. Come, Emma. (AUNT EMMA *and* LUCY *go to door up center and open it, just as* FOXY FALCRON *enters.*)

FOXY (*Bowing*): Ah, ladies, the sight of you has made this night complete for me.

AUNT EMMA: Foxy Falcron, save your blarney for the idiots who put you in office.

FOXY: Alas, a sharp tongue—a sharp tongue. But I shall turn the other cheek.

LUCY: Do not turn it too far; you might get a crick in your neck. (AUNT EMMA *and* LUCY *exit.*)

FOXY (*Coming to center*): Good evening, Josiah. Good evening, Gudgeon, my son, and the fair Stella. May I offer my heartfelt felicitations on your approaching marriage. Ah, wedded bliss, wedded bliss! Mrs. Falcron and I have been like two lovebirds ever since that glorious day when I slipped the little gold ring onto the finger of her tiny hand.

GUDGEON: Wedded bliss. That's right.

FOXY: Ah, you speak with elegance and feeling, Gudge.
—as well you might with such a treasure as the lovely
Stella soon to be yours forevermore. But Stella, my dear,
you do not look as happy as one would expect.

STELLA: I'm not happy.

STARLIGHT: Pay no attention to the foolish child. She
labors under the incredible delusion that a girl should
choose her own husband. I do not know what is hap-
pening to the younger generation. My father chose my
wife, his father chose his, and so it should be. No girl is
capable of reasoning well enough to make so important
a decision.

STELLA: But, Father, this is 1890.

STARLIGHT: Exactly. A splendid year for marriage—to the
young man of your father's choice.

GUDGEON: That's me.

STELLA: For pity's sake, Gudgeon, stop acting like a parrot.
I know very well it's you. That's the trouble. (*Turns
away from him*)

FOXY: Aha! The plot thickens! Has our little wren been
casting her eyes longingly at another young man?

STARLIGHT: That rascal, Richard Alldare, has been casting
sheep's eyes at her—and she has returned the glances.
Imagine, a young and impecunious lawyer bold enough
to expect my daughter's hand in marriage.

FOXY: Be of good cheer, friend Josiah. After the election
results are announced, young Alldare's name will be
mud. And as for Stella's marriage, (*He smiles*) I am certain she knows that life in the poorhouse is not the
utmost in luxury.

STARLIGHT (*Hurriedly*): I am sure that our engaged couple would like to be alone to exchange confidences.
Stella, will you and Gudgeon go into another room so

that Foxy and I can talk without interruption. (*Coyly*) I know very well that two is company but three's a crowd.

GUDGEON: That's right. Three is company, but two's a— no, that's not it. Two is—

STELLA (*Wearily*): Please, Gudgeon, don't bother to figure it out. Come along. (*She exits left, followed by* GUDGEON.)

STARLIGHT: I have written a list of names for possible appointments, Foxy. I shall get it. (*Starts off*)

FOXY: Splendid, Josiah. I rely on your excellent judgment. (STARLIGHT *exits left.* FOXY *comes to down center and addresses the audience.*) Ah, friends, how pleasant to see your smiling faces. I wish to share a secret with you. As you know, a good politician prepares for all contingencies. (*He chuckles.*) And I am not only a good politician, but a statesman as well. The beautiful Stella Starlight is a headstrong girl. Unknown to her, I have intercepted a note she has written to Richard Alldare. Although the note does not clearly say so, I suspect she may intend to elope with the rascal—even though I have threatened to dismiss her father from his job and send him to the poorhouse. (*Rubbing hands together*) But I shall get the fair Stella in my clutches and she shall marry my son Gudgeon or my name is not Foxy Falcron. If Richard Alldare should by some strange quirk of circumstance win the election—and I assure you that my henchmen are stuffing the ballot boxes to prevent this, heh, heh— then it is vital that Stella marry Gudgeon, for then, inasmuch as Richard Alldare loves Stella, he would do nothing to me for fear of hurting her. In fact, the marriage could prove a stumbling block to Alldare's reforms.

Consequently, dear friends, I have concocted a delightful scheme. Shortly after I leave here, I shall return. I shall inform the unsuspecting Stella—heh, heh—that I wish to take her to my home for my victory party. Instead, I shall drive her in my buggy to my hunting lodge on the outskirts of town. She will remain there under the watchful eyes of two generously muscled women of my acquaintance until her marriage to Gudgeon next week. I shall circulate the story that she is visiting relatives. (*Laughing evilly*) Now, I ask you, is that not a plan worthy of a genius? (STARLIGHT *enters at left with piece of paper in his hand.*)

STARLIGHT: Here are my suggestions. (*Hands* FOXY *paper*)

FOXY: My heartfelt thanks. I am returning to City Hall to check on matters. I shall see you shortly, friend Josiah. (FOXY *exits up center.* STARLIGHT *exits left. After a moment,* STELLA *and* GUDGEON *enter at left. She sits on sofa and* GUDGEON *sits beside her. She moves away.*)

GUDGEON: I don't understand you, Stella. Our families practically run this city. We should be united.

STELLA: I do not like to be threatened.

GUDGEON: But think of the life we shall have as man and wife. I need company, Stella. I get lonesome sitting around the house all day.

STELLA (*Sarcastically*): Have you ever thought of working?

GUDGEON (*Shocked*): Whatever for? As Father has told me many times, he has built up his own career—

STELLA: Through threats, crooked deals, and worse.

GUDGEON: He has built up his own career so that his son —that's me—can live like a gentleman. No true gentleman soils his hands with work.

STELLA: You amaze me, Gudgeon. You really do. Assume that we're married. Just how shall we spend each day?

GUDGEON: At leisure, of course. We shan't rise much before ten. Plenty of sleep is something I've always needed. After breakfast, I usually work with my stamp collection until lunch.

STELLA: It sounds positively thrilling so far.

GUDGEON (*Unaware of her sarcasm*): I knew you would be impressed. After lunch, I usually take a nap. It doesn't pay to overdo things, you know. Then after my nap, I work on my coin collection until dinner time.

STELLA: How exciting!

GUDGEON: After dinner, you and I would take a short stroll around the grounds. Our garden is lovely, and everyone should get a breath of fresh air.

STELLA: Yes, I can see that fresh air would be welcome.

GUDGEON: Then after our stroll, we would have a cosy little chat with dear Father and sweet Mother. I make it a rule to be in bed by nine. By following that rule, I never become overtired.

STELLA (*Sarcastically*): A nine-o'clock curfew would be imperative after so fatiguing a day. (*Seriously*) And, Gudgeon, do you really spend every day in that manner?

GUDGEON: Yes. Isn't it wonderful? Of course, if you think it's too much, we could cut down a bit. I could shorten my time with my coin collection.

STELLA: Oh, no. If you want to live dangerously, I would never think of trying to tame your restless spirit. (JENNY *bursts in, out of breath.*)

JENNY (*Puffing*): They're still counting the votes.

STELLA (*Eagerly*): How is Richard progressing? Is he ahead? Are his chances good?

JENNY: Foxy Falcron is leading, they say. Aunt Emma and Lucy Holler look as gloomy as owls.

STELLA: Oh, poor Richard. Defeat will be such a disappointment to him.

GUDGEON: What can the fellow expect? He had no right to run against dear Father.

STELLA: This is a free country, isn't it, Gudgeon—at least for men?

JENNY: I'll go back to keep an eye on things. I'll need to sleep for three days after tonight.

STELLA: Gudgeon can advise you on that. He's an authority on sleep. (JENNY *hurries out up center.*)

GUDGEON (*Complacently*): It's what I expected. The citizens of our fair city cannot be misled by a handsome face and a cocky manner.

STELLA: Richard is not cocky—but he is handsome. (*The doorbell rings.* STELLA *rises, goes to door up center and opens it.* RICHARD *enters.*) Richard!

RICHARD: Stella!

STELLA: Dear Richard!

RICHARD: Sweet Stella!

STELLA: Richard, you should not have come here. You know that Father has forbidden you to enter the house.

RICHARD (*Following* STELLA *to center*): I had to see you, Stella. (*Dramatically*) In a man's darkest hour, what light is there for him but the face of the woman he adores?

GUDGEON: Now see here, Richard, watch your language. That's my fiancée you're addressing.

RICHARD: Oh, hello, Gudgeon.

GUDGEON: Hello me no hellos. If I were not a peaceful man, I would eject you from the premises.

RICHARD (*Menacingly*): I wish you'd try, Gudgeon. The way I feel tonight, I wish you'd try. (*He approaches*

GUDGEON.) Seize me, Gudgeon. Use those manly muscles of yours, and throw me bodily from the house. (*Advancing*) Please do, Gudgeon. (GUDGEON, *terrified, rushes toward door left, trips, falls flat on his back, bumping his head on floor. He lies still.* RICHARD *goes to him and bends over him.*)

STELLA (*Worried*): Is he hurt?

RICHARD: He has knocked himself out. But I am certain that he will be all right. At least while he is unconscious, we can talk. (*He puts his arm around her waist and leads her to sofa, where they sit.*)

STELLA: Jenny has informed me that the election is not going well for you.

RICHARD: Jenny speaks the truth. I have fought the good fight, but to no avail. Oh, Stella, my desire was to win the election, to fight for justice and honor, and to shower you for the rest of your life with the good things to which you are accustomed.

STELLA: Dear Richard, recall to mind what Mr. Whittier has written, "Of all sad words of tongue or pen, the saddest are these: it might have been."

RICHARD: True, too true. Knowing, however, on this bitter night that all our dreams are shattered, I have come to see you for what may well be the last time.

STELLA (*Beginning to weep*): Richard.

RICHARD: We are the victims of our times and traditions. I know that you cannot go against the expressed wishes of your father.

STELLA: Oh, Richard, if I had only myself to consider, I would. But Foxy Falcron has threatened to send Father over the hills to the poorhouse if I do not marry Gudgeon.

RICHARD: I know, I know. If I had my way, I would steal

away with you. But that would not be fair. Your father would end his days in poverty. Society would look askance at you. This I could never allow.

STELLA: Richard, you are so noble.

RICHARD: Yes, I am. It is perhaps my one fault. After to-night, I shall leave Fairview. I could not bear to remain here where I would see you every day and know that you could never be mine. (*Dramatically*) So I come to bid you one last farewell (*He takes her hand*), and to assure you that all my life, no matter where I am, no matter how old I become, I shall always treasure the memory of your sweet face and pure heart. Needless to say, I shall never marry.

STELLA: How I wish I could say the same. But (*She points at* GUDGEON's *inert form.*) there lies my future husband.

RICHARD (*Emotionally*): Oh, Stella, Stella! (*He takes her in his arms and is about to kiss her as* STARLIGHT *appears at left.*)

STARLIGHT (*Shocked*): What's this? Unhand my daughter, sir. (*Noticing* GUDGEON) And what has happened to Gudgeon? (*He stoops and lifts* GUDGEON's *head.*) Richard Alldare, I have forbidden you to set foot in this house. Stella, what do you mean by allowing this upstart to cross my threshold? Are you mad? Do you have the audacity to go against your father's wishes?

RICHARD: Please, Mr. Starlight, do not blame Stella for what has happened. As always, she is pure of heart. It is I who forced my way in. The crime, if any, lies wholly on my broad shoulders. (GUDGEON *stirs.*)

GUDGEON (*Sitting up and looking about vaguely*): Did the thieves make away with my stamp collection?

STARLIGHT: There, my boy, you have not as yet recovered that keenness of mind for which you are so well known

throughout the area. Let me help you. (*He helps* GUDG-
EON *to stand.*) What dastardly deed has been done to
you? What foul hand felled you?

STELLA: No foul hand felled him. He tripped and hit his
head on the floor.

GUDGEON (*Rubbing his neck*): Richard Alldare threatened
me with bodily harm. He must have struck me when I
was pleading with him to behave like a gentleman.

STARLIGHT: Aha! So you struck him, Mr. Richard Alldare.
You deliberately laid your hand on my daughter's fiancé.
I might have expected such conduct from a rascal of
your stamp. You are a disgrace to American manhood.

RICHARD: I did not strike Gudgeon Falcron, although I
must confess I was sorely tempted. He ran away from
me with such speed that I would have had to be a grey-
hound to catch him. (JENNY, *still out of breath, bursts
in.*)

JENNY: The—the—

STARLIGHT: Great Caesar, child, say what you have to say!

JENNY: The election—

STELLA: Has Richard won? Has he achieved his noble purpose?

STARLIGHT (*Laughing*): No man can defeat Foxy Falcron.
He is loved and honored by all.

JENNY: Richard has lost, I am afraid. The results are
close—and there are only a few ballots left to be
counted.

STARLIGHT (*Beaming*): Naturally, the citizens know a
talented and honest man when they see one.

GUDGEON: That's right. Talented and honest.

STELLA: Oh, Richard, I am so sorry.

RICHARD (*Drawing himself up proudly*): The mark of the

mature man is that he accepts whatever life offers—the joy and the sorrow—without complaint. I bow to my fate.

STELLA: Richard, you are so wonderful.

STARLIGHT: Fine words. Fine words. But now I'll trouble you, sir, to remove yourself from these premises. If you will not obey, I shall ask Gudgeon, who is, after all, a younger man than I, to use all his strength to escort you forcibly from this house.

GUDGEON (*Worried*): I have a frightful headache, Mr. Starlight. I am not sure that I am at my physical best.

RICHARD: I sense that my presence is not wanted. I shall take my leave. (*He moves toward up center.*) But I know that in this breast (*He strikes himself dramatically on the chest.*) there beats an honest heart.

STELLA (*Weeping*): Richard, you are magnificent.

RICHARD (*At door*): Farewell, dear Stella. Remember what I have told you. Always, wherever I go, to the very end of time, I shall carry with me the indelible memory of your beauty and goodness. (RICHARD *exits.*)

STARLIGHT: And good riddance to bad rubbish.

GUDGEON: That's right. Bad rubbish.

STELLA: He isn't bad rubbish. He's everything good and honorable. (FOXY FALCRON *enters up center.*)

FOXY: Back again, friend Josiah, back again. Your list is, as always, magnificent.

STARLIGHT: We have just heard good reports of the election, Foxy.

FOXY: They were to be expected. The voters love me.

GUDGEON (*Holding head*): I feel a bit faint.

STARLIGHT: Poor boy. Come with me, Gudgeon. I shall give you a pill for your head and perhaps a drink of water to make you feel better. Jenny, you come along, too, in the event that further help is desired. (STAR-LIGHT, GUDGEON, *and* JENNY *exit left.*)

FOXY: How pleasant it is to be alone with my future daughter-in-law. (*Moving toward* STELLA) Ah, my son Gudgeon is, indeed, a most fortunate young man.

STELLA: Sir, I wish I could share your pleasure. But you seem to forget: It is your threat of the poorhouse for my father that has made me consent to a marital alliance with Gudgeon.

FOXY (*Suavely*): *Threat?* My dear child, I am as meek and kindly as a lamb. You misjudge me. But come, we must become better acquainted. I am here to invite you to my victory party. Mrs. Falcron, a woman in a million, was especially desirous that you attend. She is so fond of you —as are all of us.

STELLA (*Firmly and proudly*): Sir, I could not be such a hypocrite as to attend your victory party. I am in no mood to celebrate an occasion that has made me an un-happy girl.

FOXY (*Coaxingly*): Oh, come now, I am sure you do not mean that. All of us have your welfare at heart. I must insist. (*He takes her arm.*)

STELLA: Unhand me, sir. I shall not come with you, no matter what brutal force you attempt to exert.

FOXY: Aha, my proud beauty, so you defy me. (*He grasps her arm more firmly, and she struggles as he attempts to drag her toward door. Suddenly* RICHARD *appears in the doorway.*)

RICHARD: You cad! Release that fair flower of American womanhood!

STELLA: Oh, Richard. How glad I am to see you!

FOXY: So, Richard Alldare, you are again attempting to cross my path. I say, this girl is coming with me.

RICHARD: You, sir, may control this once-fair town, but you shall never have power over this ever fair young maiden. (*He takes* STELLA *in his arms. Suddenly* AUNT EMMA, LUCY, *and* FIVE SUFFRAGETTES *burst into the room. They wave ballots and hit* FOXY *over the head with the papers as they parade around the room.* FOXY *protests as they hit him, but he finally slumps to the floor.*)

SUFFRAGETTES: Down with Foxy Falcron! Foxy is out forever! Get the rascal out of here! (*As the women are shouting,* STARLIGHT, GUDGEON *and* JENNY *enter from left.*)

STARLIGHT: Silence! What is the meaning of this? (*All quiet down.*)

GUDGEON (*Bending over* FOXY): Father, you do not seem to be yourself.

STARLIGHT: Richard Alldare, how dare you return to my home?

AUNT EMMA: Richard Alldare! (*Runs to him*) I did not know you were here! (*She holds up his arm.*) All hail to our new mayor, Richard Alldare.

SUFFRAGETTES: Hurrah for Mayor Richard Alldare!

JENNY: You mean Richard has won?

AUNT EMMA: The last ballots did it, Jenny. (*She waves a piece of paper.*) I have here the official certification of Richard's election. Foxy's followers tried to stuff the ballot boxes, but women have small hands, and can easily remove fake ballots from the boxes. Right, girls? (*She hands paper to* RICHARD, *who smiles broadly as he reads it.*)

1ST SUFFRAGETTE: Right as rain.

2ND SUFFRAGETTE: And our husbands listened to our advice, too.

3RD SUFFRAGETTE: They knew their domestic lives would be stormy if they didn't.

4TH SUFFRAGETTE: If there's one thing a man wants, it's comfort and security in the home.

5TH SUFFRAGETTE (*To* FOXY, *who has been helped to his feet by* STARLIGHT *and* GUDGEON): And you can put that in your pipe and smoke it, Foxy Falcron.

FOXY: There must be some mistake. I cannot believe that the citizens of this community, loving and honoring me as they do, would desert their idol.

AUNT EMMA: You're living in a dream world, Foxy. A new day has dawned.

LUCY: And Richard Alldare is the rising sun. Right, girls?

SUFFRAGETTES: Right!

FOXY (*Moving toward door*): I shall go down to City Hall to correct this error. We'll all laugh about it in the morning. (RICHARD *rushes to* FOXY *and grabs him by the coat collar*.)

RICHARD: Not so fast, Foxy Falcron. I intend to expose you for the nefarious villain that you are. (*Keeping a firm grip on* FOXY *and dragging him to center*) This man is a cad to end all cads. Not content with his corrupt attempts to hoodwink the citizens of this community, he was endeavoring to kidnap the fair Stella and to hold her incommunicado until she could be married to this—this clod. (*He nods scornfully at* GUDGEON.)

GUDGEON: I'm not a clod.

FOXY (*Wriggling in* RICHARD'S *grasp*): I have been misjudged. I shall consult my attorney.

STELLA (*Angrily*): The error was yours, Foxy Falcron.

What Richard says is true. Foxy was attempting to abduct me, but Richard rescued me in his usual magnificent manner.

RICHARD: Foxy Falcron, I discovered your treacherous plot because one of your henchmen, Greasy Gear, whom I met right outside this house, has a mouth as big as the Grand Canyon. He sidled up to me and said, "You won't be seeing the fair Stella for a while—Foxy is taking care of her."

FOXY: The garrulous oaf!

RICHARD: I used a bit of physical persuasion on the wily Greasy. It was not difficult to learn all the details of the scheme from him.

FOXY: The miserable traitor!

RICHARD: But now my cup of joy is filled to overflowing. I have shown Foxy Falcron to be a serpent among men —and I have won the election.

STELLA: Oh, Richard, what a happy night this is for us!

RICHARD: Yes—it is, indeed, a night to remember. Naturally, there will now be many changes for the better in the government of our fair city.

GUDGEON: You will, of course, find a job for my dear father.

RICHARD: Foxy Falcron's days as a parasite are over.

GUDGEON: Do you realize what this means? I may have to go to work.

RICHARD: Well, Gudgeon Falcron, work is good for a man's soul.

GUDGEON: I shall never be able to work properly with this splitting headache. (*Going to* STELLA) Stella, this terrible news has changed our situation. I could never ask you to marry a man who comes to you with hands soiled by labor.

STELLA: I shall try to bear up bravely under this blow.

GUDGEON: I shall go home now to work on my stamp collection. Perhaps it will relax my shattered nerves. (*Goes to door up center and turns before he exits*) Work! It is a prospect almost too horrible to contemplate. (*He exits dejectedly.*)

RICHARD: And now, Mr. Starlight, I ask for your daughter's hand in marriage. I was once a poor but honest lawyer, but now I am a man of position.

STELLA: Please, Father.

FOXY: Don't be cloth-headed, Josiah.

STARLIGHT: What can I say? I must, I suppose, bow to my fate. Very well, Richard Alldare. As they say in less elegant circles than those in which I travel, you can't fight City Hall. (*Walks dejectedly toward left*) As for me, I know my doom. It is over the hills to the poorhouse for me.

RICHARD: Stop, sir. I am a generous man. I shall temper justice with mercy. You may remain in your position as City Treasurer

STELLA: Dear Richard.

RICHARD: Sweet Stella. (*They embrace.* FOXY *attempts to exit up center, but this time* AUNT EMMA, LUCY, *and the* SUFFRAGETTES *block him.*)

AUNT EMMA: Not so fast, Foxy.

FOXY (*Eluding them*): Drat all of you! Women! It was a sad day for all of us when they emerged from the kitchen.

LUCY: And don't forget this, Foxy Falcron, some day women will have the vote.

FOXY: Curses! And bah! I'll yet have my revenge. (*He exits hurriedly.*)

RICHARD (*Holding up his hand*): And now I vow before

all of you that I, Richard Alldare, shall devote my life
to two things: to making Stella the happiest, most con-
tented woman in the world, and to making Fairview the
most progressive and honestly run city in the nation.
And these things will I do—or my name is not Richard
Alldare. (*He again embraces* STELLA. *The* SUFFRAGETTES
*applaud, and begin to parade around the room. They
are joined by* JENNY *and by* STARLIGHT, *who looks bewildered. Quick curtain.*)

THE END

Production Notes

BEAUTY AND THE BALLOT

Characters: 4 male; 9 female.

Playing Time: 25 minutes.

Costumes: Appropriate dress of the Gay Nineties. The women wear long skirts, gay blouses. The men wear dark suits, and may have mustaches. Starlight has a pocket watch.

Properties: Placards (with slogans as indicated in the text), paper for Starlight, ballots, paper for Aunt Emma.

Setting: A Victorian living room. At center is a large table and some comfortable chairs. There is a sofa down right and an easy chair down left. There are bookcases up left and right. A door at left leads to another room. A door up center leads onto the veranda.

Lighting: No special effects.

Not for Publication

Characters

MRS. GRAY
PROFESSOR THOMAS GRAY, *her husband*
PRESIDENT JAMES SWIFT, *president of Coleman College*
ENID ROSS, *an attractive reporter for "Click"*
GREGG HASKELL, *a photographer for "Click"*
HAL GRAY, *a boy of sixteen*
JUNE GRAY, *his seventeen-year-old sister*
MARILYN SIMPSON, *a girl of sixteen*
RUSS HOLMES, *a boy of seventeen*

SCENE 1

TIME: *Morning.*

SETTING: *The living room of the Gray household in a small college town in New England.*

AT RISE: MRS. GRAY *is standing at window, anxiously looking out. Suddenly, she turns excitedly and rushes to door right.*

MRS. GRAY (*Loudly*): Tom! President Swift! There's a taxi coming around the corner! It must be the people from *Click*. (*She rushes back to window and looks out again.* PROFESSOR THOMAS GRAY *and* PRESIDENT JAMES SWIFT *of Coleman College enter.*)

PROFESSOR: So the zero hour approaches.

PRESIDENT (*Cheerfully, in a booming voice*): This is a great day for Coleman College.

MRS. GRAY: The taxi's stopping now, and two people are getting out. Why, they're both quite presentable.

PROFESSOR (*Smiling*): After all, *Click* is a respectable magazine.

PRESIDENT: And don't forget, Tom, it has a circulation of more than six million.

PROFESSOR: I realize that, President Swift.

PRESIDENT: So this story they're doing on your book will bring nationwide publicity to Coleman College (*Rubbing his hands*), especially important now that we're beginning our new fund-raising program!

MRS. GRAY (*Moving away from window*): They're coming up the stairs now. Tom, do fix your tie, dear.

PROFESSOR: I hope they won't be disappointed. To be perfectly frank, I don't see how my book can possibly interest the six million readers of *Click*.

PRESIDENT: Don't be modest, Tom. That book of yours is a fine job—though I must admit I might have preferred a slightly more—well, more academic title. Still, you're a credit to Coleman College. (*Doorbell rings.*)

PROFESSOR (*Going to door and opening it*): How do you do. (ENID ROSS *and* GREGG HASKELL *enter.* GREGG *has a camera strapped over his shoulder.*)

ENID: Good morning. We're from *Click*. I'm Enid Ross, the writing end of this combination, and this is Gregg Haskell, our photographer. (PROFESSOR *shakes hands with both.*)

PROFESSOR: This is my wife, Mrs. Gray. (*More hand-*

shaking) And this is President Swift of Coleman College. (*More handshaking*)

ENID: We've both read your book, Professor Gray, and enjoyed it thoroughly.

GREGG: I like your title—*The Care and Feeding of Teen-Agers.*

PRESIDENT: We're all very proud of Tom. And (*To* ENID *and* GREGG) I'm certainly delighted to welcome you both to Coleman College. (*Glances at watch*) Unfortunately, I must run along now. I have an appointment in exactly five minutes with a wealthy alumnus who cannot be kept waiting.

ENID: Oh, certainly not. We know how important wealthy alumni are to colleges these days.

PRESIDENT: No more important than you are, Miss Ross. You and the six million readers of *Click.* I won't pretend this national publicity is not very welcome just now, when we're initiating our fund drive. (*Moves toward door*) Mr. Haskell, I hope you will take some handsome pictures of our campus.

GREGG: I'll do my best, sir. (*Grins*) Should I also take some shots of the wide-open spaces where you hope the new buildings are going to be?

PRESIDENT: Better concentrate on what we already have, in the hope of encouraging what we eagerly seek. (*Bows to* ENID) Goodbye, Miss Ross. I'll drop around later and see how things are progressing. Meanwhile I leave you in Tom's capable hands. (*Looks meaningfully at* PROFESSOR.)

PROFESSOR: Thank you for coming, sir. (PRESIDENT SWIFT *exits.*)

ENID: Now, professor, we're eager to see those two teen-agers of yours.

PROFESSOR (*To* MRS. GRAY): Where are Hal and June, by the way?

MRS. GRAY: They're down in the playroom with a couple of their friends. Probably making plans for the big prom tonight.

ENID: Perhaps a little later I can go down and meet them. Those two youngsters are the key to our story, you know.

GREGG: Right. One of the chief reasons our editor sent us out here, Professor, was that you and Mrs. Gray have two teen-agers of your own.

ENID (*Picking up book from the coffee table*): There was a passage in your book, Professor, that particularly impressed our editor.

PROFESSOR: Oh? Which passage was that?

ENID: Let me see if I can find it. (*She thumbs through the book. Everyone is watching her attentively, and nobody notices* HAL, *who appears in doorway and stands listening quietly as* ENID *reads aloud from book.*)

GREGG: Let's hear it, Enid.

ENID (*Reading aloud*): "The teen-ager is a natural rebel. He considers many aspects of the society about him dull and stupid, and is consequently critical of it. With his fellow teen-agers, he creates a world of his own to which he has a sense of belonging. Thus the special jargon, the interest in hot rods, fads in fashions, and the idolizing of certain figures in the entertainment world." (*Pauses*) I like that passage. And I suppose it grows out of your experience with your own teen-agers.

PROFESSOR (*Chuckling*): Well, not exactly, I'm happy to say. (HAL *clears his throat.* PROFESSOR *looks up and sees him.*) Oh, hello, Hal. Come in, son.

HAL (*Retreating*): I can't, Dad. I'm all dirty. (*Holds out his hands)* Russ and I were trying to fix his bike and I have grease all over me.

MRS. GRAY: Well, get yourself cleaned up, dear. Then you and June come up and meet Miss Ross and Mr. Haskell, our guests from *Click.*

HAL: O.K. (*He starts to exit, but then stops as* MRS. GRAY *speaks. He turns, stands again partly hidden behind the doorway, listening.*)

MRS. GRAY: Miss Ross, I'm afraid you won't find that Hal and June quite fit their father's description of a teen-ager.

PROFESSOR: That's right. As a matter of fact, I got very little use out of my children as source material.

GREGG: I must say from the little glimpse I had of your son he seems very normal.

PROFESSOR: Happily for us, Hal and June are the exceptions that prove the rule.

ENID: Happily for you, Professor, but not so happily for our story. The normal isn't exactly news. (HAL *exits quickly.*)

GREGG: You understand how it is in the world of popular journalism, Professor. It's the old story—a dog biting a man isn't news, but a man biting a dog is. When I read your book I realized what a monster I must have been at sixteen.

MRS. GRAY: I'm afraid we can't offer you any monsters.

ENID: Too bad. Monsters make good copy—teen-age or otherwise. (*Disappointedly*) But we'll do the best we can. First I'd like a long interview with you, Professor Gray.

PROFESSOR: I'll be happy to cooperate.

GREGG: And I'll want to shoot some campus pictures: your

office, Professor, and some of the college buildings, that sort of thing. I'll do the house and family this afternoon.

PROFESSOR: I'm sure that Mrs. Gray will be happy to act as your guide, Mr. Haskell.

MRS. GRAY: Of course. The campus is lovely this time of year.

ENID: After that, I'd like to talk to the teen-agers.

PROFESSOR: I'm sure they'll be delighted. Being interviewed by a reporter from *Click* is pretty exciting for any teen-ager, monster or not!

MRS. GRAY: Why don't you and Miss Ross go into the study, Tom? You can work undisturbed there.

PROFESSOR: Good idea. This way, Miss Ross. (*He and* ENID *exit right.*)

MRS. GRAY: And now, Mr. Haskell, shall we start on our guided tour?

GREGG: I'm in your hands, Mrs. Gray. On to the campus! (GREGG *and* MRS. GRAY *exit right.* HAL *enters immediately from left, looks around room.*)

HAL (*Calling loudly towards left*): All right, everyone, the coast is clear. (JUNE GRAY *and* MARILYN SIMPSON *enter, followed by* RUSS HOLMES.)

JUNE: Gosh, Hal, I hope Mother won't be angry because we didn't come up to greet the *Click* people.

HAL (*Goes to sofa and sits down dejectedly*): It's just as well you didn't show up. We're in for plenty of trouble.

MARILYN (*Sitting next to* HAL): Trouble?

RUSS (*Sitting in chair left of table*): You'd better let us in on it. We might have to plan our strategy.

JUNE (*Sitting in chair near table*): Has it anything to do with the reporters from *Click*?

HAL: Everything! I did some eavesdropping outside the door when they were here with Mother and Dad. I didn't mean to be sneaky; in fact, I was going in to say hello, but Enid Ross, the girl reporter, stopped me in my tracks.

RUSS: What does she have to do with our problems?

HAL: She read a passage from Dad's book out loud, and when I heard her reaction to it, I stayed put.

MARILYN: But why? We've all read your father's book and didn't see anything wrong with it. He really understands teen-agers.

HAL: Sure he does, but Enid's favorite passage is the one which says that all teen-agers are rebels.

JUNE: That's where he explains why teen-agers have fads in clothes, speech, and hobbies, and create a small world of their own.

HAL: That's the part. But the trouble is that after she read it, she began to ask Dad a lot of questions about June and me. She said she imagined that Dad got a lot of his material from observing us.

MARILYN (*Laughing*): You and June? You seem perfectly normal.

HAL (*Dejectedly*): That's what Dad and Mother said, but Enid and the photographer with her seemed pretty disappointed that June and I aren't the type of teen-agers Dad talks about in his book. They said that a story for *Click* needs monsters to make good copy—not normal teen-agers.

JUNE: You mean they think we might spoil the story?

HAL: Use your own judgment. Dad says teen-agers are rebels at heart. Are we rebels?

RUSS: I haven't staged a rebellion since Miss Smith gave me a "C" on an English theme when I thought I deserved a "B."

JUNE: Do you mean that *Click* might not even use the story?

HAL: Not unless we can somehow turn into monsters or rebels, I guess!

MARILYN: No story, no publicity for Coleman.

RUSS: Are we mice or men? Let's put our heads together and do something about it.

HAL: Spoken like a true non-mouse!

JUNE (*Suddenly inspired*): Well, I've got an idea! Let's create that small world.

MARILYN: You mean really become rebels?

JUNE: That's exactly what I mean. We can put on an act, can't we?

MARILYN: I'll rely on my Dramatic Club experience.

JUNE: The important thing is to plan this carefully.

HAL: Incidentally, our girl, Enid, wants to interview us this afternoon.

JUNE: Wonderful!

RUSS: That'll make things easier. That is, if you and Hal don't mind if Marilyn and I rebel with you.

HAL: The more the merrier.

JUNE (*Rising*): Let's go to the basement. I think better there—besides, living-room walls sometimes have ears.

RUSS (*Rising*): On to victory!

HAL (*Rising*): It's do or die for dear old Coleman College. (*They exit quickly, as the curtain falls.*)

*   *   *   *   *

SCENE 2

TIME: *Two o'clock in the afternoon, the same day.*

SETTING: *The same.*

AT RISE: HAL, *dressed like a beatnik, is lying on the sofa.*

JUNE *is humming along with a rock 'n' roll record in background, as she does a popular teen-age dance.*

JUNE: How am I percolating, Hal? Am I swinging? Am I doing justice to Rocky Mellow's latest hit?

HAL: You're in the swing, thing. You're real gone.

JUNE (*Opening eyes*): You look pretty wild yourself.

HAL: That's the idea, isn't it?

JUNE: Won't Mother and Dad be surprised?

HAL: Surprised and pleased at what we're doing for the cause.

JUNE: Mother is still roaming the campus with that photographer from *Click*.

HAL: The last I heard they were taking pictures of Dad's psychology lab.

JUNE: Let's hope they don't disturb the white mice. Those little fellows are very sensitive.

HAL: And Dad's still closeted with the beautiful Enid. That's a long interview.

JUNE: Well, you know how Dad is when he gets going on his favorite subject. (ENID Ross *enters suddenly. She stops in doorway and gazes in astonishment at* JUNE *and* HAL. JUNE *catches sight of her and does another dance step.* HAL *jumps from sofa, yawns, and stretches his arms over his head.*)

HAL: Hiya, friend. I'm Hal Gray, and this is my sister, June.

JUNE: We heard you want to talk to us.

ENID (*Still in doorway*): Er—yes. Your father is writing a statement for me in his study. He thought this would be a good time for me to see you.

JUNE (*Chewing gum vigorously and dancing around room with her eyes closed*): Sure thing, journalist.

HAL (*Closing eyes and also doing a dance step*): Shoot, chum. You'll find us on the beam.

ENID: You're not exactly what I expected. I sometimes wonder if parents really know their children. (*She walks into room, and tries to avoid being bumped by either* JUNE *or* HAL, *who continue to dance with eyes closed. She manages to get to chair at left of table, where she sits.*)

JUNE (*Still dancing*): We're way out. We're up in the clouds. We're on our way to cuckoo-land.

ENID: I can believe that.

HAL (*Opening his eyes*): Fire away, sister. Make with the questions. We'll tell you our teen-age secrets.

ENID: I wish you'd both sit down. You're making me dizzy.

HAL: Anything to oblige a slick chick. Park the carcass, June.

JUNE: All rightie, blightie. (*She dances over to sofa and plunks herself down on it.* HAL *dances to table, shuts off record player and sits down; he puts one leg over the arm of the chair.*)

ENID: You know, you're not at all the way your father described you.

HAL: This is the *real* me.

JUNE: Just a couple of normal adolescents. After all, you've read Dad's book, haven't you?

ENID: Yes. Tell me, what did you think of the book?

JUNE: Dad's a sharp cookie. He's got us pegged right.

HAL: For a square, he certainly hit the nail on the head.

ENID: You mean you agree with him that teen-agers are rebels at heart?

HAL: Of course we are. Who wouldn't be? The adult world is full of squares.

JUNE: Right. (*She outlines a square with her hands.*)

HAL: The world's a mess—and we didn't make it that way. It makes us sick, sick, sick.

ENID (*Smiling in spite of herself*): I suppose you think that what your father calls your own "small world" is a better place?

HAL: It's a swinging world. It's in the groove, and we're with it.

ENID (*Still smiling*): Are blue jeans the accepted fashion for teen-agers in your world?

JUNE (*Smoothing her jeans*): These are comfortable. They're the greatest.

HAL: They give you room to move in, chum. They're the most.

ENID: I have a suspicion that Pucci might call them the least.

JUNE: I hate to say it, Miss Ross, but you must be a square. And that's bad, because you're still young.

HAL: You should get with it, Miss Ross. Live a little. (MARILYN *and* RUSS *enter, dressed like* HAL *and* JUNE.)

MARILYN: Give us some tunes, goons.

RUSS: We're from the equator, alligator.

HAL: Miss Ross, this is my personal doll, Marilyn Simpson. And this is June's steady, Russ Holmes.

ENID (*Bewildered*): Glad to meet you.

MARILYN: How's tricks, Miss Ross?

ENID: Confused, to say the least.

RUSS: We've just come from a real rough drag race. Joe Sykes wrecked his wheels.

ENID: Good heavens! Was he hurt?

RUSS: No, but his hot rod is strictly for the junk pile. It was a crazy caper.

JUNE (*Dancing toward record player with her eyes closed, turns record on again*): Have you heard Rocky Mellow's new record, Marilyn? It's the living end. Listen!

MARILYN (*Listening intently with her eyes closed*): That Rocky—he's so dreamy!

ENID: Rocky Mellow? You mean that new rock'n'roll rage who wiggles and gyrates like a top when he sings, if you can call it singing?

HAL: Watch it, Miss Ross. Rocky is one of us. He made good in a big way. Listen to that record. It gets me right here. (*Tapping his heart*)

MARILYN: Doesn't he really send you when he sings, Miss Ross?

JUNE: The trouble with you adults is that you're jealous of Rocky. He's really hip—and he understands us teen-agers.

ENID (*Firmly*): Believe me, if there's one person in this world of whom I'm not jealous, it's your Rocky Mellow. He can't sing. He doesn't send me anywhere, except far away. He's just the product of a shrewd publicity campaign.

JUNE (*Angrily*): Can't sing!

MARILYN: He's got golden pipes!

HAL: Let's demonstrate, Russ. Let's show Miss Ross how wrong she is.

RUSS: I'm with you. (HAL *jumps from easy chair and joins* RUSS. *Both pretend they are strumming guitars, and begin to sing in time with the record, with appropriate acrobatics. As they sing,* MARILYN *and* JUNE *clap their hands ecstatically.* PRESIDENT SWIFT, MRS. GRAY *and* GREGG HASKELL *enter.*)

MRS. GRAY (*Amazed*): What in the world is going on here?

PRESIDENT: Bless my soul! Can this be the Gray household?

(*Goes center, places hat on table, then turns and stares at* HAL *and* RUSS.)

MRS. GRAY (*Angrily*): Now let's stop this nonsense. Turn that racket off! And where did you get those terrible clothes?

JUNE: Don't be square, Mother. (*Keeps dancing.*)

PRESIDENT: I assure you, Mr. Haskell, that this state of affairs is not a normal one. I don't know what has got into these young people.

RUSS: You have to go along with the times, President Swift.

MARILYN: That's right. You have to get with it.

GREGG: I don't know what this is all about, but I certainly want to take pictures of it. I can see the caption now: "Typical Teen-Agers in Action on Coleman College Campus."

PRESIDENT (*Grabbing* GREGG's *arm as he prepares to snap picture*): Please, Mr. Haskell. No photographs of such goings-on. What will your readers think?

GREGG: They're interested in typical teen-agers.

PRESIDENT: But, my dear man, all this would be most damaging to Coleman College. What would the Board of Trustees say?

MRS. GRAY: They'd say plenty.

ENID: I don't see what all the shouting is about. After all, Professor Gray's chief premise in his book is that teen-agers are rebels, that they create their own small world in their revolt against adult society.

HAL: Now you're really with it, Miss Ross.

MRS. GRAY: Don't be vulgar, Hal. What's got into you? (PROFESSOR GRAY *enters quickly.*)

PROFESSOR: I have the statement ready for *Click*, Miss Ross. (*He stops short and looks with astonishment at* JUNE *and* HAL.) What is the meaning of those outlandish clothes?

PRESIDENT: Tom, I am most annoyed—most annoyed, indeed. These young people have been behaving disgracefully. When we arrived, Hal and Russ were engaged in a most bizarre kind of performance—barbaric, in fact.

MRS. GRAY: They looked as though they were indulging in pagan revels.

HAL (*Grabbing* MARILYN's *hand*): Shall we dance?

MARILYN: A pleasure, treasure. (*They begin to do a popular step.*)

RUSS (*To* JUNE): Let's join the mob. (*He and* JUNE *begin to dance.*)

PRESIDENT: This is disgraceful! (GREGG *tries to photograph the dancing.* PRESIDENT SWIFT *grabs his arm.*)

GREGG (*Angrily*): Look, President Swift, Miss Ross and I came here to get a story. And a story means the whole story. The Professor's book is about teen-agers, and here are teen-agers in action. I'm going to take pictures of them.

MRS. GRAY (*Loudly*): Stop that dancing at once! And turn that record off!

PROFESSOR (*Angrily*): And we mean at once! (HAL, JUNE, MARILYN *and* RUSS *stop dancing.* HAL *turns off record. They look startled.*)

PRESIDENT (*To* PROFESSOR): I had no idea that publicizing your book would lead to such outrageous conduct, Tom.

PROFESSOR: I assure you, President Swift, that I am as angry and as disappointed as you are.

PRESIDENT: I will admit that Coleman College could profit from a story in *Click* at this time. (*Pauses and looks seriously at the gathering*) But a college must also maintain its dignity. If the story in *Click* has photographs of this performance, the college will suffer. (*Crosses to* PROFESSOR GRAY) So will you, Tom. The children of a college professor—and particularly of a psychologist—should behave with decorum. (*Turning to* GREGG) There is just one thing to do, and it is my right and my duty to do it. (*Firmly*) As president of the college, Miss Ross and Mr. Haskell, I forbid publication of the story or the pictures. And Tom, I shall want a word with you in my office tomorrow morning at ten o'clock. Good afternoon. (*Goes to center door.*)

GREGG (*Heatedly*): Now just a moment, President Swift. There's such a thing as freedom of the press, you know. Our editor sent us here for a story, and we're going to have it.

PRESIDENT: Young man, I forbid—

GREGG: You can't forbid—at least, not us. Our editor would be furious if we returned empty-handed. After all, you invited us to do a story on Coleman, and we're going to do it. Besides, the way things have turned out, the story will be even better than we expected. The actions of these kids will give it plenty of zip.

PRESIDENT (*Sputtering*): Sir, I have had my say. You know my feelings. (*Exits angrily.*)

MRS. GRAY: You just cannot publish that story over President Swift's objections.

PROFESSOR: With that story in print, I may as well bid a fond farewell to my career. President Swift isn't to be trifled with. (*Angrily, to* HAL, JUNE, MARILYN *and* RUSS) I don't know what has been going on here, but I must say that I am ashamed and astounded. I have never before seen you young people dressed in such a ridiculous way. And I have never before seen you indulge in such inane shenanigans.

MRS. GRAY: A fine mess you've got us into. What's happened to you?

PROFESSOR: Miss Ross and Mr. Haskell, I must apologize to you for this display. (*Going toward door*) I'm going now to try to overtake President Swift. I hope I can manage to soothe his ruffled feathers. (*Exits.* HAL, JUNE, MARILYN *and* RUSS *look dejected.*)

JUNE (*Sighing*): We were only trying to help.

MARILYN: We didn't mean any harm.

RUSS: In fact, we thought we were doing the Professor a big favor.

ENID: Favor? How?

HAL: Well, Miss Ross, this all grew out of my overhearing you read from Dad's book. Then I heard you say that you wondered if June and I were typical teen-agers.

JUNE: As you know, Dad's chief point is that teen-agers are rebels. He says they create their own small world.

GREGG (*Laughing*): You've certainly proved that this afternoon.

HAL: That's just what we were trying to do. Don't you see? The four of us are strictly normal. We're not revolting against anything. The trouble is we're too normal. And we were afraid you wouldn't find enough life and zip for your story unless we put on an act.

ENID (*Laughing*): And all this was just to help Professor Gray?

JUNE: That's the truth.

ENID: You know—that's rather sweet.

HAL (*Gloomily*): But the whole thing's boomeranged.

GREGG: Say, wait a minute. Do you know something? You kids have actually proved that Professor Gray was right.

HAL (*Astonished*): We have?

GREGG: Sure thing. Look at it this way. What you've done is actually rebellion—rebellion against your father's book. You feel he was wrong about most teen-agers. You rejected his adult ideas, so you rebelled by putting on this act.

ENID: Your father was so upset, he didn't realize that you proved his theory.

JUNE: You mean we're really rebels, anyway?

GREGG: No question about it. You're just not the blue-jeaned, leather-jacket kind of rebel. But you're rebels nevertheless.

ENID (*Excitedly*): What a story it will make! Listen. How does this sound? "The teen-age son and daughter of Professor Thomas Gray, both sensible, well-behaved youngsters, were faced with a problem. Worried because their normal, everyday behavior might disprove their father's thesis that the adolescent is a rebel at heart, they joined forces with two of their young friends in a remarkable demonstration of loyalty to their parent. Putting on an act worthy of Broadway, they masqueraded as jive-happy, blue-jeaned, leather-jacketed youngsters devoted to acrobatics on the dance floor and gyrating singers, with a jargon all their own. And in this attempt to help Professor Gray, they unknowingly proved the thesis of his book —for their performance was really a gesture of rebellion against Professor Gray's major premise in *The Care and Feeding of Teen-Agers*."

JUNE: Golly, I wish you'd write my English themes for me.

HAL: I see what you mean. Dad was right, after all.

MARILYN: The only trouble is—nobody knows it except us.

(PRESIDENT SWIFT *enters hurriedly, followed by* PROFESSOR GRAY.)

PRESIDENT (*Going to table*): I forgot my hat. (*Picking up hat, glares angrily at the young people*) I hope *you're* all pleased with your disgraceful behavior.

ENID (*Charmingly*): President Swift, I can't tell you how

much I admired the stand you took on this issue. I just adore men of integrity.

PRESIDENT (*Softening*): Why, thank you, Miss Ross. A man has to live with his own conscience.

ENID: But what you did was magnificent. So few people today have the courage to stick to their principles.

PRESIDENT (*Beaming*): Let me assure you, Miss Ross, that nothing I said was meant to be a criticism of either you or Mr. Haskell. You are merely the unfortunate victims of circumstance.

ENID: How generous of you! (*She grasps his arm.*) But you'll be happy to know that everything has turned out all right.

PRESIDENT (*Perplexed*): It has?

ENID: You see, what these young people have done merely proves the chief thesis of Professor Gray's book.

PROFESSOR: With the demonstration they put on?

ENID: What these young people attempted to do was to come to the aid of Professor Gray and Coleman College.

GREGG: And it was wonderful of them to do it.

ENID: You know yourself, President Swift, that these peculiar clothes and zany actions are not characteristic of these four youngsters. But, unknowingly, they proved they are rebels, because they were rebelling against Professor Gray's opinion of teen-agers. Thus, the Professor's theory is right, and we have a peg on which to hang our story.

GREGG: In fact, the story will do credit to Professor Gray, the college, and these young people.

PRESIDENT (*Hesitatingly*): Well—

ENID (*Quickly*): Forgive me for explaining in such detail to a man of your intelligence. I know that you must have seen the point at once.

PRESIDENT (*Flattered*): Yes, my dear. I see exactly what you mean. These young people meant well. (*Beaming*) And as you say, what they have done can serve a most useful purpose.

GREGG: You mean it's all right to shoot some pictures of these kids swooning over a Rocky Mellow record?

PRESIDENT: I don't know who Rocky Mellow is, but you can shoot anything you want. I trust Miss Ross's judgment implicitly.

ENID (*Sweetly*): Thank you, President Swift.

PRESIDENT: Thank *you*, my dear.

GREGG: Come on, Hal and Russ. Let's have Rocky's record again. The girls can join you for a dance. (MARILYN *turns on record. She and* JUNE *begin to dance, as* HAL *and* RUSS *pretend to strum guitars and sing along with record while* GREGG *takes their picture.*) Great! This'll wow our readers. Now for the real dance. (PROFESSOR GRAY, *still somewhat bewildered, sinks into easy chair and looks dazed.*)

PROFESSOR: Did I really start all this? (HAL *and* MARILYN *and* JUNE *and* RUSS *team up and begin dancing while* GREGG *aims his camera.*)

JUNE (*Dancing over to* PROFESSOR): There's just one thing missing from this picture. The real hero of all this. (*To* PROFESSOR) May I have this dance? (*The* PROFESSOR *looks up, notices everyone smiling happily at him, shrugs his shoulders, stands up, and breaks into a wide grin.*)

PROFESSOR: O.K., June, let's give it a whirl! (*He and* JUNE *begin to dance, while the others clap their hands. Curtain.*)

THE END

Production Notes

NOT FOR PUBLICATION

Characters: 5 male; 4 female.

Playing Time: 30 minutes.

Costumes: Modern everyday dress. In Scene 2, Hal and Russ wear leather jackets, pegged trousers and cowboy boots; June and Marilyn wear dungarees and sloppy sweaters. President Swift wears a suit and a hat.

Properties: Record of hit rock 'n' roll song, camera, book.

Setting: The living room of the Gray household in a small college town in New England. Door up center leads to front porch. Windows are at either side of this exit. Exits at left and right lead to rest of house. A bookcase, sofa, chairs, and a table at center complete the furnishings. On the table are magazines, a copy of the Professor's book, and a record player.

Lighting: No special effects.

Sound: Record is played, as indicated.

Thar She Blows

Characters

CAPTAIN ABEL LONGSHORE
MINERVA LONGSHORE, *his wife*
COOKIE BURNEM, *the ship's cook*
JEREMIAH CLAM, *a handsome young Harvard man*
EZEKIEL FOGHORN, *the first mate*
JAKE BLAKE, *the harpooner*
SAMSON SPRY, *the master-at-arms*
SEDONIA LONGSHORE, *the Captain's pretty daughter*
TWO SAILORS

TIME: *An afternoon in the late 1850's.*
SETTING: *The Captain's cabin aboard the whaling bark, "Never Ready," out of New Bedford.*
AT RISE: CAPTAIN ABEL LONGSHORE *is seated at table, center, with a navigation chart unfolded before him. His wife,* MINERVA, *is busily sweeping the cabin.*

MINERVA: Never thought there could be so much dust raised at sea, Abel. Our house in New Bedford—and, gracious, how I long for it—never attracted as much dirt as this cabin does. Land sakes, it's all a body can do to keep it clean.

ABEL: Avast there, Minerva! Don't be carrying on with your landlubber's domestic chatter. I wish you'd throw that broom through a porthole. (*He gazes at chart intently.*) Can't you see I'm trying to figure out just where this good ship is? (*Frowning*) One thing's certain as ice storms in January, the *Never Ready* is either in the Atlantic or the Pacific.

MINERVA: It's real comfortin', Abel, to have you at the helm. A body knows she's in good hands.

ABEL (*Spinning globe and placing finger on it*): Aha! I think I have it. If my calculations are correct—and Captain Abel Longshore isn't one to make mistakes—we're close to the area where Whistling Waldo, that devilish whale, is up to his blasted shenanigans.

MINERVA (*Stopping her sweeping and going to* ABEL, *and putting hand on his shoulder*): Oh, Abel, I do wish you'd try to forget Whistling Waldo. That's all you've been talkin' about on this voyage. The crew is beginnin' to mutter behind your back.

ABEL: Let 'em mutter. If they keep it up, I'll throw their leathery hides to the sharks. I'm captain of the *Never Ready,* and my word is law.

MINERVA: But the poor fellows want to return to New Bedford. We've already got a good catch of whales— and that's what they signed up for. They don't want to be roamin' over the high seas forever just keepin' their weather eyes peeled for one whale—your everlastin' Whistling Waldo.

ABEL (*Banging fist on table*): I made a vow, Minerva, that I'll get Whistling Waldo if it's the last thing I ever do. I'm not forgettin' what he did to my whaleboat on our last voyage. He just flipped his blasted tail, and overboard we all went. And that dratted whale just whistled in our faces. I'll never forget that sight!

MINERVA: Abel, whales don't whistle.

ABEL: Woman, Whistling Waldo does. He knows how to wound a man's pride. (COOKIE BURNEM, *wearing a chef's cap and a food-spotted apron, enters carrying a large coffeepot.*)

COOKIE (*With a careless salute*): Afternoon, Captain. Will you be wantin' hot biscuits tonight?

ABEL: Let me tell you, Cookie Burnem, that those last biscuits of yours set on my stomach like a load of anchors.

COOKIE (*Pained*): It was a new recipe, Captain. I picked it up in Singapore.

ABEL: Well, you'd better put it down again—permanently.

COOKIE (*Coming to table*): Would you like some coffee to wet your whistle, Captain?

ABEL (*Knocking coffeepot from COOKIE's hand*): Avast there, you blasted landlubber—I thought I told you never to mention the word *whistle* in my presence. (*Banging fist on table*) I'll get that whistling mammal and whistle the daylights out of him.

COOKIE (*Nervously*): There's somethin' I must be tellin' you, Captain. (*Backing away carefully*) The crew has picked a committee to speak to you. They don't like the way things are goin'.

ABEL: Nobody asked 'em.

COOKIE: They're waitin' outside, Captain.

ABEL: Who are the nervy water rats? I'll have 'em in irons.

MINERVA: Now, Abel, try to be reasonable.

COOKIE: It's Ezekiel Foghorn, Jeremiah Clam, and Jake Blake.

ABEL: I might have known. Just because Clam is a Harvard man, he thinks he knows it all. But he doesn't know a typhoon from a summer shower. It was a mistake to let him come on this voyage—even though he's plannin' to write a book on it and let the world know what a great whalin' captain I am.

MINERVA: Jeremiah Clam's a fine young man, Abel, and our daughter, Sedonia, is mighty sweet on him.

ABEL: I'll not have her marryin' a Harvard Clam. A whaling ship is the only college that teaches a man anything. As for Jake Blake, let him stick to his harpoonin'. His job is to nail Whistling Waldo. And Ezekiel Foghorn should know better. Since when does a first mate question his captain? Well, bring in the scurvy lot of 'em.

COOKIE: Yes, Captain. (*He picks up coffeepot and opens door.*) Come in, boys. (JEREMIAH CLAM, EZEKIEL FOGHORN, *and* JAKE BLAKE *enter.* COOKIE *sneaks out.*)

ABEL (*To crew*): Speak your minds—if you can call 'em that—and get out.

JAKE: Y-y-yes, Captain.

ABEL: And don't just stand there like a sardine out of water, Jake Blake.

FOGHORN: We have a complaint, Captain, and we're here to tell it.

ABEL (*Sarcastically*): So you have a complaint, Ezekiel Foghorn. Well, well, let the lighthouse bell ring out. There's nothin' I enjoy more than hearin' a salt-pork-chewin' first mate make complaints. Just about makes my day, it does.

FOGHORN: Jeremiah Clam is our appointed spokesman.

ABEL: He is, is he? A landlubber for a spokesman. Well, it all fits. It's what I'd expect from a crew that doesn't know port from starboard.

JEREMIAH: Sir, all we ask is that you listen to us with equanimity.

ABEL (*Roaring*): With what? Watch your language, Clam! There's a lady present.

JEREMIAH: Equanimity is a perfectly respectable word, sir. It means composure, calmness.

ABEL: Are you accusin' me of not bein' calm? A captain who's taken this ship through monsoons and hurricanes?

JEREMIAH: No, Captain, not at all. But let me state our view as succinctly as possible.

MINERVA: My, it's a pleasure to hear you talk, Jeremiah. Such nice big words.

JEREMIAH: Thank you, ma'am. You see, Captain, we of the crew feel that it is high time to return to New Bedford. We have a full quota of whales—

ABEL (*Banging fist on table*): Oh, no we don't! We don't have Whistling Waldo!

JEREMIAH: But the crew longs for home and loved ones.

FOGHORN (*Turning globe and placing finger on it*): Here's good old New Bedford. It's over a year since I've seen my wife.

JAKE (*Looking longingly at spot on globe*): And my girl friend, Hepzibah Fish, must be pinin' for me.

ABEL (*With mock emotion as he pretends to wipe tears from his eyes*): Oh, boo, hoo, hoo! I didn't know you boys were so lonely. Boo, hoo, hoo! (*All look at him expectantly.*) Why, you lopsided oysters, I'll never turn back until I have my revenge on Whistling Waldo.

JEREMIAH: Sir, you leave us no alternative. (*He takes a small book from his pocket.*) I have here Dr. Harwell Snide's famous work, *Handbook for Mutineers*. It was part of a course—Mutiny 101—which I took at Harvard. Monday, Wednesday, and Friday at 9 a.m. (*He opens book*.) Let me read a passage from Chapter Four, page 96: "Certain cases of mutiny are justifiable in an instance such as the following: If a captain pursues an unreasonable and fanatical course, such as concentrating on one whale only with vengeance in mind, the crew is within its rights to take matters into its own hands. This was done on the *Periwinkle* in October, 1842, the *Striped Bass* in January, 1845, and the *Quahog Chowder* in June, 1847." So you see, sir, we have the law on our side.

ABEL: Interestin' passage. Now let me quote to you an observation by Captain Abel Longshore of the whaling bark, *Never Ready*. "Any blasted crew members who attempt to mutiny aboard my ship will be thrown into irons and hanged when we get back to port." (SEDONIA LONGSHORE *enters breathlessly*.)

MINERVA: Daughter Sedonia, where have you been?

SEDONIA: I was feeding the sea gulls, dear Mother. Ah, what graceful creatures they are! But it seemed, as I watched the gulls in their flight, that I could hear loud voices coming from here. (*Going to* JEREMIAH) I hope that nothing is amiss, Jeremiah.

JEREMIAH: Sweet Sedonia, I have been explaining to your father the reasons why the crew feels so strongly that we should return at once to New Bedford. I mean no harm —but justice must be done. As for you, you know that I would not hurt a hair on your lovely head. After all, we are betrothed, are we not?

SEDONIA (*Drawing herself up proudly*): Sir, I could never marry a man who planned to mutiny against my dear father.

ABEL: That's my daughter who said that.

JEREMIAH: But sweet Sedonia, be reasonable. We have our quota of whales. It is time to head for port.

SEDONIA: But we have not captured Whistling Waldo.

ABEL: Right you are, daughter. And I'll not stir from the high seas until I have that whistling devil in my clutches —and I don't care if it takes half a lifetime.

JAKE: Jumpin' mackerel, Captain, I don't aim to spend the rest of my life aboard the *Never Ready*. I'm not gettin' any younger.

FOGHORN: Me either. A man needs a rest on land once in a while.

ABEL: You'll get a rest—in irons. That'll relax you.

JEREMIAH: Sir, you leave us no alternative but to seize the ship. (ABEL *reaches into the table drawer and brings out a gun, which he aims at* JEREMIAH.)

ABEL: Take one step toward any scurvy mutiny, and I'll blast you down to Davy Jones's locker!

MINERVA: Abel, be careful. That thing might go off.

SEDONIA (*Standing in front of* JEREMIAH): Oh, Father, you would not shoot the man I love!

JEREMIAH: Thank you, Sedonia. At Harvard, I was always taught to be grateful for such favors.

SEDONIA: Alas, I am torn between two loves—my regard for my dear father and my warm affection for handsome Jeremiah Clam. What is a girl to do?

ABEL: Get away from him, and I'll shoot him full of portholes.

SEDONIA: Oh, Father, I know that blood is thicker than water, but Jeremiah has such pretty blue eyes, and he is so well educated.

JEREMIAH: My thanks again, fair Sedonia. You are the brightest blossom in the garden of life.

FOGHORN: Just remember this, Captain, if you shoot Jeremiah, the crew won't take kindly to it—even if he is a Harvard man.

JAKE: That's right. We don't hold with killin', we don't.

FOGHORN: And the crew will refuse to obey your orders, Captain. You'll be one man against many.

ABEL: I'm more than a match for all of you.

MINERVA: Abel, I do think you're bein' just a mite headstrong.

ABEL: Daughter, go out on deck and get master-at-arms Samson Spry. I'm goin' to have him put these sharks in irons.

SEDONIA: Alas, I must respond to the call of loyalty to my dear father. (*She goes to door.*) But, Father, promise not to shoot Jeremiah—at least, not until I return.

ABEL: My trigger finger itches, daughter, but I'll control it for a while.

SEDONIA: I knew I could rely on your kindness, dear Father. (*She exits.*)

JAKE: If you put me in irons, Captain, I won't be able to harpoon Whistling Waldo. A man needs his arms free for harpoonin'.

FOGHORN: Jake's right, Captain. And I won't be able to steer the whaleboat when we go after Whistling Waldo.

ABEL: I'll do the blasted steerin' myself. And the harpoonin', too. And what's more, I'll do 'em both better than either of you.

JEREMIAH: A man can do only so much, Captain. None of us is superhuman.

ABEL: I'm superhuman, Clam. And I didn't have to go to Harvard to learn to be so.

MINERVA: Oh, Abel, I sometimes wonder if you're not bein' just a mite peculiar about all this. (SEDONIA *re-*

turns, followed by SAMSON SPRY. SPRY *has guns at his belt and also carries a whip.*)

SPRY (*Snapping whip enthusiastically*): Somebody you want given a taste of the cat-o'-nine-tails, Captain? Always ready to oblige.

ABEL: Oh, there you are, Spry. I want you to put these three barracudas in irons.

SPRY: What for, Captain?

ABEL (*Angrily*): You questionin' my authority, Samson Spry? These men are plannin' a mutiny, that's what for. You know the law of the sea.

JEREMIAH: But there is a higher law—that expressed by Dr. Harwell Snide in his book.

SPRY: Jeremiah's right, Captain. He showed me that book. I can't read printin', but he read it to me. I can read numbers, though—at least, most numbers.

ABEL (*Banging his hand on table and pointing gun at* SPRY): Quiet, fool! Do you think I'm interested in the state of your blasted education? Get these men into irons.

SPRY: I'm sorry, Captain, but I can't do it. I get real enjoyment from clappin' fellows into irons and maybe givin' 'em a taste of my trusty cat-o'-nine-tails (*He cracks whip.*), but I can't do it—and I won't do it. They want to be gettin' back to New Bedford—and so do I.

ABEL (*Angrily*): You know what this means, Samson Spry. You'll be hangin' from the yardarm when we get back to port.

1ST SAILOR (*Offstage*): Thar she blows! (*Offstage whistle is heard.*)

2ND SAILOR (*Offstage*): Where away?

1ST SAILOR (*Offstage*): Just off starboard and spoutin' away! (COOKIE BURNEM *rushes in.*)

COOKIE: The lookout's sighted whales, Captain. And he thinks one of 'em is Whistling Waldo!

SEDONIA: Oh, Father, your chance has come.

ABEL: And I'm ready for it. Now that whistling devil will meet his match in Captain Abel Longshore.

FOGHORN: I'm willin' to let bygones be bygones, Captain. If it's Whistling Waldo, let's get him and then head for port.

JAKE: Me, too, Captain. My harpoons are sharp and rarin' to go.

JEREMIAH: And I also am willing to contribute whatever skills I possess to the pursuit of Whistling Waldo.

ABEL (*Sarcastically*): Well, now, isn't that just too sweet for words. You boys will be bringin' tears to my eyes. Anyway, for the time bein', all right. You can come with me, Ezekiel, and you, too, Jake. But as for you, Clam, the answer is no. You're the leader of the so-called mutiny. And you're goin' to stay right here. (*He hands gun to* SEDONIA.) Keep him covered, daughter. If he tries anything peculiar, don't shoot to kill. Just wing him in the shoulder or the leg. I want him alive for hangin'.

SEDONIA: Alas, dear Father, I shall, of course, follow your instructions, for a daughter's duty is first and foremost to her sweet papa.

ABEL: Spry, you'd better come along, too. I want you to have that cat-o'-nine-tails ready just in case some misguided swab doesn't do his job properly.

SPRY (*Cracking whip*): Aye, aye, Captain.

ABEL: You come, too, Minerva. It'll be a rare sight.

MINERVA: I wouldn't miss it, Abel.

ABEL (*Taking* JEREMIAH *by the shoulders and pushing him down into chair*): You just sit here, Jeremiah Clam, and reflect on your sins. (*Goes toward door*) Come on, boys. You, too, Minerva. (ABEL, COOKIE, MINERVA, SPRY, FOGHORN, *and* JAKE *exit hurriedly*.)

SEDONIA (*Sitting in chair opposite* JEREMIAH *and keeping gun pointed at him*): Oh, dear, Jeremiah. I never dreamed that I would be in such a plight. Alas, that I am the chosen instrument to punish you for your indiscretions.

JEREMIAH: Do not fear, sweet Sedonia. At Harvard, I was taught to accept the bitter with the sweet. But may I ask a favor? Will you please allow me to watch the action through a porthole? I give you the word of a Harvard man that I shall not attempt to escape.

SEDONIA: How can I refuse you?

JEREMIAH (*Rising and going to porthole*): Thank you, sweet Sedonia. (*He takes a pamphlet from his pocket.*) I happen to have here Captain Ahab Saltpork's brilliant pamphlet, "How to Catch a Whale." (*He observes through porthole, reading aloud from pamphlet at the same time.*) "When the whale is sighted, the whaleboats for pursuing the monster of the deep should be lowered. Each whaleboat should contain four men, with the harpooner standing, his harpoon poised to strike, in the bow of the boat." (*Peering intently*) Ah, yes, Captain Abel is now supervising these matters—and how excited he is.

SEDONIA: This is Father's day of days! (*Water splashes through porthole into* JEREMIAH'*s face.*)

JEREMIAH (*Sputtering*): The water seems a bit rough. (*Reading again from pamphlet*) "If possible, the whaleboat should be kept within fifty feet of its quarry." (*More water splashes through porthole.*)

1ST SAILOR (*Offstage*): Avast there!

2ND SAILOR (*Offstage*): Heave ho, you lubbers!

JEREMIAH: Alas, my pamphlet is water-logged. (*Peering again through porthole*) Ah, yes, there are five whales out there.

SEDONIA: What a catch it will be!

JEREMIAH: Great heavens! There seems to be a great deal of trouble out there. The crew is running aimlessly over the deck. Captain Abel is stamping his feet and gesturing wildly. The crew seems bewildered. (*Peering intently*) There is a shoal off starboard that seems very familiar.

SEDONIA: Familiar? What do you mean, Jeremiah?

JEREMIAH (*Excitedly*): Can it be? I wonder. (*He goes to globe, examines it intently, and then looks with interest at the navigation chart.*) Aha! I note that Captain Abel has been calculating the bearings of the ship. (*Using a pencil, he makes some quick notations of his own.*) There! It is just as I suspected. The poor man has made a grave error.

SEDONIA: An error? But Father never makes a mistake. He has told me so himself.

JEREMIAH (*Figuring rapidly*): I fear that he has. You see, at Harvard, I had a course in the subject. Advanced Navigation 302. Tuesday, Thursday, and Saturday at 10 a.m. Professor Northstar in charge. And although I do say it myself, I learned my lessons well. In fact, I received an A in the course.

SEDONIA: You are so brilliant, Jeremiah.

JEREMIAH: Thank you. You are right. (*He continues his figuring and then looks up suddenly, very surprised.*) Great heavens! It can't be possible! (*He checks the figures.*) But, yes, it is. (*He laughs delightedly.*) Oh, Sedonia, this is the very cream of the jest.

SEDONIA: What do you mean, Jeremiah? What is all this mystery?

JEREMIAH: Do you know where the *Never Ready* really is at this moment?

SEDONIA: Either in the middle of the Atlantic or the Pacific. Father was sure of that. And he is one of the world's great whaling captains.

JEREMIAH: Sedonia, figures do not lie—at least not the figures compiled by a Harvard man. Brace yourself for a surprise. The *Never Ready,* right now, is no more than ten miles from New Bedford. Your dear father has unwittingly piloted his ship homeward.

1ST SAILOR (*Offstage*): Drat the luck!

2ND SAILOR (*Offstage*): Ahoy!

SEDONIA: Oh, Jeremiah, are you sure?

JEREMIAH: Sweet Sedonia, I am sure I am right—or my name is not Jeremiah Clam. Come here, and I shall demonstrate the veracity of my computations.

SEDONIA: Dear Jeremiah, I cannot come there. I have vowed to keep you covered with this gun. I cannot break my promise.

JEREMIAH: Sweet Sedonia, do you think that I would take advantage of you—you who have displayed the sterling loyalty of a woman who adheres to the ancient and true adage that blood is thicker than water? After all, Sedonia, I *am* a Harvard man.

SEDONIA (*Rising*): Forgive me for doubting you, dear Jeremiah. I shall look at your calculations, although I must confess that mathematics has never been my strong point. (*She goes to* JEREMIAH *and looks over his shoulder.*)

JEREMIAH (*Pointing to chart*): You note the latitude and longitude accurately computed. (ABEL *enters, leaning on*

SAMSON SPRY *and* COOKIE BURNEM. ABEL *is limping badly.* MINERVA, *looking worried and flustered, follows.*)

SEDONIA: Alas, dear Father, what has happened?

ABEL (*As* JEREMIAH *rises and* COOKIE *and* SPRY *help* ABEL *into the chair*): The fates are against me. That devil, Whistling Waldo, has 'em on his side.

MINERVA: Poor Abel. Just as he was goin' over the side of the ship to get into his whaleboat, he stubbed his toe.

ABEL (*Hopping about, holding foot*): Stubbed! I tell you, woman, it's broken. Ouch! (*Suddenly seeing* JEREMIAH) What's this man doin', roamin' around the cabin, Sedonia? You're supposed to keep that gun aimed at him.

SEDONIA: Fear not, dear Father, Jeremiah has given me his word as a Harvard man that he will attempt nothing underhanded.

JEREMIAH: Thank you, Sedonia, for your kind words. (*To* ABEL) You must soak that toe in hot sea water, sir. It will do you good.

COOKIE: I'll go boil the water.

SPRY: Just use last night's soup. That was watery enough.

COOKIE: That was good soup. I picked up the recipe in Hong Kong. (COOKIE *exits.*)

ABEL (*Rubbing his toe*): Drat that foot of mine. Now that blasted whale will get away. I'll have to begin the search all over again.

MINERVA: Land sakes, Abel, we're not goin' traipsin' over the high seas till eternity! (EZEKIEL FOGHORN *enters excitedly.*)

FOGHORN: I tell you, there's an amazin' sight out there. Whistling Waldo is close to the ship, and he has four little whales with him.

JEREMIAH: They are his children undoubtedly.

FOGHORN: He keeps jumpin' out of the water and sort of bowin' to us. And then the little fellows jump out of the water and bow, too.

ABEL: That whale is crazy. I always said so.

JEREMIAH (*Holding up his hand*): No, Whistling Waldo is not crazy. What you have been witnessing, Ezekiel Foghorn, is something that has occurred only twice before in the history of whaling—and it is a miraculous compliment to Captain Abel Longshore.

ABEL (*Holding his foot*): You're the one who's insane, Clam.

JEREMIAH: Not at all, sir, and I shall prove my sanity. At Harvard, I took a course, Whaling History 302, Monday, Thursday, and Saturday at 1 p.m. Professor Seabreeze in charge. Our textbook was Dr. Henry Oilkeg's *Whales I Have Known*. It so happens that I have a copy of the book with me.

FOGHORN: You're a walkin' library, Jeremiah Clam.

JEREMIAH: Thank you, Ezekiel Foghorn. You pay a pretty compliment. But now to Dr. Oilkeg's book. (*He takes the book from his pocket.*) I read now from page 35, Chapter Two, entitled "The Courage and Intelligence of Whales." Listen well. (*He reads aloud.*) "The whale is a most courageous and intelligent creature, and above all else, he admires courage and intelligence in others, including human beings. He particularly admires those valiant whaling captains who pit their strength against his and who pursue him personally—often for years on end."

SEDONIA: Like dear Father.

JEREMIAH: Exactly, sweet Sedonia. I continue. "The whale demonstrates his admiration in a most unusual manner. And this unique demonstration of admiration has occurred twice in whaling history. The first instance concerns Captain Sealeg Scrimshaw of the whaling bark, *Codfish,* out of Nantucket. Captain Scrimshaw spent two years in pursuit of a whale named Dandy Dan. He was never able to capture him. But on June 3, 1842, when the Captain was approaching his home port of Nantucket, Dandy Dan appeared suddenly with three small whales—his children. Dandy Dan and his offspring began to leap from the water, each bowing in the direction of Captain Scrimshaw. This was the whale's way of saying, 'Captain, I pay tribute to your courage and determination. You are a great man. Let us now call it quits—each with his high opinion of the other.' "

SEDONIA (*Wiping her eyes*): Oh, how touching!

MINERVA: Makes a body have goose flesh all over!

JEREMIAH: I continue. "The second instance occurred on August 8, 1845, in exactly the same manner. A whale named Bonny Bob, along with his two children, gave the same tribute to Captain Amber Griss of Mystic, Connecticut, as he sailed into his home port." (*Closing book*) You see, sir, what Whistling Waldo is doing out there is paying his tribute to you. (*Offstage whistle is heard.*)

SEDONIA: Isn't that wonderful, brave Father?

ABEL (*Puzzled*): Might be true at that. Only trouble is we aren't in New Bedford. My calculations say we're either in the middle of the Atlantic or the Pacific.

JEREMIAH: I fear that I have news for you, sir. Your calculations are incorrect.

SEDONIA: That's right, Father. Jeremiah told me—

ABEL (*Wearily*): I know. He took a course at Harvard.

JEREMIAH: That I did, sir. I have figured the bearings of

the *Never Ready,* and I am happy to inform you that we are only a few miles out of New Bedford.

MINERVA: Heaven be praised! I'll be able to get to my spring cleanin' back home.

JEREMIAH: Think of it, sir—Whistling Waldo has made you immortal. You are only the third captain in all of whaling history to receive this tribute—and the first from New Bedford.

SPRY: You'll be a famous man, Captain.

FOGHORN: Your name'll go down as the mightiest of all.

ABEL (*Visibly pleased*): No more than my due.

JEREMIAH: And in the book I shall write about this voyage, I shall tell the world of this memorable event.

ABEL (*Leaping up*): I must go up on deck. I must receive my tribute from Whistling Waldo in person.

MINERVA: Abel, be careful of that toe.

ABEL: It feels better already. (*He limps toward door and then turns.*) And to show you what a great man I am, I won't say a word in port about the mutiny. Let bygones be bygones.

JEREMIAH: Sir, you're a prince of good fellows.

ABEL: Prince! I'm a blasted king! (*He opens door and collides with* COOKIE, *who enters, carrying pail of water.* COOKIE *sprawls on the floor, dropping pail.*)

COOKIE: Oops! Sorry, Captain, but I was bringin' water so you could bathe your toe.

ABEL: Use it for soup. I've better things to do. Come on, all. (*He exits, followed by* SPRY, FOGHORN, *and* MINERVA. COOKIE *rises, shakes his head, and also exits.*)

SEDONIA: Oh, dear Jeremiah, how happy I am that all our problems are solved. No more must I be torn between daughterly duty and love for you.

JEREMIAH (*Embracing her*): I knew that all would be well. For every cloud has a silver lining—

SEDONIA: And it is a long road that has no turning.

JEREMIAH: As soon as we reach port, we shall be married in the Whaleman's Chapel in New Bedford.

SEDONIA (*Ecstatically*): We shall! We shall! And I hope we will be happy.

JEREMIAH (*Placing his arm around her and leading her to door*): There is no question about it. At Harvard, I took a course, Marriage and the Family 401. Monday, Wednesday, and Saturday at 2 p.m. Professor Bliss in charge. I can guarantee that I shall make the perfect husband.

SEDONIA: Oh, Jeremiah, Harvard has prepared you for everything.

JEREMIAH: Yes, sweet Sedonia, it is, indeed, a great and noble thing to be a Harvard man. (*They exit as whistle is heard and curtain falls.*)

THE END

Production Notes

THAR SHE BLOWS

Characters: 8 male; 2 female.

Playing Time: 35 minutes.

Costumes: Minerva and Sedonia wear appropriate dress of the mid-nineteenth century. Cookie Burnem wears a chef's cap and a dirty apron. Others wear suitable nautical costume. Captain Abel wears boots; Samson Spry has a walrus mustache. He has guns at his belt and carries a whip. Jeremiah has two books and a pamphlet in his pockets.

Properties: Broom, coffeepot, whip, pail of water.

Setting: Captain Abel's cabin aboard the whaling ship *Never Ready*. At center is a table on which are an oil lamp, a compass, books, a large navigation chart, a pencil, and a globe. There is a gun in drawer of table. Up left is a bunk; raincoats and sou'westers hang on hooks on left wall. There is a door up center, and a porthole at left.

Lighting: No special effects.

Sound: Offstage whistling, as indicated.

The Knights of the Square Table

Characters

KING HAYPENNY, *the absent-minded ruler of Shillingshire*
QUEEN GIDDYVERE
ALBERT, *a page*
WILHEMINA, *a lady-in-waiting*
SIR WALDO, *an elderly knight*
BATTYMUSS, *a magician*
LADY CRUMPET, *an attractive but evil woman*
SIR FERDINAND, *a poetic knight*
SIR PERCIVAL, *a handsome knight*
PRINCESS LORRAINE, *an attractive girl of 18*

TIME: *Many, many years ago, when knighthood was in flower, but beginning to wither.*

SETTING: *A room in the castle of King Haypenny in the kingdom of Shillingshire. At center is a large square table with chairs around it. Down left are two thrones for the King and Queen. There is a fireplace on right wall, with cauldron hanging on a hook.*

AT RISE: KING HAYPENNY *and* QUEEN GIDDYVERE *are seated on their thrones.* KING HAYPENNY *is eating apples from a bowl held for him by* ALBERT, *a page.* QUEEN

GIDDYVERE *is knitting. Her ball of yarn is held by* WILHEMINA, *a lady-in-waiting.*

ALBERT (*Holding bowl toward* KING HAYPENNY): Have another apple, Your Majesty.

HAYPENNY (*Still chewing previous apple*): Don't mind if I do, Albert. These are splendid apples—splendid. Wish we could grow them like this in Shillingshire. But these are from Piccalilli, are they not?

ALBERT: Yes, Sir Percival brought them back from Piccalilli on one of his quests. (HAYPENNY *takes another apple and bites into it.*)

GIDDYVERE: If you eat any more of those, you'll have indigestion, Haypenny. And you know what indigestion does to your disposition.

HAYPENNY: Just one more, my dear—just one more. (*Chewing*) Delicious. I must say our enemies in the kingdom of Piccalilli grow delicious apples. By the way, where is Lorraine?

GIDDYVERE: I suspect that our fair daughter is walking in the garden with Sir Percival. I hope she doesn't get a cold in all that dampness.

HAYPENNY: Sir Pervical? Who's that?

GIDDYVERE: Heavens, Haypenny, your memory gets more like a sieve every day. Sir Percival is one of your Knights of the Square Table.

WILHEMINA (*Coyly*): And the most handsome—except for Sir Ferdinand.

HAYPENNY: Of course, now that you mention it, my dear Giddyvere, I know him well. Charming fellow—and a roaring lion in battle. (SIR WALDO *enters hurriedly at center, rushes toward throne, trips, and falls flat on his face.* WILHEMINA *and* ALBERT *giggle.*)

GIDDYVERE: Now, Wilhemina, now, Albert, it's not polite to laugh at another's misfortunes. But ods bodkins, Sir Waldo, you're about as graceful as a wounded bear.

SIR WALDO (*Picking himself up*): Drat these floors! They're mighty treacherous for a man my age—especially when he's in a hurry.

HAYPENNY: What's the news, Sir—er—what's your name?

GIDDYVERE (*Sighing*): It's Sir Waldo, Haypenny. You ought to know him. He's lived in the castle now for a month. Your memory is just terrible.

HAYPENNY: Of course, Sir Waldo it is. Fine fellow.

SIR WALDO (*Excitedly*): I have dreadful tidings, Your Majesty. Simply horrible.

HAYPENNY (*Munching*): These apples are the quintessence of juiciness. It's a pity they grow in the kingdom of Piccalilli.

SIR WALDO: I've been scouring the countryside for dragons —and beastly elusive creatures they are. I haven't come across one in weeks. Seems to be a definite dragon shortage in these parts.

ALBERT (*Suppressing a giggle*): Into every life some rain must fall, Sir Waldo.

GIDDYVERE: Please get to the point, Sir Waldo.

SIR WALDO: I'm coming to it, Your Majesty. Being tired, dusty, and discouraged, I stopped at an inn not ten miles from here. There I learned—and I shudder to say it—that Sir Belvidere de Nasty of Piccalilli, who has been terrorizing the people of Shillingshire for many months, is now advancing on the castle with his band of cutthroats. He means to overthrow Your Majesty. I suggest that Your Majesty be certain that the castle's defenses are in good order.

GIDDYVERE: Oh, dear, we are headed for calamity and catastrophe!

SIR WALDO (*Drawing himself up proudly*): Not while the good Knights of the Square Table are here to give battle to the evil Sir Belvidere de Nasty.

HAYPENNY: Bravely spoken, Sir—er—what's your name?

GIDDYVERE: Waldo.

HAYPENNY: Exactly. (*He takes another bite of apple.*) Only one thing to do. I must call a meeting of the Knights of the Square Table immediately. No time to lose. Albert, fetch everybody. (ALBERT, *taking the apples along with him, begins to leave, but* HAYPENNY *grabs his arm.*) I'll keep the apples. (*He takes bowl from* ALBERT.) They're positively superb. (ALBERT *rushes out up center, and* HAYPENNY, *carrying the bowl of apples, goes to square table and sits at head.* SIR WALDO *also sits at table.* QUEEN GIDDYVERE *remains on her throne and continues to knit.*)

GIDDYVERE (*Shaking her head*): I hope we're not headed for calamity and catastrophe. Oh, drat! I'm so nervous that I've dropped a stitch.

WILHEMINA: Be of good cheer, Your Majesty. With so many brave knights at hand, we shall be as safe as babes in their mothers' arms. (ALBERT, *out of breath, enters up center.*)

ALBERT (*In a loud voice*): The magician Battymuss and Lady Crumpet! (LADY CRUMPET *and* BATTYMUSS *enter. Both bow, first to* HAYPENNY, *then to* GIDDYVERE. BATTYMUSS *takes a seat at the table while* LADY CRUMPET *goes to stand beside* GIDDYVERE'S *throne.* ALBERT *exits up center.*)

HAYPENNY: Bad news, bad news, Lady Crumpet and Battymuss. Sir—what's his name—I have it on the tip of my tongue—

SIR WALDO: Sir Belvidere de Nasty, Your Majesty.

HAYPENNY: That's the fellow. He's on his way to attack the castle.

BATTYMUSS: Want me to cast a spell, Your Majesty? I've learned a lot of new ones recently. (ALBERT, *even more out of breath, appears at center.*)

ALBERT: Sir Ferdinand—the poetic knight.

WILHEMINA (*Admiringly*): The pearl of chivalry! (SIR FERDINAND *enters. He is busily writing on a scroll. He bows to* HAYPENNY *and* GIDDYVERE, *smiles at* WILHEMINA *and blows her a kiss. She sighs rapturously. He takes his seat at the table.* ALBERT *exits up center.*)

SIR FERDINAND: All morning I've been searching for a rhyme for "iced tea."

LADY CRUMPET (*Nastily*): Try "Sir Belvidere de Nasty." He'll be here soon.

SIR FERDINAND: Thank you, Lady Crumpet. (*He writes.*) That may well do it.

WILHEMINA: Oh, Sir Ferdinand, you're so brilliant.

SIR FERDINAND: Yes. And I owe it all to plain living and high thinking. (ALBERT, *really out of breath, appears up center.*)

ALBERT: The Princess Lorraine and Sir Percival. (PRINCESS LORRAINE *enters, hand in hand with handsome* SIR PERCIVAL. SIR PERCIVAL *escorts her to* GIDDYVERE's *throne, bows, kisses* LORRAINE's *hand, and then goes to take his place at the table.*) I believe all are now present, Your Majesty. The other knights are busy on quests throughout the kingdom.

HAYPENNY: Oh, are there other knights? Splendid, splendid. I always say there's safety in numbers.

GIDDYVERE: Heavens, Haypenny, get on with the business. We haven't much time.

HAYPENNY (*Munching on apple*): These apples are absolutely mouth-watering. Very well, my dear. (*Coughs*) Er—the meeting of the Knights of the Square Table will come to order. Er—we will hear the secretary's report.

SIR PERCIVAL: Your Majesty, you forgot to appoint a secretary at the last meeting.

GIDDYVERE: Really, Haypenny, this is the last straw. Get Battymuss to cast a spell so that your memory will improve.

BATTYMUSS: And I'm the man to do it. I have a spell guaranteed to give you a memory like an elephant's. (*He rises and bows to* HAYPENNY.) Just look at me, Your Majesty. (HAYPENNY *does so.*) Now repeat after me, "Wacko! Dracko! Slacko!"

HAYPENNY: Incredible! Incredible! I feel my memory improving already. Battymuss, you're an invaluable fellow.

BATTYMUSS: When better spells are cast in the kingdom of Shillingshire, I will cast 'em.

HAYPENNY: I'm certain you will. Wacko—wacko. (*Furrowing brow in concentration*) I forgot the words. What were they? (GIDDYVERE *sighs audibly.* WILHEMINA *and* LORRAINE *giggle.* LADY CRUMPET *shakes her head disdainfully.*)

BATTYMUSS: Wacko! Dracko! Slacko!

HAYPENNY: Of course. I remember now. Wacko. (*He smiles triumphantly.*) Right?

BATTYMUSS: Amazing!

HAYPENNY: And—er—

LADY CRUMPET: A little bird told me that the other words are "Dracko" and "Slacko," Your Majesty.

HAYPENNY: Naturally. Dracko! Slacko!

BATTYMUSS: Now before you go to sleep tonight, Your Majesty, place a peach pit under your pillow.

GIDDYVERE: That is, if he remembers.

HAYPENNY: Oh, my dear fellow, wouldn't an apple core do as well? I have a good supply of them.

BATTYMUSS: For the proper spell, only a peach pit is appropriate.

HAYPENNY: Very well. Now where were we?

SIR PERCIVAL: You had just called the meeting to order, Your Majesty.

HAYPENNY: I had? Yes, to be sure, I had. Thank you, Sir Percival. We will hear the secretary's report.

SIR FERDINAND: If I may speak in verse, Your Majesty.
(*Reciting*)
The absence of a secretary is due
To the fact that none was appointed by you.

WILHEMINA: How lovely!

HAYPENNY: Beautiful! Beautiful! There's nothing like a good poem to make a morning brighter.

SIR PERCIVAL (*Wearily*): I suggest that we omit the secretary's report.

HAYPENNY: If you wish—but I do like these meetings to be conducted according to the rules. And speaking of meetings, what's the purpose of this one?

SIR WALDO: Your Majesty, Sir Belvidere de Nasty is advancing on the castle with his villainous cohorts.

HAYPENNY: Why didn't you say so? We must take action at once.

GIDDYVERE: At last!

HAYPENNY: The chair is open to suggestions.

SIR PERCIVAL: I crave a boon, Your Majesty.

HAYPENNY: Granted, Sir—er—

LORRAINE: Percival, Father.

HAYPENNY: Right you are.

SIR PERCIVAL (*Rising*): Fellow Knights of the Square Table.

HAYPENNY: Really, Sir—er—

LORRAINE (*Exasperatedly*): Percival, Father!

HAYPENNY: Thank you, daughter. Really, Sir Percival, I have told you before. Always refer to your colleagues as Fellow Squares.

SIR PERCIVAL (*Bowing*): I'm sorry, Your Majesty. Fellow Squares, I move that each of us take charge of a particular aspect of the castle's defense. I shall man the walls with archers.

HAYPENNY: Good.

SIR PERCIVAL: And I request that Wilhemina take charge of boiling plenty of oil in yonder cauldron. (*He points to cauldron in fireplace.*) We shall pour it on the forces of Sir Belvidere de Nasty.

LADY CRUMPET (*Sarcastically*): There'll be a hot time in the old castle tonight.

WILHEMINA: I'll bring the oil to a boil at once, Sir Percival. (*She goes quickly to fireplace and begins to stir contents of cauldron.*) I always use one of Mother's old recipes.

SIR FERDINAND (*Rising*): I, too, crave a boon, Your Majesty.

HAYPENNY: Granted.

SIR FERDINAND: Fellow Knights of the—(HAYPENNY *coughs in warning.*) I mean, Fellow Squares, I shall as usual fight with the heart of a tiger and the skill of a Lancelot.

WILHEMINA: That's my Ferdinand who said that.

SIR FERDINAND: In addition, I should like, as usual, to be made official chronicler of the coming struggle so that I may set down in deathless verse the valiant deeds that are soon to be performed for the glory of Shillingshire.

SIR WALDO: Hear! Hear!

HAYPENNY: Splendid, Sir—er—what's that name?

LADY CRUMPET: Ferdinand.

HAYPENNY: Ah, yes, that name does ring a bell. Ferdinand.

SIR WALDO (*Rising*): I crave a boon, Your Majesty.

HAYPENNY: My, the boons are flying thick and fast this morning. Granted.

SIR WALDO: Fellow Knights—I mean, of course, Fellow Squares—because of my intimate knowledge of the surrounding countryside, gained in my perpetual search for dangerous dragons—

LADY CRUMPET: Now, Sir Waldo, you know that no one has seen a dragon around here since one ate Lady Doughnut two years ago.

SIR WALDO (*Firmly*): In view of my experience, I volunteer to leave the castle and to keep an eye out for the coming of the dastardly Sir Belvidere de Nasty and his insidious villains from Piccalilli. By so doing, I shall keep you all informed.

HAYPENNY: Sounds sensible. Very sensible. Permission granted.

SIR WALDO: Thank you, Your Majesty. Then I shall be about it at once. (*He starts to exit up center, stumbles, and falls.*) Drat these floors. Some day I'll hurt myself. (*He exits, limping.*)

SIR FERDINAND: Sir Waldo walks with ease through doors, But has his troubles with old floors. (*Rising*), I, too, shall be off to do my duty. But first, I ask the aid of the muses to inspire us all.

WILHEMINA: My hero!

HAYPENNY (*Wiping tears from his eyes*): Beautiful! Touching! You're an example to us all!

SIR FERDINAND: Thank you. (*He blows a kiss to* WILHEMINA, *who sighs, and then he exits.*)

HAYPENNY: Come, Giddyvere. We must speak to the vassals below and stir their hearts to valor and victory.

GIDDYVERE (*Taking up her knitting and ball of yarn*): I just hope we're not headed for calamity and catastrophe. (HAYPENNY *and* GIDDYVERE *exit up center.*)

SIR PERCIVAL (*Going to* PRINCESS LORRAINE, *bows and kisses her hand*): Fair princess, know that I shall fight the good fight with the memory of your lustrous eyes and ruby lips before me. In the ensuing battle, I ask permission to wear your favor. (*She smiles and gives him her handkerchief.*) Ah, this is a banner bright enough to inspire me to great heights of chivalry and daring. And should our forces win the day—and by St. George and good King Haypenny, they shall—I intend to ask your hand in marriage.

LORRAINE (*Quite overcome*): Oh, Percival, my goodly knight, how proud I am that you shall wear my favor. I am of all women in the world the most honored. And, dear Percival, my hand is yours, whenever you desire it. (*Hand in hand, they exit.* LADY CRUMPET *goes to fireplace.*)

LADY CRUMPET: I'll stir that foul brew for a while, Wilhemina. You had better go out to see if you can be of any help to the Queen.

WILHEMINA: Yes, Lady Crumpet. And perhaps I can catch a glimpse of wonderful Sir Ferdinand. (WILHEMINA *and* ALBERT *exit up center.* LADY CRUMPET *and* BATTYMUSS *come to center.*)

LADY CRUMPET (*Venomously*): Now that was a sickening little scene if I ever saw one. That bragging Percival and that simpering Lorraine make my blood boil.

BATTYMUSS: Don't be hard on them, Lady Crumpet. (*Laughing*) Poor Sir Percival is not long for this world. As for the Princess Lorraine—well, we know what's in *her* future.

LADY CRUMPET (*Rubbing her hands together with malicious delight*): Ah, yes, Sir Belvidere will make a few changes around this silly castle. He wants the Princess Lorraine for himself—men are always easy marks for a pretty face. Why he wants her when I'm around, I'll never know. But who can tell what goes on in men's pointed heads? Anyway, you know what you're to do, don't you?

BATTYMUSS: Of course. When the attack begins, I shall, with my customary cleverness, let down the drawbridge so that Sir Belvidere and his cohorts can cross the moat and enter the castle. King Haypenny usually controls the drawbridge, but it will be child's play to hoodwink him. I won't even have to cast a spell.

LADY CRUMPET: Save that stuff for the country boys, Battymuss. You couldn't cast a spell across a one-foot puddle. As a magician, you're good only for laughs.

BATTYMUSS: Really, Lady Crumpet, I resent such talk.

LADY CRUMPET: That's your privilege. But you can give up all your foolish magic, anyway, as soon as Sir Belvidere seizes the castle. He'll be King of Shillingshire then, and we'll be rid of that bumbling idiot, Haypenny.

BATTYMUSS: And *I'll* be prime minister. That's the reward Sir Belvidere promised me for my brilliant aid.

LADY CRUMPET: And I'll be a power in the kingdom, too. There'll be some common sense around here for a change. (*Laughing nastily*) Oh, what a joyful day this will be! Well, we know what we must do. I shall give Princess Lorraine a sleeping potion and then lock her in her bedroom. What she doesn't know won't hurt her.

BATTYMUSS: You know, I have just been thinking—what a furor would be caused if they knew the greatest secret of all. (WILHEMINA *appears in doorway*.) If they knew that —(LADY CRUMPET *claps her hand over* BATTYMUSS' *mouth*.)

LADY CRUMPET: Be quiet, you fool. (*She nods toward doorway*.) Oh, hello, Wilhemina. I was just attempting to remove a shred of barley from Battymuss' teeth.

WILHEMINA: You should be stirring the oil, Lady Crumpet. Mother always said the secret was in the stirring.

LADY CRUMPET: And Mother knows best. You go right ahead with the stirring. Come, Battymuss, we'll leave the dear child to her cooking chores. (LADY CRUMPET *and* BATTYMUSS *exit up center.* WILHEMINA *begins to stir contents of cauldron. After a moment,* ALBERT *enters excitedly up center*.)

ALBERT: Sir Belvidere de Nasty and his men are now in sight of the castle. Sir Percival saw them first.

WILHEMINA: And what of Sir Ferdinand?

ALBERT: The last I saw of him, he was busy writing.

WILHEMINA: He's the most brilliant knight in the world.

ALBERT: Yes, if pens were swords, he'd be a one-man army. (BATTYMUSS *and* KING HAYPENNY *enter hurriedly at center*.)

HAYPENNY: The oil! We're ready for the boiling oil. The wretches will never be able to scale the castle walls when we pour the stuff on 'em.

WILHEMINA: The oil is bubbling and hot, Your Majesty.

HAYPENNY: Splendid. Albert, take the cauldron out to the oil-pouring brigade.

WILHEMINA: I'll help. (*She and* ALBERT *carry cauldron out at center*.)

HAYPENNY: Now, let's see, there's something I must do. Oh, yes, I must return to the moat. Mighty important duty I have there.

BATTYMUSS: Your Majesty, I have a suggestion. I have been gazing into my crystal ball—the one given to me by Merlin, who is the president of the magicians' society— and I saw a terrible thing.

HAYPENNY: Terrible?

BATTYMUSS: Yes, the crystal ball warns—and I have never known it to be in error—that in any battle, you should remain in this room. After all, your life is important to the welfare of Shillingshire. (*He reaches into pocket of his gown and produces a small scroll.*) I have here an account of apple growing in Piccalilli. Since you will soon capture Piccalilli—and since you are *so* fond of that country's apples—perhaps you would like to study this scroll.

HAYPENNY (*Taking scroll*): Indeed, I would. You're a thoughtful fellow, Battymuss—the most kindly and generous magician I've ever known. (*He goes to throne, where he sits.*) But, dash it all, I was supposed to do something. (*Striking forehead*) Ah, yes, the moat.

BATTYMUSS: I shall be happy to guard the moat, Your Majesty.

HAYPENNY: Anything for the glory and honor of Shillingshire. Battymuss, your loyalty is touching. (*Looking at scroll*) Ah, pruning the apple trees regularly—that's the secret. (BATTYMUSS *exits quickly up center. After a moment,* PRINCESS LORRAINE, WILHEMINA, *and* LADY CRUMPET *enter.* LADY CRUMPET *is carrying a goblet.*)

LORRAINE: How exciting the battle is! How nobly Sir Percival is directing the defense of the castle!

WILHEMINA: Not to mention Ferdinand. How amazing it is that he can write so well in the heat of battle.

LORRAINE: I am sure that the day soon will be ours. Sir Belvidere de Nasty and his evil men have been unable to storm the walls of the castle.

WILHEMINA: Thanks to Mother's recipe.

LORRAINE: And because the bridge over the moat is up, the attackers cannot get into the castle. Our brave archers are sending arrows into the hides of our enemies.

HAYPENNY (*Still reading*): Soil is important, too. Mighty important. Must be the secret of their juiciness.

LORRAINE: What in the world are you speaking about, Father?

HAYPENNY: Apple growing, my dear. Apple growing in Piccalilli. Clever people, those Piccalillians.

LADY CRUMPET (*Evilly*): Princess Lorraine, you must be tired and thirsty from all this perilous excitement. I have mixed a soothing potion for you.

LORRAINE: Thank you, Lady Crumpet. You are most kind.

LADY CRUMPET: Yes, I have a heart as big as the world. Drink, my dear. (*She holds out goblet.* LORRAINE *takes it and drinks from it.*)

LORRAINE: It is good, but there is a slightly bitter taste to it.

LADY CRUMPET: Ah, that's the secret of it. That's what will bring the roses to your cheeks. (ALBERT *rushes in.*)

ALBERT: They are attacking again, but we shall drive them off! Sir Percival is magnificent!

LORRAINE (*Sleepily*): Of course. (SIR FERDINAND, *in knight's armor, enters, dragging a struggling* BATTYMUSS *by the collar.*)

BATTYMUSS: Drat you, Sir Ferdinand, I'll cast a spell on you. I'll turn you into a toad.

FERDINAND:

When bigger spells are made and cast

Yours will be the worst—and last. (FERDINAND *drags* BATTYMUSS *to* HAYPENNY'S *throne.*) Your Majesty, this malevolent magician was about to do a deed of terrible treachery. He lowered the drawbridge of the castle moat.

WILHEMINA: Oh, how vile!

LADY CRUMPET (*Excitedly*): Did any of the enemy cross the bridge?

SIR FERDINAND: Only one, Lady Crumpet. The leader, I believe—yes, the dirty, dastardly, disgusting Sir Belvidere de Nasty. (LADY CRUMPET *smiles.*)

BATTYMUSS: This is all a dreadful mistake, Your Majesty. I was merely testing the bridge. Wanted to be sure the chains weren't rusty.

SIR FERDINAND (*Taking piece of rope from his pocket*): And I shall test this rope for size and strength. (SIR FERDINAND *ties* BATTYMUSS' *hands behind his back and also ties his feet together so that* BATTYMUSS *is lying on the floor.*)

BATTYMUSS: I'll cast seven evil spells on all of you! (*From offstage, there is the sound of clanking swords. Suddenly,* SIR PERCIVAL *and* SIR WALDO, *both in knight's armor, enter, fighting furiously in a display of sword play.* LORRAINE *sinks to the floor, obviously fast asleep.*)

WILHEMINA (*Frightened*): But why do our knights fight with each other?

HAYPENNY (*Looking up from scroll*): Why, indeed? What's the situation here? Not going by the rules at all. Knights of the Square Table should be fair and square. (*Notic-*

ing LORRAINE) Who's that girl on the floor? Her face seems familiar.

LADY CRUMPET: That's your daughter, Your Majesty. (SIR PERCIVAL *and* SIR WALDO *continue fighting.*)

SIR FERDINAND (*Drawing sword*): I'll put an end to this. (*He is about to enter the fray.*)

LADY CRUMPET (*Suddenly taking a dagger from her pocket and holding it at* KING HAYPENNY's *heart*): Not so fast. Make one move, Sir Ferdinand, and Shillingshire will be without a king.

HAYPENNY: Oh, I say, Lady Crumpet, that's not at all friendly. (SIR FERDINAND *looks baffled and sheathes his sword.* GIDDYVERE *enters at center.*)

GIDDYVERE: A day of calamity and catastrophe!

BATTYMUSS (*From floor*): I'll cast a spell that will make everyone wish he were somewhere else! (ALBERT, *unseen by the others, enters from left. He creeps on hands and knees and hides behind* KING HAYPENNY's *throne. Suddenly, he jumps up and knocks the dagger from* LADY CRUMPET's *hand.* ALBERT *grabs dagger quickly.*)

HAYPENNY: Oh, good show, er—

GIDDYVERE: Albert. (*She rushes to* KING) Are you all right?

HAYPENNY: Splendid. But somewhat confused. And that's odd, because my thinking is usually clear as a bell. (SIR PERCIVAL *knocks the sword from* SIR WALDO's *hand.* SIR WALDO *is now weaponless.* SIR PERCIVAL *places the point of his sword at* SIR WALDO's *throat.*)

SIR PERCIVAL: Yield, miserable villain!

SIR WALDO: I yield.

GIDDYVERE: But, Sir Percival, why are you so cruel to a fellow knight? And, Lady Crumpet, why did you wish to stab dear Haypenny?

LADY CRUMPET: That's the sixty-four-shilling question.

SIR PERCIVAL: I can make everything clear, Your Majesty. (*Noticing* LORRAINE *on floor*) But what is this? Why is the fairest flower of Shillingshire in a horizontal position?

WILHEMINA: I believe I know. Lady Crumpet must have given her a sleeping potion.

SIR PERCIVAL: Lady Crumpet, you are an evil woman. Mother warned me there were people like you in the world. Sir Ferdinand, see that this cur does not escape. (SIR FERDINAND *draws his sword and stands guard over* SIR WALDO. SIR PERCIVAL *kneels by* LORRAINE'*s side and gently shakes her shoulder*.) Awaken, pretty maiden. All is well, and the day is ours. (*There is no response*.) Ah, well, then I know what to do. (*From his tunic,* SIR PERCIVAL *draws a small bottle*.) I have with me an ancient antidote which was given to me by an Arab, Ali Nik Kildare, when I went on my last crusade. It is guaranteed to awaken the sleeping, and make loud the silent. It is called Nik's Rub. (SIR PERCIVAL *pours some of the liquid into his hand and rubs* LORRAINE'*s forehead with it. She stirs*.) Ah, the sleeping beauty is roused.

LORRAINE (*Faintly*): What are the minstrels playing, Mother?

SIR PERCIVAL: Princess Lorraine, it is I, Sir Percival.

LORRAINE: Oh, my brave knight, how happy I am to see you. (*To* LADY CRUMPET) Something was wrong with that drink you gave me.

LADY CRUMPET: My, you draw a quick conclusion, don't you?

SIR PERCIVAL: Let me now explain. That repulsive knight

(*Pointing to* Sir Waldo) is a trickster of the lowest order.

HAYPENNY: Oh, really, that can't be. I know the fellow's face well—though I can't, at the moment, recall his name.

SIR PERCIVAL: Listen well, Your Majesty. For a long time, I have been suspicious of him and of his forays into the countryside when he was supposedly looking for dragons. I spoke recently with Sir Humbert Disney, president of the Shillingshire Society for the Preservation and Encouragement of Dragons, and he informed me that there are now no dragons in Shillingshire. Now hear this. Sir Waldo merely went through the countryside to lead evil forces in raids on our good peasants.

SIR WALDO: I deny everything. And I refuse to comment on the grounds that—(SIR PERCIVAL *seizes* SIR WALDO *by the hair and yanks.* SIR WALDO's *hair, really a gray wig, comes off in* SIR PERCIVAL's *hands. All gasp.*)

SIR PERCIVAL: Note! The supposed Sir Waldo is really that loathsome knight, Sir Belvidere de Nasty, from Piccalilli.

GIDDYVERE: Sir Belvidere! Oh, calamity and catastrophe!

SIR PERCIVAL: He was able to cross the drawbridge before Sir Ferdinand discovered Battymuss' treachery. Needless to say, de Nasty, Lady Crumpet, and Battymuss were in league in this cowardly attempt at treason. If their plan had succeeded, Sir Belvidere would have been king.

SIR WALDO: And Lorraine would have been my queen.

LORRAINE: Oh, horrible! A fate worse than death!

SIR PERCIVAL: Fear not, sweet princess. Now, without their leader, Sir Belvidere's forces have retreated in wild disorder.

BATTYMUSS (*From floor*): Alazambo! Calazambo! Rem-axambo! Let these ropes be loosed! (*He struggles, but to no avail.*)

LADY CRUMPET: A faker to the end, Battymuss. Why I ever joined forces with a half-wit like you, I'll never know. Oh, well, you can't blame a girl for trying. That's the way the meat pie crumbles.

SIR PERCIVAL: With your permission, Your Majesty, I shall put this evil trio in the castle dungeon where they shall be held until their trial for treason.

HAYPENNY: Permission granted. Much obliged to you, Sir—

LORRAINE: (*Rapturously*): Percival, Father. (SIR PERCIVAL *goes to* LADY CRUMPET *and takes her by the arm.* SIR FERDINAND, *sword still drawn, takes charge of* SIR WALDO.)

SIR PERCIVAL: Albert, you can drag Battymuss along.

ALBERT: A pleasure. (*He grabs* BATTYMUSS *by the collar, with* BATTYMUSS *still uttering words of magic.* PERCIVAL, LADY CRUMPET, SIR FERDINAND, SIR WALDO, ALBERT, *and* BATTYMUSS *all exit up center.*)

LORRAINE: Oh, how fortunate we are to have in our midst a knight so brave and commanding as Sir Percival!

WILHEMINA: Sir Ferdinand isn't exactly a cream puff either.

GIDDYVERE: And let us not forget Albert. I really do believe that we have been safely delivered from calamity and catastrophe. (SIR PERCIVAL, SIR FERDINAND, *and* ALBERT *return.*)

SIR PERCIVAL: We have delivered the miserable three into the hands of some of our stalwart vassals who will escort them to the dungeon.

HAYPENNY: Splendid.

SIR FERDINAND: A boon, Your Majesty.

HAYPENNY: The boon is yours.

SIR FERDINAND: A poem in honor of this most auspicious occasion. (*He recites dramatically.*)

An ode in honor of the fray

That saved for us this shining day.

Good Percival, long may he wave

In Shillingshire, strong and brave.

May Albert win his just acclaim—

Honor and glory to his name.

Good Percival deserves the hand

Of the princess of this land.

(SIR PERCIVAL *and* LORRAINE *embrace happily.*)

And, yours truly, poetic Ferd

Would like these words now to be heard:

He plights his troth to Wilhemina (*Thinking*)—er—mina

(*Triumphantly*)

Than whom no girl could be keener! (SIR FERDINAND *embraces* WILHEMINA. *All applaud.*)

HAYPENNY (*Wiping a tear from his eye*): Moving! Touching! Highly emotional! Nothing like a good poem to stir the heart. (*He goes to square table.*) But we must get to our business. Must have a meeting at once. (*Waving scroll as he sits*) Need to consider methods of improving apple growing in Shillingshire.

LORRAINE: Father, do I have your permission to marry this goodly knight?

HAYPENNY: Certainly. Who is he?

LORRAINE: Percival, Father.

HAYPENNY: Fine fellow. Look forward to having him as a son-in-law.

WILHEMINA (*Eagerly*): And I, Your Majesty, may I marry this poetic knight?

HAYPENNY: Don't see why not. The more the merrier.

GIDDYVERE: Blessings on you, my children.

HAYPENNY: And now the meeting will come to order. We shall hear the secretary's report.

GIDDYVERE: Oh, Haypenny, must we go through all that again! (*All shout "No!" The knights bang spears or swords on floor, women stamp their feet, and* KING HAYPENNY *covers his ears as the curtains close.*)

THE END

Production Notes

THE KNIGHTS OF THE SQUARE TABLE

Characters: 6 male; 4 female.

Playing Time: 30 minutes.

Costumes: Typical royal robes for all but Battymuss. Albert, and knights. Battymuss wears a cone-shaped hat, and a gown decorated with various symbols. Albert wears a page's costume. The knights put on "armor" at the end of the play.

Properties: Bowl, apples, long spoon, goblet, swords, dagger, scrolls, pen, lace handkerchief, knitting, rope, small bottle, gray wig.

Setting: A room in a castle. On the walls of the room hang shields and swords. At center is a large square table with heavy chairs around it. At right is a fireplace with a cauldron, hanging on a hook. At left is a throne, a large, heavy, preferably ornate chair. Next to it is a similar chair, but smaller, for Queen Giddyvere's throne. Up center there is an entrance.

Lighting: No special effects.

The Sand Dune Hillbillies

Characters

BETTY BRANDON, *19, desk clerk at the Surfside Hotel*
DUDLEY MURGATROYD, *an aging actor*
FELICIA FARADAY, *an attractive but sarcastic actress*
MISS LUCRETIA THORPE, *a fussy prospective guest*
HENRY BILLINGS, *the bellhop*
ZEKE BILLINGS, *Henry's hillbilly uncle*
AMOS BILLINGS, *Henry's hillbilly cousin*
DAISY SUE BILLINGS, *18, an Ozark belle*
MR. CRAIG, *manager of the Surfside Hotel*
SEPTIMUS BOYD ⎱ *hotel guests*
MRS. RENNICK ⎰

TIME: *A morning in July.*

SETTING: *The lounge and lobby of the Surfside Hotel on Cape Cod.*

AT RISE: BETTY BRANDON *is sitting on stool behind registration desk.* DUDLEY MURGATROYD *sits at table, sipping coffee and reading newspaper.* FELICIA FARADAY *sits opposite him, studying a playscript. Telephone rings.*

BETTY (*Answering phone*): Surfside Hotel, Cape Cod's finest. Betty Brandon speaking. . . . Oh, good morning, Mrs. Blaisdell. . . . Yes, the chef says we'll be needing fifty pounds of lobster, twenty of scallops, and at least two gallons of clams. . . . Fine, as long as you can deliver by noon. . . . Right. Goodbye, Mrs. Blaisdell. Remember me to the Captain. (MISS LUCRETIA THORPE, *enters, followed by the bellhop,* HENRY BILLINGS, *who is carrying her bags.* MISS THORPE *goes to registration desk.*)

MISS THORPE: Ah, how pleasant is to be back on Cape Cod after the noise and confusion of the city. Good morning. I'm Lucretia Thorpe.

BETTY: Good morning, Miss Thorpe. We have your reservation, and your room is ready.

MISS THORPE: Splendid. I hope it is the same room I have had for the past five summers; it has a lovely view of the ocean.

BETTY: Yes, indeed, Miss Thorpe. It's 546.

MISS THORPE: Good. When I arrive each summer at the Surfside Hotel, it's almost like being home again. It's such a restful place.

HENRY (*Smiling*): The Surfside guarantees satisfaction, Miss Thorpe. (ZEKE *and his son,* AMOS BILLINGS *enter, carrying rifles. They are obviously in an exuberant mood, laughing noisily, aiming their rifles, and shouting "Ping! Ping!" They are barefoot but apparently dressed in their Sunday best—poorly fitting suits, badly in need of pressing.*)

ZEKE: Mornin', Miss Brandon. Mornin', nephew Henry. Great day for a bit of shootin'. (*He aims his rifle at a spot above the registration desk*) Ping! Ping!

MISS THORPE (*Frightened*): Gracious, is it necessary for

you to wave those firearms about? I've never seen such a sight at the Surfside before!

AMOS: Shucks, ma'am, these guns aren't dangerous. Paw and me know how to handle 'em. Right, Paw?

ZEKE: Right as rain, Amos.

AMOS (*Aiming rifle at* HENRY): We can hit a mosquito's eye at a hundred paces.

ZEKE (*Smiling amiably at* MISS THORPE): Sure can, ma'am. (MISS THORPE *looks terrified.*) Of course, my son Amos is foolin'. He doesn't really intend to shoot his cousin Henry. Anyhow, come on, Amos. We've got things to do.

AMOS: Right, Paw.

ZEKE (*To* MISS THORPE): Now don't you be a-worryin', ma'am. (ZEKE *and* AMOS *exit.*)

MISS THORPE: Well, I never! Are those creatures guests at this hotel?

BETTY: Yes, they are, Miss Thorpe, but they're harmless.

MISS THORPE: Harmless! With those deadly guns! Well, young woman, if they're the sort of clientele that the Surfside is specializing in this season, I'm leaving. Young man, take my bags out to the car. I'll get a room at the Breakers Hotel.

BETTY: But Miss Thorpe—

MISS THORPE: But me no buts. The bags, young man. I'll not live in a madhouse. (*She goes toward center door.* HENRY *sighs, shrugs his shoulders, and follows with her bags.* MISS THORPE *pauses briefly and talks to* BETTY.) And you can tell your manager, Mr. Craig, that I've never seen anything more outrageous in my life. (*She and* HENRY *exit.* DAISY SUE BILLINGS, *enters, barefoot and wearing a simple dress. She is followed onstage by* SEPTIMUS BOYD, *who wears wrinkled slacks and a loud sports shirt.*)

DAISY SUE: Shucks, Mr. Boyd, I don't rightly know if I should accompany you to the theater tonight. Paw might not like it.

SEPTIMUS: Ah, Daisy Sue, the evening would be a most pleasant one.

DAISY SUE: We don't hold much truck with plays and things back in the Ozarks.

SEPTIMUS: Then it's time you tasted some of the pleasures of a more sophisticated civilization, my dear. (DAISY SUE *and* BOYD *exit*.)

FELICIA (*Angrily*): Miss Brandon, must this hotel lounge be infested by mountain nymphs being pursued by middle-aged millionaires and by fugitives from a TV hillbilly program? I'm trying to learn my lines for a play which, as you well know, opens tonight.

BETTY: I'm sorry, Miss Faraday. But the entire Billings family seems to have caused plenty of confusion around here.

FELICIA: Confusion is a mild word to describe the shenanigans we've been exposed to for the last few days. I was told that the Surfside Hotel is exclusive. It's about as exclusive as the Ringling Brothers Circus.

BETTY: You see, Miss Faraday, the Billings family is from the Ozarks. Our bellhop, Henry, is related to them. As I understand it, they inherited a bit of money so they came here for a Cape Cod vacation to surprise Henry. They made reservations in the regular manner. And they certainly did surprise poor Henry!

FELICIA: And they've horrified me.

DUDLEY: Now, now, Felicia, my dear. Try not to be snobbish. Tolerance is the keynote of the day.

FELICIA: Not with me, buster. And you might learn your

lines, too, Dudley. You muffed plenty at last night's dress rehearsal.

DUDLEY: Fear not, Felicia. (*Proudly*) Dudley Murgatroyd always rises to the occasion before an audience. (HENRY *re-enters. He goes to desk.*)

HENRY (*Wiping brow*): Golly, Betty, if Zeke and Amos and Daisy Sue stay here much longer, I'll lose my job. Mr. Craig is getting fed up with their doings. Zeke and Amos are out on the beach right now, busy with their target practice. They set up a lot of sand pails out on the raft, and they've been shooting at them from shore. Mr. Craig is having a fit.

BETTY: You certainly picked a peculiar set of relatives, Henry.

HENRY (*Sadly*): We can choose our friends, but not our relatives. And I certainly need this job if I'm going to return to college in the fall.

BETTY: So do I. But if the Billings clan continues its fun and frolic, there won't be any guests left around here —and we'll all be out of jobs.

HENRY: And it's just my luck that Mr. Craig should be right outside when I escorted Miss Thorpe to her car. When he heard her story, I thought he'd flay me alive. (ZEKE *and* AMOS *re-enter.*)

AMOS: We've been havin' a parcel of fun out there on the beach. This Cape Cod is sure a beautiful place.

ZEKE: Can't compare to the mountains, son, but it is real purty. Makes a man glad to be alive. I see that Boyd's botherin' our Daisy Sue again. Never trust a Boyd, I say. The only good Boyd is a dead Boyd.

AMOS: That's right, Paw. We Billings have been feudin' with the Boyds for nigh onto a hundred years.

HENRY (*Impatiently*): I've told you, Amos, that this isn't one of the mountain Boyds. This is Septimus Boyd—a respectable millionaire.

ZEKE: A Boyd is a Boyd, Henry, and it's no matter how much money he's made off other people.

AMOS: The only good Boyd is a dead Boyd.

ZEKE: You said a mouthful, Amos. And I want you to keep a watch on the ornery galoot. Don't let him out of your sight.

AMOS: Right, Paw. I'll stick to him like dew on mountain grass. (AMOS *goes to right door and almost collides with* MR. CRAIG, *the manager of the hotel*.) Oops! You and me nearly came a cropper there, Mr. Craig. But no harm done. (AMOS *exits*.)

CRAIG (*Coming to center, angrily*): No harm done, he says! They frighten the life out of the other guests with their target practice on the beach. (*His voice rises excitedly*.) We lose a valued guest, and you say, "No harm done!"

ZEKE: Just havin' a bit of fun, Mr. Craig. After all, we're here for a little vacation. And we're really enjoyin' it!

CRAIG: Henry, I'm holding you personally responsible for all these goings-on. These people are your relatives. If they don't begin to act like civilized human beings, I'm going to throw them out—and you with them.

ZEKE: Now, looky here, Mr. Craig, we paid good money in advance. And we're not doin' anybody a bit of harm.

CRAIG: The first thing you can do is to put away that gun.

ZEKE: Aw, shucks. All right, if you say so. We don't want to cause any trouble. But back home, we don't step out of the cabin without this. (*He pats gun affectionately*.)

HENRY: I'll have a talk with Uncle Zeke and with cousin Amos and Daisy Sue. I know they'll behave, Mr. Craig.

ZEKE: We'll behave sure as shootin'. The Billings always do the right thing. (CRAIG *shrugs his shoulders in exasperation, shakes his head, and exits.*)

HENRY: Uncle Zeke, you'll just have to let up a bit. I know you mean well, but things are different here—not like the Ozarks.

ZEKE: Shucks, Henry, the only reason we moseyed here to Cape Cod to see you was to bring you a mite of joy. You and your Maw and Paw have lived in the East for a heap of years, and we wanted to see how you were doin'.

HENRY: I appreciate it, Uncle Zeke.

ZEKE: We're sorry if we've caused a ruckus. Guess things are different here. But— (*He goes over to* FELICIA *and* DUDLEY)—we're a-goin' to do things right. Ma'am, we're a-comin' to your play tonight. We've never seen any play-actin' before.

FELICIA: Now that is the most joyful news to hit these dainty ears since I won an Academy Award. (*She looks at his feet.*) Wear shoes, will you, buster. The Surfside Summer Theater is a high-toned place.

ZEKE: Oh, we got shoes all right. But they're a mite tight.

FELICIA: So is your suit.

ZEKE: Nice suit, isn't it? Ordered it direct from the catalogue.

DUDLEY (*Sarcastically*): Indeed? I could have sworn you had it custom-made in London.

ZEKE: Never been to London.

DUDLEY: I'd never have guessed it.

FELICIA (*Rising*): I'm going to my room where I hope I can find some peace and quiet. This scintillating conversation is too much for me this early in the morning.

ZEKE: And the best of luck to you tonight, ma'am.

FELICIA (*Going right*): I suspect I'll need it! (*She exits.*)

DUDLEY: I'll have to tear myself away from such invigorating company, too.

ZEKE: In-invigorating, my, that's a purty fine word!

DUDLEY: I'm a purty fine fellow. (*Exits*)

ZEKE: The actors aren't over-friendly people, are they?

HENRY: They have a job to do, Uncle Zeke.

BETTY: Their nerves are probably on edge. (DAISY SUE *re-enters, followed by* SEPTIMUS BOYD, *whom* AMOS *is holding by the collar.*)

ZEKE: Now, looky here, Daisy Sue, why are you gallivantin' around here with this Boyd galoot?

DAISY SUE: Shucks, you got no call to worry, Paw. I like the exercise. And I can outrun him any day in the week. Keeps a girl slim and fit.

SEPTIMUS (*Struggling*): Unhand me, you country bumpkin!

AMOS: You got no call to bandy names at me.

SEPTIMUS: Do you know who I am? I'm Septimus Boyd, chairman of Wilkins Consolidated.

DAISY SUE (*Giggling*): Let him go, Amos. He's as harmless as a kitten.

AMOS: There's no good Boyd but a dead Boyd.

ZEKE: And that's just what he'll be if he keeps botherin' our Daisy Sue. (AMOS *releases* SEPTIMUS.)

SEPTIMUS (*Angrily*): I shall complain to Mr. Craig. You have threatened me and inflicted bodily injury on me. (*He rubs his neck.*)

ZEKE: You Boyds were always great ones for complainin'.

SEPTIMUS: I don't know what Boyds you're thinking of.

ZEKE: We got ourselves a parcel of Boyds back there in the Ozarks. And there's not one you could trust with a baby's piggy bank.

SEPTIMUS (*Exasperatedly*): You're a bunch of barbarians! I'll see Mr. Craig at once. (*Exits right*)

ZEKE: Keep on his trail, Amos. He's not to be trusted.

AMOS: Right, Paw. There never was a Boyd that was anything but a skunk. (AMOS *exits*.)

DAISY SUE: You want to come swimmin' with me, Miss Betty?

BETTY: I'd like to, Daisy Sue, but I'm on duty until noon.

ZEKE: I'll mosey onto the beach with you, Daisy Sue. I'm not one for swimmin', but I'll do some wadin'.

DAISY SUE: That'll be fine, Paw. The salt water is good for you.

ZEKE: See you folks later. (DAISY SUE *and* ZEKE *exit*.)

BETTY: You know, I can't help liking them, Henry, but let's face it. They are a problem. Isn't there anything you can do?

HENRY: I had a brain storm this morning.

BETTY: Good. Let's hear about it.

HENRY: I phoned Mother and Dad and explained the whole situation to them. I asked them to send a telegram here to Zeke inviting him and Amos and Daisy Sue for a visit. I told them to pour it on and say how they haven't seen each other for years and have so much to talk about, that kinfolk ought to see each other, and so on.

BETTY: The question is, will it work? They seem to be having a good time here, and they may not want to tear themselves away from Cape Cod's salty breezes and sandy shores.

HENRY: I thought of that. Mother and Dad are going to say that they themselves will be leaving for a vacation in a week, so it's important that Zeke and the others go there now.

BETTY: The old Cape won't seem the same without them.

HENRY: It will certainly be quieter. My chief worry is Mr. Craig. If this doesn't work, I'm done.

BETTY: Courage, friend. We'll be back on that ivy-covered campus yet.

HENRY: I hope so. You're good in English, and I'm good in math. We make an unbeatable combination. (MR. CRAIG *enters.*)

CRAIG: Betty, have you taken care of those reservations for the Carson family?

BETTY: Yes, Mr. Craig. I'm putting them in 401 and 402.

CRAIG: Good—good, that is, if we still have a hotel here by the time the Carsons arrive. Where is the pride of the Ozarks? Shooting at guests or rollicking in the waves?

HENRY: I don't think he'll be here much longer, Mr. Craig.

CRAIG: Henry, those words are as sweet to my ears as a Mozart symphony. I'm a broad-minded man, a kindly man. I give to charity, I do my duty as a citizen. But there's a limit to my patience—and I'm afraid I'm fast reaching it. I'm trying to run a good hotel here, but lately I've felt as though I were in the middle of a variety show.

HENRY: I've got a plan, Mr. Craig. I think you'll be seeing the last of Uncle Zeke and Amos and Daisy Sue before long.

BETTY (*Loyally*): And it's a good plan, Mr. Craig. Henry's—

CRAIG (*Holding up his hand*): Please, don't tell me. Let me bask in the sunshine of anticipation. Let me look forward to that happy hour—and it had better be soon—when the Billings ride forth from here in their rattling jalopy. When that time comes, I shall declare a holiday and serve a free meal with champagne to all surviving guests. (FELICIA FARADAY *enters excitedly, followed by* DUDLEY MURGATROYD)

FELICIA: Mr. Craig, this is the straw that has broken the camel's back! I've put up with plenty, but this really does it.

DUDLEY: It's a confounded outrage!

CRAIG: Miss Faraday, what has happened?

FELICIA: I'll tell you what's happened, buster. My diamond earrings have been stolen from my room!

CRAIG: Oh, no!

DUDLEY: Not to mention her jade ring—and fine jade it was.

CRAIG: Miss Faraday, I can assure you that we've never had anything like this happen before at Surfside.

FELICIA: Isn't that just great! Well, it's happened now. And I want you to call the police at once. That jewelry is valuable.

CRAIG: Perhaps you've just mislaid it. Maybe it will turn up. I dislike having the police on the premises. It's bad publicity for the hotel.

FELICIA: If that jewelry isn't recovered, and pronto— you'll be up to your ears in bad publicity. And I haven't mislaid the stuff.

DUDLEY: Of course not. Felicia is most careful with her jewelry.

FELICIA: You can bet your sweet life I am. Diamonds really are a girl's best friend.

CRAIG: I'm sure that if we investigate the matter with a minimum of fuss, we'll be able to do something. I really cannot understand how such a thing could have happened. Our clientele is above suspicion.

FELICIA: Are you kidding? What about those three hillbillies who have been cavorting around here with all the charm and grace of uncaged tigers? I'd be willing to bet they're behind the theft.

DUDLEY: Anybody who wears suits like those Zeke and Amos are sporting I distrust on sight. Clothes may not make the man, but they reveal a good deal about him.

FELICIA: And I second the motion. All I know is that I had planned to wear that jewelry at the press party after tonight's performance. In other words, I want that jewelry recovered by tonight, or the Surfside Hotel will look like a ghost town after I'm through talking to reporters and anybody else who will listen.

CRAIG: Miss Faraday, I'll get onto the matter at once.

FELICIA: And take my advice—start with those hillbillies. Frisk them, and you'll probably find my jewels. (ZEKE enters.)

ZEKE (Cheerfully): Hello, folks. Jumping 'gators, but that water is cold this mornin'. Fair chilled my feet, it did. And I stepped on a bloomin' shell, too. Guess all these here water sports is only for young rapscallions.

FELICIA: Save the philosophy for a rainy day. What I want to know is, have you been sneaking around my room and getting your grubby hands on my jewelry?

ZEKE (Surprised): Just what are you aimin' to say, ma'am? I haven't been sneakin' anywhere. Been doin' a bit of wadin' in the chilly water is all.

DUDLEY: Miss Faraday's diamond earrings and handsome jade ring have been stolen from her room.

ZEKE: Well, now, I'm right sorry to hear that ma'am. Valuable stuff, was it?

FELICIA: You can bet your boots it was valuable. And you needn't act so innocent. Search him, Mr. Craig.

HENRY: Miss Faraday, I think you're being hasty. I know that Uncle Zeke may seem a little out of place here, but I certainly don't think he'd do anything dishonest.

ZEKE: I get it now. You think I took your doodads, ma'am.

FELICIA: That's the general idea, you or that son of yours.

ZEKE (*Turning his coat pockets inside out*): I'm hurt, ma'am. Zeke Billings never took anything in his life that didn't rightly belong to him. And you got no call to say I did. (*Showing empty pockets*) Satisfied? (*He also turns trouser pockets inside out.*) See anything?

DUDLEY: I don't imagine that even you would be silly enough to carry the jewelry in your pockets.

ZEKE: Now, looky here. You folks seem to be sayin' that I'm a crook. (*Angrily*) You've no call to say such a thing.

FELICIA: Mr. Craig, we're just wasting time. My advice to you is to get on the ball. Get your investigation going. You know how I feel. (*She exits huffily, followed by* MURGATROYD)

ZEKE: I said it before, those actors sure don't seem too friendly.

BETTY: Miss Faraday is upset, and she has a right to be.

HENRY: But she doesn't have the right to call Uncle Zeke a thief with no evidence at all. (AMOS *enters.*)

AMOS: That fella Boyd has gone to his room, Paw. Guess he's goin' to settle down for a nap.

CRAIG: Most of the guests are out on the beach at this time of day. I think I'll just have to search their rooms. I hate to invade a guest's privacy, but what else is there for me to do? I certainly don't want the police here if I can avoid it.

BETTY: Want any help, Mr. Craig?

CRAIG: No, thanks, Betty. The maids will give me any as-

sistance I need. (*He shakes his head.*) What a day!
(*Exits*)

AMOS: What's all this about the police, Paw?

ZEKE: That there actress woman has gone and got her
jewelry swiped. Seems to think I took her tinny trinkets
—and so does that other actor fellow.

AMOS (*Angrily shadow boxing*): Let me at 'em, Paw.
There's nobody goin' to call you a thief and get away
with it.

HENRY: Now, Amos, control yourself.

AMOS: The last critter that insulted Paw, I put in the
hospital for a month.

ZEKE: You're a good boy, Amos, but Henry's right. We
don't want to make any more trouble. Cool heads are
what we need. (DAISY SUE *enters.*)

DAISY SUE: My, that water is so refreshin'. Even better
than the spring back home. This is a real purty place.

AMOS: Not so purty as it was, Daisy Sue. Folks here been
accusin' Paw of stealin' that actress woman's jewelry.

DAISY SUE: Accusin' Paw? But that's plain foolish.

BETTY: Well, somebody stole her jewelry, and I hope we
can find the culprit. Mr. Craig's searching empty rooms
now.

AMOS: If you ask me, that actor fellow, Murgatroyd, looks
like he'd steal the gold teeth from his own Maw. (*The
phone rings. Betty answers it.*)

BETTY: Surfside Hotel. . . . Oh, hello, Gert. How are
things at the telephone company? . . . A telegram?
Yes, I'll take it down. (*She takes pad and pencil from
desk and begins to write down message. After a moment
or two, she speaks*) Yes, I have it. Thanks, Gert. I'll see
that he gets it. Bye. (*She tears sheet from pad and hands
it to* ZEKE) A telegram for you, Mr. Billings.

ZEKE: A tellygram? Say, this is a real surprise. Never got one of those in my whole life. (*He reads the message, his lips moving slowly.*) Well, now, this is real nice. It's from your Maw and Paw, Henry. They want Amos and Daisy Sue and me to pay 'em a visit. They want us right away on account of they're leavin' soon for their own vacation.

HENRY (*Eagerly*): That's wonderful. You haven't seen Mother and Dad in years. You'll have so much to talk about.

ZEKE: Sure will. Only trouble is, it just wouldn't look right if we left just yet, what with all this talk about our stealin' jewels from that actress woman. No, we got to clear the Billings name before we can go traipsin' out of here.

AMOS: That's right, Paw.

ZEKE: And I've been a-thinkin'. I got a notion that Amos and Daisy Sue and me can act like the detective fellows I was watchin' the other night on TV. Yes, sir, I got a real fine idea.

DAISY SUE: What is it, Paw?

ZEKE: You and Amos come with me. I'm goin' to need both of you.

HENRY (*Worried*): Uncle Zeke, you're not fixin' to do anything hasty, are you?

ZEKE: Don't you be a-worryin', Henry. Sure as shootin' I'm on the right track. Come on, Daisy Sue, Amos, we got us some sleuthin' to do. (ZEKE, AMOS, *and* DAISY SUE *exit*.)

BETTY: I shudder to think what Zeke may be up to.

HENRY: Things can't get any worse around here, that's for sure.

BETTY: Perhaps Mr. Craig should have called the police. After all, they know how to deal with these matters.

HENRY: But I can see his point. The publicity wouldn't do the hotel any good.

BETTY: The way Felicia Faraday has been making threats, I'm afraid we're in for some bad publicity, anyway. (MR. CRAIG *enters.* BETTY *and* HENRY *look at him expectantly.*)

CRAIG (*Sighing*): No success so far. I've left the maids to continue the search, and they seem to be enjoying it. What a morning! Septimus Boyd just nailed me in the corridor and told me that Amos had threatened him with bodily harm. Boyd is upset, to put the matter mildly. That's all we need around here to top things off—an angry millionaire. He went into his room, slammed the door, and locked it. Said that the Surfside Hotel is a dangerous place and that it's filled with lunatics. I'm beginning to think he's right. (MRS. RENNICK *enters excitedly.*)

BETTY: Why, good morning, Mrs. Rennick. You're not usually up at this hour.

MRS. RENNICK (*Breathlessly*): Oh, Mr. Craig, thank heaven you're here! There is a dreadful commotion going on in the room next to mine—Mr. Boyd's room, you know. Gracious, there's all kinds of groaning and screaming and chairs falling and banging. I'm positive someone's being murdered up there!

CRAIG: Oh, now it's murder!

MRS. RENNICK: Somebody had better go up to investigate. The noise is simply frightful.

CRAIG (*Wearily*): I'll go up.

HENRY: You may need help, Mr. Craig. (CRAIG *and* HENRY

exit quickly. MRS. RENNICK *goes to chair and sinks into it.*)

MRS. RENNICK: I had planned to sleep late this morning because I'm going to the theater tonight. But I was frightened out of my wits by those goings-on in Mr. Boyd's room.

BETTY: Maybe Mr. Boyd is just taking a nap and having a nightmare.

MRS. RENNICK: Miss Brandon, no one person, whether he is having a nightmare or not, could produce all that hullabaloo. I just don't understand it. The Surfside Hotel used to be such a restful place.

BETTY: Things have been humming lately. (*There is the sound of voices offstage.* ZEKE *and* AMOS *enter. They are carrying the unconscious form of* SEPTIMUS BOYD. MR. CRAIG, HENRY, *and* DAISY SUE *follow, excitedly.*)

MRS. RENNICK (*Jumping to her feet and rushing over to look at* BOYD.): It's just as I thought—he's been murdered! (AMOS *and* ZEKE *put* BOYD *down on a chair.*)

ZEKE: No, he's just a mite tired, ma'am.

DAISY SUE: Maybe you hit him a bit too hard, Amos.

AMOS: Shucks, I never even smacked him with my real Sunday punch. Just a little tap, was all.

BETTY: What happened?

HENRY: Uncle Zeke, I thought you weren't going to do anything hasty.

ZEKE: Wasn't anything hasty about this, Henry. No, sir, just moseyed up to Boyd's room on account of there never was a Boyd you could trust as far as you could throw him.

DAISY SUE: And I helped, didn't I, Paw?

ZEKE: I'm real proud of you, Daisy Sue. (*Turning*) You see, folks, when we got to Boyd's room, it was locked. So

I had Daisy Sue use her purtiest voice to get Boyd to open the door. He's kind of sweet on her, so open it he did.

SEPTIMUS (*Opening eyes and beginning to gain consciousness*): Where's the truck that hit me? (*He blinks and looks around him.*) Help! Those lunatics are still here! (*Noticing* CRAIG) Mr. Craig, I demand protection. I shall sue this hotel for all the money it has. These idiots forced their way into my room and began accusing me of—

ZEKE: And, by golly, we knew what we were talkin' about. Show 'em, Amos. (AMOS *reaches into his pocket and takes out the diamond earrings and the jade ring*)

AMOS: Here's Miss Faraday's jewelry, safe and sound.

CRAIG (*Excitedly*): Hurray! Betty, phone Miss Faraday's room and tell her to come down here at once. (BETTY *goes to phone and dials.*)

BETTY (*Into phone*): Miss Faraday? Will you please come down to the lounge? Your jewelry has been found. (*Hangs up, then to others.*) She's whooping like an Indian.

ZEKE: And the creepin' snake that took 'em was this here Boyd.

AMOS: There never was a good Boyd but a dead Boyd.

SEPTIMUS: Mr. Craig, this is preposterous. I ask you, why would I, the chairman of Wilkins Consolidated, stoop so low as to filch a couple of trinkets such as those. (*He points to jewelry in* AMOS' *hands.*)

ZEKE: Shucks, Boyd, you're not pullin' the wool over our eyes. (ZEKE *takes a wallet from his trousers and holds it up for inspection.* BOYD *tries to stop him.*)

SEPTIMUS (*Reaching for wallet*): That's my wallet. (*He*

rises and goes toward ZEKE) I demand that you return it.
(AMOS *grabs* BOYD *by the collar and pushes him down
in the chair again.*)

AMOS: Sit down, Boyd. It's rest you're needin'.

ZEKE: Folks can learn a heap by inspectin' a man's wallet.
Yes, sir. (*Takes a small card from wallet.*) Listen to this
one. "Septimus Boyd, handwriting expert." (*Takes another card from wallet*) "Septimus Boyd, Personal Rep-
resentative for the Smith Uranium Company." (*Takes
another card from wallet*) "Septimus Boyd, Travel
Agent." (*Takes another card from wallet*) "Septimus
Boyd, Agent for Lackluster Insurance Company."
(*Takes another card*) "Septimus Boyd, Actors' Agent."

MRS. RENNICK: Why, Mr. Boyd, you're really a jack-of-all-
trades, aren't you?

ZEKE: There's more, but what's real interestin' is this
here newspaper clippin'. Don't know why you saved it,
Boyd. (ZEKE *takes clipping from wallet*) This here
headline says, "Well-Known Confidence Man, Septimus
Boyd, Released from State Prison After Serving Five-
Year Sentence."

HENRY: Uncle Zeke, you're a whiz. Perry Mason and
Sherlock Holmes could take lessons from you.

CRAIG: What I don't understand, Mr. Billings, is just what
led you to suspect Boyd.

ZEKE: Plain as the nose on your face, Mr. Craig. Down in
the Ozarks, whenever anything crooked takes place—
robbery or just plain swindlin'—we always go out after
the Boyds. They're all snakes in the grass.

AMOS: Never was a Boyd you could trust.

DAISY SUE: A Boyd is the lowest rung on the ladder. That's
what old Grandpaw Billings used to tell me when I was

just a little girl. (FELICIA FARADAY, *followed by* DUDLEY
MURGATROYD, *rushes in.*)

FELICIA: Where is it? Where's my jewelry?

AMOS (*Handing it to her*): Here it is, ma'am, and none the
worse for wear. Found it all hidden in this here galoot's
shavin' kit.

DUDLEY: Whose shaving kit?

CRAIG: Mr. Boyd is the culprit, sir.

DUDLEY: Boyd! But he's a millionaire!

ZEKE: He's no more a millionaire than I am. He's a jail-
bird, that's what he is.

FELICIA: And you were able to find my jewelry?

ZEKE: Shucks, it wasn't anythin', ma'am. Me and Amos
and Daisy Sue just did our duty. Couldn't have you
goin' around suspectin' we were the crooks.

FELICIA: Mr. Billings, I owe you an apology.

DUDLEY: And so do I. After all, clothes do not make the
man.

FELICIA: I wish that you and Amos and Daisy Sue would
come to the theater tonight as my guests. It's the least
I can do to make amends to you. (*To* BOYD) And as for
you, you're as low as a night-crawler.

SEPTIMUS: There has been a mistake.

MRS. RENNICK: And I guess you made it, Mr. Boyd. (*She
goes toward door.*) Perhaps now, I can get some sleep.
(*Exits*)

ZEKE (*To* FELICIA): Ma'am, it's real good of you to invite
us to the play-actin'. But I guess we just can't come.
I got a tellygram a while ago, and me and Amos and
Daisy Sue have to pay a bit of a visit to Henry's maw
and paw.

CRAIG: I was just about to suggest, my dear man, that you

and Amos and Daisy Sue remain here as my guests for as long as you like.

ZEKE: Now that's real kind, Mr. Craig. But we Billings have a real strong family feelin'. Wouldn't do for us to disappoint our kin.

CRAIG: You know best. But the Surfside Hotel won't be the same without you.

FELICIA: And that's the understatement of the year.

HENRY: What shall we do with Mr. Boyd?

FELICIA: Feed him to the crocodiles.

CRAIG: Henry, bring the station wagon around front, and you and I will escort friend Boyd to the police station.

AMOS: I'll come, too. We won't be leavin' for a while, will we, Paw?

ZEKE: Not for a bit. Got to pack our duds and all. You go along, Amos—just in case that Boyd varmint tries to make trouble.

AMOS: I'll be ready for him, Paw. (HENRY *exits.* CRAIG *and* AMOS *take* BOYD *by the arms and lead him toward door.* BOYD *attempts to get away, but* AMOS *pins his arms back*) One more move like that and I'll be a-usin' my Sunday punch. (*They exit.*)

FELICIA: Well, as the Bard so aptly puts it, "All's well that ends well."

DUDLEY: And to quote him again, this time hopefully, "The rest is silence."

FELICIA: Silence—oh, blessed word. I'm going to try to take a nap.

DUDLEY: I, too. I owe it to my audience to be completely rested. (FELICIA *and* DUDLEY *go left.*)

FELICIA (*At door*): And thanks again, Mr. Billings. You're a diamond in the rough. (FELICIA *and* DUDLEY *exit.*)

ZEKE: We'd better start packin' our duds, Daisy Sue. Got a long drive ahead of us.

DAISY SUE: All right, Paw. (ZEKE *and* DAISY SUE *exit. The phone rings.* BETTY *answers it.*)

BETTY: Surfside Hotel. . . . Yes. . . . Well, ordinarily, we'd be filled up, but just this morning two of our rooms have become unexpectedly vacant. Yes. . . . Of course, *(Picks up pencil and writes)* Mrs. Walter Williams. Yes, we'll expect you tomorrow about three. Thank you. (HENRY *enters.*)

HENRY: Betty, Mr. Craig wants you to call the police station and tell them we're on our way.

BETTY: A pleasure. Oh, Henry, it looks as though we'll be back on that ivy-covered campus.

HENRY: You bet we will. Isn't it great? Oh, I tell you, the Billings family is talented. (*He goes toward door, singing, then Exits.* BETTY *chuckles and lifts phone as the curtain falls.*)

THE END

Production Notes

THE SAND DUNE HILLBILLIES

Characters: 6 male; 5 female.

Playing Time: 35 minutes.

Costumes: Zeke, Amos, and Daisy Sue are barefoot and wear ill-fitting, out-of-style clothes. Boyd wears a loud sports shirt and wrinkled slacks. Henry wears a bellhop's uniform—dark trousers and a short, red mess jacket. All others wear modern casual clothes. Zeke and Amos have rifles. Mrs. Rennick wears several pieces of costume jewelry.

Properties: Play script, pad of paper and pencil, suitcases, "diamond" earrings, a "jade" ring, wallet, several business cards, newspaper clipping, coffee cups.

Setting: The lounge of the Surfside Hotel. There is a registration desk right, with a stool behind it and a telephone and desk pen and registration book on top. A door center leads outside and other doors left and right lead to other parts of the hotel. There are several tables and chairs around, with magazines and newspapers on the tables. A writing desk is at one side with a chair in front of it.

Lighting: No special effects.

My Fair Monster

Characters

JERRY LARKIN, *a young writer*
SIGMUND SIGNOFF, *president of Signoff TV Productions*
SUSAN GARTH, *his secretary*
PEGGY SHORE, *a publicity agent*
LENA LAMPOON, *a lady detective*
MR. WEIRD ⎱
MRS. WEIRD ⎰ *characters in a TV show*
CREEPY ⎱
GRUESOME ⎬ *the Weirds' daughters*
REPULSIVE ⎰
GRAVES, *the Weirds' butler*
HELENA FAIRWEATHER, *president of the Slimonade Company*
HECTOR GRANT, *president of the Woofie Dog Food Company*

TIME: *A snowy morning in winter.*
SETTING: *The offices of Signoff TV Productions. Signoff's desk is at right; a conference table and chairs are at center, and a sofa is down left.*

At Rise: Sigmund Signoff *is seated at his desk.* Susan Garth *sits beside the desk, and* Peggy Shore *sits at conference table.* Jerry Larkin *is pacing the floor.*

Jerry (*Glancing anxiously at his watch*): Ten o'clock, and still no sign of that detective.

Susan: Miss Lampoon is supposed to be dependable. She comes highly recommended.

Peggy: We would get a blizzard on an important day like this. Let's just hope that Miss Lampoon does get here—and, most of all, that Helena Fairweather and Hector Grant arrive on time.

Signoff: You're sure everything is all set, Peggy?

Peggy: Mr. Signoff, you wound me with such a question. Haven't I been publicity director for Signoff Productions for two years? Haven't you learned to trust me?

Signoff (*Contritely*): Sorry, Peggy, I was just sending up a smoke signal to see if the Indians said Ugh! You can't blame me for worrying, though. We have a good property in "My Fair Monster." Jerry's done a good job of writing. It could be the biggest situation comedy we've ever had.

Jerry: That is, if Woofie Dog Food and the Slimonade Company will agree to sponsor it. (Lena Lampoon *enters up center. She wears a man's trench coat, a Sherlock Holmes hat, dark glasses, and high boots. She carries a battered briefcase.*)

Lena: Lena Lampoon to the rescue, folks. Bet you thought I wouldn't make it. But good old Lena is like the boys at the Post Office—nothing stops her from the swift completion of her appointed rounds.

Signoff (*Rising*): Welcome, Miss Lampoon.

Lena (*Sitting at table*): I'm loaded with information. In

fact, it's pouring out of my ears—or is that snow? Ha! Ha! (*Takes a thermos from briefcase*) But first a drink of good old java. (*She pours herself a cup of coffee*) Ah, that hits the spot. (*Takes a sandwich from briefcase*) And a little snack won't do me any harm either.

JERRY (*Impatiently*): Miss Lampoon, I hope you're not planning a ten-course dinner.

LENA: Keep your shirt on, sonny. I work better with a few victuals in me. (*Takes a bite of sandwich*) Mm-m. Nothing like salami with plenty of hot mustard. (*Takes another bite and then removes several papers from briefcase*) Here's the stuff. Now, which of you kids is the efficient secretary?

SUSAN: I'm Mr. Signoff's secretary. (*Ironically*) And Susan Garth is the name.

SIGNOFF: And the best secretary I ever had.

LENA: Swell. Well, kid, you probably want to take this down in shorthand or Sanskrit or Swahili or whatever you use. (SUSAN *takes pad and pencil from desk and is poised for action.*) Let's take Helena Fairweather first. President of the Slimonade Company. Maiden lady, but a mighty glamorous one. Has a sharp tongue and thinks that her product, Slimonade, is the best low-calorie drink ever invented. Thinks the curse of Americans is the bulging tummy, and wants to do something about it. I might add that she has her weaker moments. She owns a dog—a mutt that looks like a cross between a kangaroo and a dachshund. He's probably a reject from Noah's ark. And she adores the pooch. All in all, she's one of the luminaries of café society. (*To* SUSAN) Got all that, kid?

SUSAN: Got it.

LENA (*Looking at another paper, taking bite from sand-*

wich, and a swig from thermos): Hector Grant, president of the Woofie Dog Food Company—now there's a real tartar for you. He's a fanatic on physical exercise—does fifty push-ups every morning before breakfast, swims in his pool three times a day, including Sundays. Blows his top if he doesn't have his own way. Fancies himself an intellectual. Fond of quoting poetry. Has a Park Avenue apartment and a country house in Brewster. (*Puts papers down*)

SIGNOFF: Miss Lampoon, I congratulate you on a thorough job. (*Looking around room*) Well, folks, let's send up a rocket and see if it hits Mars.

LENA (*Taking apple from briefcase and biting into it*): Just one question, Mr. Signoff. What's the reason for this investigation?

SIGNOFF: I assume, Miss Lampoon, that you can keep a confidence.

LENA: Don't be insulting. My lips are sealed about anything connected with my profession.

SIGNOFF: Of course. Well, it's this way. Jerry here has created a new situation comedy, "My Fair Monster."

LENA: My fair what?

JERRY: Monster.

SUSAN: It's a scream.

JERRY: We've already made the pilot film, which both Helena Fairweather and Hector Grant have seen. And we've made four other episodes. (*Taking SUSAN's hand*) "My Fair Monster" means a lot to Susan and me. We want to be married, but it takes money to set up housekeeping. If "My Fair Monster" is successful, we'll be the happiest newlyweds on the block.

LENA: Bless you, my children. There's nothing like young

love to brighten up a bleak winter morning. But what's "My Fair Monster" all about?

PEGGY: You know how popular monsters always are on television? Well, "My Fair Monster" tops them all. It's about a man-and-wife song-writing team, the Weirds. They're horrible to look at but essentially nice people, and they're working on a musical called "My Fair Monster."

SUSAN: The husband looks like a combination of the Frankenstein monster, Count Dracula, and the Wolf Man. The wife is thin, with long black hair. She always dresses in black.

LENA: They sound dreamy.

JERRY: And they have three daughters—Creepy, Gruesome, and Repulsive. And a butler named Graves.

SIGNOFF: And all we need now are the commercials. So you see why we wanted your information. We wanted to know the interests, likes, and dislikes of our two potential sponsors. That way we can use the old psychology on them. We can plant an acorn and see if an oak tree grows.

LENA (*Closing briefcase and rising*): So you want to impress Helena Fairweather and Hector Grant. Well, kids, here's a bit of advice. Get in a bevy of fat girls and give 'em Slimonade to drink. Then, for Mr. Grant, invite Sir Laurence Olivier and Richard Burton to read selections from the poetry of T. S. Eliot and E. E. Cummings. And you might call in the New York Giants football team to do deep knee-bends. That ought to cover everything. (*Goes toward up center door*) It's been a real treat. I'll send you the bill, Mr. Signoff. But now it's out to the old dog sled and mush-mush through the drifts. Good luck to "My Fair Monster." (*She exits.*)

PEGGY: That's what I call a character. You ought to work her into the script, Jerry.

JERRY: But first we'll have to work the sponsors in.

SIGNOFF: The die is cast. We'll just have to run the locomotive into the station and see if it stops for water.

PEGGY: Hector Grant's an exercise bug. We ought to do something with that.

JERRY: Leave it to good old Jerry Larkin. I'll make like an Olympic champion.

PEGGY: And he likes poetry.

SUSAN: Leave that to me. I took poetry courses in college, and I had to memorize plenty of lines. Hector will think that the Muses and I are sisters.

PEGGY: And Hector must like dogs, or he wouldn't be in the dog food business. Besides which, Helena Fairweather also has a dog she adores. So I'll come on strong as a 24-carat dog lover.

SUSAN: And we'll extol the beauty of a slim waist in honor of Slimonade.

JERRY: Right—exercise, slim waists, poetry, and dogs.

SIGNOFF (*Enthusiastically*): As far as dogs go, Helena and Hector will think we originated Lassie by the time we're through with them. (*Looks at watch*) It won't be long now. (*Patting stomach*) I need a little solace for my ulcers. (*Goes to left and stops at door*) Shouldn't the cast be here by now? Hector and Helena specifically requested that the cast of "My Fair Monster" be present at the conference. (*Offstage voices are heard.*) Ah, that sounds like them. (MR. *and* MRS. WEIRD, CREEPY, GRUESOME, REPULSIVE, *and* GRAVES *enter up center.* MR. *and* MRS. WEIRD *are wearing overcoats over their costumes;*

MR. WEIRD *carries a mask.* CREEPY, GRUESOME, *and* REPULSIVE *are carrying an assortment of musical instruments.*)

MR. WEIRD (*Taking off his coat*): I brought along a mask because I knew I wouldn't have time for make-up. (*Puts on mask*)

SIGNOFF: Most becoming. Glad you're all here. Be with you in a moment. (*He exits left*)

MRS. WEIRD (*Removing coat and speaking in low, sultry voice*): Gracious, it's cold and blizzardy out. I hope that Helena Fairweather and Hector Grant make it.

GRAVES: So do I. But it's tough playing a butler in this weather. (MR. *and* MRS. WEIRD *and* GRAVES *sit on sofa. The three girls stand behind them.*)

MR. WEIRD: I hope I don't get a cold out of this. I'm very susceptible to the sniffles.

JERRY: I think we'll have you folks do two scenes for Helena and Hector. First, I suggest the sequence in which the interior decorator arrives to re-do the Weirds' home.

MRS. WEIRD: That's a good bit. Gives us all a chance to go over big in a sight gag. (*The three girls nod happily.*)

JERRY: And then the spot where you all sing the theme song of the musical. (*Voices are heard from offstage.*)

PEGGY: It won't be long now. Here they come. (JERRY *throws* SUSAN *a kiss.*)

JERRY: That's for luck.

SUSAN: Thanks. That reminds me of the days when Peggy and I were in college. Before an exam, we always shook hands and threw a textbook over our shoulders. That was for luck, too.

PEGGY: Let's just hope Jerry's good-luck charm has better results! (HELENA FAIRWEATHER *and* HECTOR GRANT *enter up center.* HELENA *wears glamorous outfit, and* HECTOR *wears loud sport clothes.* HECTOR *has overcoat on and* HELENA *wears fur coat over her dress.*)

SUSAN (*As* HELENA *and* HECTOR *take off their coats*): Good morning, Miss Fairweather. Good morning, Mr. Grant. I'll tell Mr. Signoff that you're here. (SUSAN *exits left.* HELENA *and* HECTOR *sit at conference table.*)

HELENA: My feet feel as though they were left in the freezer over night. I hope "My Fair Monster" is worth my making like a human iceberg.

HECTOR: Nonsense, Helena. This is the kind of day that brings the roses to your cheeks. Splendid air—clear, crisp.

JERRY (*Quick to take advantage*): Right you are, sir. I even walked to the office this morning. Of course, it's only four miles so I haven't really had my exercise for the day. (*Smiling at* HELENA) Have to keep that tummy from bulging. (JERRY *begins to do push-ups and does five or six before stopping.*) There. That's better. Nothing like a little workout for the circulation. (SUSAN *returns with* SIGNOFF.)

SIGNOFF (*Shaking hands with* HELENA *and* HECTOR): Welcome. Welcome. (*Goes to his desk*) Let's raise the curtains and see if any sunshine breaks through. Does everybody know everybody?

HELENA: After seeing the pilot film, I'd know this crew anywhere. The Weirds aren't exactly like everybody's next-door neighbors, you know.

HECTOR: Right. Right. Take Mrs. Weird—she looks like a refugee from a haunted house.

MRS. WEIRD: Mr. Grant, you're just what the doctor ordered for a girl's ego.

HELENA: And Mr. Weird, you're like something out of a nightmare. So are the three creepy little Weird sisters. (*The children smile;* JERRY *has now begun to do deep knee-bends.*)

HECTOR (*Regarding* JERRY *with approval*): That's a smart young writer you have there, Signoff. Knows the value of a sound mind in a sound body.

PEGGY: In the summer, Jerry runs five miles through Central Park every morning.

SUSAN: That's on weekdays. On Sundays he does ten.

HECTOR: Good sense. Good sense. Ever try this one? (*He rises, raises hands over his head, bends down, and touches his toes several times.*) Excellent for the waistline. You won't find any flab on me. (*Tensing stomach muscles and "punching" them with his fist.*) That's what you call keeping fit.

HELENA: O.K., Hector, you've made your point. We all know you are the perfect blend of Superman, Tom Swift, and Hercules.

PEGGY: I admire a muscular man. And I try to keep fit, too—chiefly by walking my dogs. I have three darling poodles.

HELENA: Good for you. A dog is a girl's best friend—next to diamonds, money, a clear skin, and an attractive figure. But now let's get down to business. "My Fair Monster" has its points—but, frankly, I'm not completely sold on it.

HECTOR: This is just off the top of my head, but let me say that I think "My Fair Monster" is promising. Still, there's something lacking that I just can't put my finger on. (*To* WEIRDS) That's why I want to see you folks in action today. I do like the music—

SUSAN: "What passion cannot Music raise and quell?"

HECTOR: John Dryden, by George! Signoff, I want to congratulate you on the intelligence of your staff. Brainy people, really brainy.

PEGGY: Susan got an "A" in her poetry course in college. We were classmates.

HELENA (*Acidly*): Look, let's save all these academic reminiscences for the next alumnae meeting, shall we?

SIGNOFF: Miss Fairweather has a point there. After all, the question before us is this: do you two fine people like "My Fair Monster" well enough to sponsor it for a season? In other words, if we run this show up the flagpole, are you going to salute?

HELENA: Let me speak for Slimonade. I think, as Hector does, that "My Fair Monster" is promising. But we're not talking about Woolworth prices. I want to be sure I'm getting my money's worth out of this. I'm interested only in one thing—keeping the nation Slimonade conscious.

HECTOR: I second Helena's words. The Woofie Dog Food Company has one purpose in mind—to have every dog in the country barking for a good square meal of Woofie. "My Fair Monster" has to accomplish this if it's going to be of any value to me. That's why both Helena and I want to get a general idea of what the rest of the series is like.

PEGGY: The fact is, Mr. Grant, that we do want to show you a couple of scenes from the other episodes.

HELENA: And about time.

JERRY: We'll do the interior decorator scene first. Mr. and Mrs. Weird have decided to have their home redone. They, along with the children and Graves, are spending a quiet evening in their cobwebby house. They are awaiting the arrival of the interior decorator, a fellow named Chauncey Pastel. I'll play the role of Chauncey.

HECTOR: Splendid.

JERRY: Ready, everybody? (*The* WEIRD *family and* GRAVES *go to* SIGNOFF's *desk.* SIGNOFF *rises and stands up center to be out of their way.* MR. WEIRD *pretends to be looking out the window.*)

MR. WEIRD: Goodness me, it's a dreadful night out. The stars are shining, the moon is bright, the air is mellow. Not a drop of rain in sight, no bats flying around, no owls hooting. Let's hope the weatherman promises something better for tomorrow.

MRS. WEIRD: Darling, do you remember the lovely storm two weeks ago? Lightning struck three houses, the streets were flooded, and Mrs. Pickle next door was knocked down by a flying billboard.

REPULSIVE (*Ecstatically*): It was beautiful!

CREEPY: It was glorious!

GRUESOME: It was stupendous!

GRAVES: It was heartwarming!

MRS. WEIRD: I'm so glad we asked Chauncey Pastel, the interior decorator, to come in tonight to give us some suggestions about improving our happy little home. Shouldn't he be here by now, Dad?

MR. WEIRD (*Looking out window*): Indeed, he should—and there he comes now up the walk.

MRS. WEIRD: I hope he doesn't do what that other interior decorator did last week—you remember him. Why, he'd no sooner entered the house, than he froze in his tracks, and ran off screaming like a madman.

MR. WEIRD: Just remember, darling, everyone isn't normal, like us. (*The doorbell rings. If possible, the bell should have a funereal, organ-like sound.*)

GRAVES: I'll let the gentleman in. (*He goes to left, pretends to open door, and* JERRY, *playing the role of* CHAUNCEY PASTEL, *"enters."*)

CHAUNCEY (*Not noticing the* WEIRDS; *surveying the room.*): Heavens to Betsy, those cobwebs must go. Simply dreadful. And oh my goodness—a mummy is hardly the sort of thing one wants in a living room. No, a mummy simply won't do. And these black curtains need livening up—something in a friendly peach brocade would be delightful. (*He is slowly approaching the* WEIRDS *who are beaming and looking their best—which is frightful.*)

MR. WEIRD: We place ourselves in your expert hands, Mr. Pastel. (CHAUNCEY *now sees the* WEIRDS *for the first time. He does a double take, gasps, and falls to the floor in a faint.*)

MRS. WEIRD: Poor man. It must be something he ate. Fetch a glass of turpentine, Graves.

GRAVES: At once, madam. (*He exits, returns quickly, and pantomimes handing glass to* MR. WEIRD.)

MR. WEIRD (*Bending down over* CHAUNCEY): Sip this, my boy. It's loaded with vitamins. (CHAUNCEY *sips, gags, and sits up.* MR. WEIRD, *still bending close to* CHAUNCEY, *smiles at him.*) Feeling better? You're in good hands, my boy. (CHAUNCEY *takes a long look at* MR. WEIRD, *at* MRS. WEIRD *and the children, utters a feeble scream, and flops down again.*)

JERRY (*Rising*): That's enough to give you an idea of what we're attempting.

HELENA: It's not bad at all. In fact, you people make Count Dracula look like one of the Campfire Girls.

HECTOR: Helena is right, grotesquely amusing.

JERRY: And now just one more brief scene. This is the one in which Mr. and Mrs. Weird sit at the piano and sing to each other—it's the theme song for the musical they've written—"My Fair Monster."

HELENA: That ought to set musical comedy back fifty years. But if it helps to sell more Slimonade, let the chips fall where they may.

JERRY: They're accompanied by the children, who play musical instruments.

SIGNOFF: Let's roll it.

MR. WEIRD: We'll pretend the desk is a piano. (MR. *and* MRS. WEIRD *sit at desk. He takes her hand, looks soulfully into her eyes, and sings the following, to the tune of "Oh, Susannah!"*)

Oh, I've come to love your messy bangs,

Your fuzzy, furry paws,

And your scrawny arms and gleaming fangs,

Your nails like eagles' claws.

(*Refrain*) My Medusa!

The dream-ghoul of my life!

I love to twirl each snaky curl—

My dear macabre wife.

(MRS. WEIRD *sighs happily and pats his cheek.*)

MRS. WEIRD (*Singing*):

Oh, you send the shivers up my spine,

When your red eyes flash with fire,

Even though you have an ogre's face,

You're my tell-tale heart's desire.

(*Refrain*) Oh, my monster,

I love your slurp and slink,
Your pointed head and shoes of lead—
You are my favorite fink.

(MR. WEIRD *beams.* MR. *and* MRS. WEIRD *may join in repeating the last refrain.*)

HECTOR: Love those lyrics. Not Shelley or Keats, but serviceable.

HELENA: They're certainly off-beat enough.

JERRY: Thanks for the fine performances, everybody. Of course, to get the real effect, you have to see the film. There are bats flapping all over the place, and Graves does a sort of jig throughout the song.

HECTOR (*Nodding*): Nice touches. Nice touches. Yes, as I've said before, young man, the program has potential.

JERRY (*Eagerly*): You mean you'll sign the contract?

HELENA: The trouble with you members of the younger generation is that you want to move too fast. Slow down, boy—this takes a lot of thinking through.

SIGNOFF (*Quickly*): Well, there's no harm in your looking over the contract, is there? We may as well put in a new bulb and see if the lamp lights up. Get the contract from the files, Susan. (SUSAN *takes contract from filing cabinet and sets it before* HECTOR *and* HELENA.)

SUSAN (*Gaily*): There you are. (*Hopefully*) And happy signing. (HECTOR *takes a pen from his pocket.*)

HECTOR (*Reading contract carefully*): Twenty-six weeks— I suppose that's fair enough. (*Continues to read, nodding head occasionally, while* SUSAN, PEGGY, JERRY, *and* SIGNOFF *look on anxiously.*)

SIGNOFF: I think you'll find that's the standard contract in the industry, Mr. Grant.

HECTOR: You'd better look it over, Helena.

HELENA: I intend to. Mother always warned me to read

the fine print in any contract. It's those little clauses that make all the trouble. (*She takes a pair of glasses from her pocket*) I'll need these to wade through this legal language—which is usually about as clear as one of the way-out modern poets.

SUSAN: How right you are. Of course, I happen to be especially fond of W. D. Snodgrass's work.

HECTOR: Really? So am I. Young woman, you're a revelation.

HELENA (*Reading while the others watch expectantly*): Just as I thought—the boys who prepare these horrors never use one word where they can use four. Let's see now. (*Speaking aloud as she reads*) "Joint sponsorship" . . . "twenty-six weeks" . . . "right to renew option" . . . (*Frowning*) Well, it all sounds aboveboard. (*She hands contract to* HECTOR) What do you think, Hector? I confess that I really haven't made up my mind. There are a lot of nice green crinkly American dollars riding on this decision.

HECTOR (*With pen poised over contract*): It seems to be a fair contract. (*His brow furrows in thought. He puts pen on table. The others regard him anxiously.*) But all this rushing to sign. As the poet says, "Had we but world enough and time."

SUSAN: Andrew Marvell.

HECTOR: Signoff, this girl is one in a million. But back to what's bothering me.

SIGNOFF: Nothing we can't take care of, I hope.

HECTOR: Here's the nub of it. Where's the identification with my product, Woofie Dog Food, or with Helena's Slimonade? You have a funny show—no doubt about it. But nothing in it that I can see or hear really makes it appropriate for sponsorship by our particular products. Right, Helena?

HELENA: Hector, you've hit right on target. We've seen the pilot film. We've watched these performers in action here this morning. But, as you say, something is missing. Where's the identification? Where's the good old gimmick? A monster family just doesn't identify with Woofie Dog Food or with Slimonade. With poison, yes. With toadstools instead of mushrooms, yes. But with Slimonade and dog food, no. (*She rises*) It's sad—but true. But into each life some rain must fall.

HECTOR: Helena's right. Believe me, folks, I'm genuinely sorry. (*He rises*) But we live in a business world, and we have to think of what is good for business. (SIGNOFF, JERRY, SUSAN, *and* PEGGY *look terribly dejected.*)

SIGNOFF (*Desperately*): But there must be something—

HECTOR: Too late. We want a show on the channels as soon as possible. We don't dislike the series but I'm afraid it's not for us. (*He holds* HELENA's *coat for her as she puts it on.*)

HELENA: Anyway, thanks. It's been an entertaining morning. (HECTOR *puts on his coat*)

JERRY (*Frantically*): Can't we talk about this? Maybe—

HECTOR (*Holding up his hand*): No, young man. And I'm sorry.

HELENA: Come on, Hector. Out into the storm. It's been fun. I only wish my doggie had been here to enjoy it.

HECTOR: Just as well he wasn't. Snow is hard on dogs. (HECTOR *goes toward door.*)

HELENA (*Following him*): I'll bet that lovely white stuff is a foot deep by now.

SUSAN (*Excitedly*): Snow—that's it! Miss Fairweather, Mr.

Grant—stop! Please don't go! Please listen to me for just a moment!

HECTOR: My dear girl, watch your blood pressure.

SUSAN: Please!

HELENA: Let's listen, Hector. **Otherwise,** this girl will jump out of her skin.

HECTOR (*Shrugging his shoulders*): All right. (*To* SUSAN) You're a charming and brainy girl. I owe you the courtesy of listening.

SUSAN: Oh, thank you! I have the most wonderful idea! It was the mentioning of dogs and snow that did it. Peggy, do you remember the terrible blizzard during our junior year in college?

HELENA: Oh, not again. Must we have these collegiate memories?

HECTOR: Let the girl continue.

PEGGY (*Puzzled*): Of course I remember. There were snow-drifts seven and eight feet high.

SUSAN: And you remember how we were snowed in in our dormitory?

PEGGY: I'll never forget it.

SUSAN: There we were, holed up in the dormitory for an entire day until the plows could get to us. And Paul Creighton—you remember him, Peggy?

PEGGY: I certainly do. He was a real gem. (*Suddenly seeing what* SUSAN *is getting at*) Oh, of course. Now I see what you mean—

SUSAN (*Quickly*): For a joke, Paul brought a St. Bernard to the dormitory. The dog had a little keg around its neck—filled with hot coffee.

HECTOR: Charming story. But I don't see the connection—

SUSAN: But it's just what we need for "My Fair Monster"

—for the identification. Why couldn't we include a St. Bernard as a member of the Weird family? In each episode, the dog would appear with a little keg around its neck—a keg filled with Slimonade, which the whole family would drink. There's your identification, there's your image—dogs, Slimonade.

HECTOR (*Interested*): Well, I suppose it might work—

HELENA: Sounds promising.

JERRY (*Inspired*): And when the dog comes in and the family drinks, they all could say something like:

Oh, Slimonade, it has the taste—

And how it slims each person's waist.

HECTOR: By George, a couple of lines of poetry never hurt anybody.

PEGGY: Best of all, the St. Bernard sequence can easily be inserted in the pilot film and the others.

HECTOR (*Looking at* HELENA): Helena, what do you think?

HELENA: I think it would work.

HECTOR (*Taking pen from pocket and going to table*): Very well. I shall now sign on the dotted line. (*He does so with a flourish.*)

HELENA: Let me borrow your pen, Hector. And may the nation become more and more Slimonade conscious. And, of course, may all the canines in this country bark happily for Woofie Dog Food. (*She signs contract.*)

SIGNOFF (*Coming to table and taking contract*): Thank you! Thank you! This is a red-letter day for all of us. We've sent up the missile and seen it hit smack on target. (*He shakes hands briskly with* HELENA *and* HECTOR.)

HELENA: And now let's get out of here, Hector, before we have to hire a pair of snowshoes.

HECTOR: Right. I want to get back, too, before the storm

gets any worse. (*He goes to door with* HELENA) We look forward to a happy future—and a top place in the TV ratings.

JERRY: We'll do our best.

HELENA: Make sure you do, boy, because I intend to hire extra help at the Slimonade plant.

HECTOR: Long live "My Fair Monster." (*He and* HELENA *exit.* SIGNOFF *kisses the contract and hugs it to him.*)

JERRY (*Going to* SUSAN) Susan, you're a genius. I'll have the most brilliant wife in the country.

PEGGY: Thank heaven we went to college. I never realized until now the glorious benefits of our days on the ivy-covered campus.

MR. WEIRD: Well, everybody, it looks as though we'll all be working for a while.

MRS. WEIRD: Those words are music to my ears. (*All now gather around conference table*)

JERRY: Shall we do our theme?

SUSAN: Why not? After all, it's our song.

ALL (*Singing*):

Oh, I've come to love your messy bangs,
Your fuzzy, furry paws,
And your scrawny arms and gleaming fangs,
Your nails like eagles' claws.
(*Refrain*) My Medusa!
The dream-ghoul of my life!
I love to twirl each snaky curl—
My dear macabre wife.
(*They begin to sing the second stanza as the curtain falls.*)

THE END

Production Notes

My Fair Monster

Characters: 5 male; 8 female.

Playing Time: 35 minutes.

Costumes: Modern everyday dress for Jerry, Signoff, Susan, and Peggy. Jerry and Signoff have watches. Lena Lampoon wears man's trench coat, Sherlock Holmes hat, dark glasses, and high boots. She carries a briefcase. Mrs. Weird has long black hair and wears black shawl over long black dress. Mr. Weird wears coat over his costume and carries a mask. Graves has a messy wig; the three girls may wear Beatle wigs, witches' hats, and black dresses. Helena wears sweater and slacks and colorful scarf at her neck; she is wearing numerous bracelets. On her entrance she wears fur coat and overshoes over her dress. Hector wears loud sports jacket, slacks, loud tie, and pink shirt. He has overcoat over his suit. Hector has pen in his pocket; Helena has glasses in a pocket.

Properties: Briefcase with thermos bottle of coffee, sandwich, papers, and apple inside it; contract, musical instruments.

Setting: The offices of Signoff TV Productions. At right are Signoff's desk and chair; a pad of paper and pencil are on the desk. Another chair is beside the desk, and a conference table and chairs are at center. A sofa is down left. A filing cabinet, with contract in it, is at one side. Doors are up center and at left.

Lighting: No special effects.

Sound: Funereal doorbell, as indicated in text.